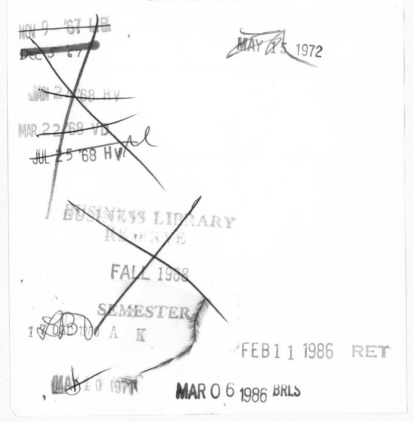

The
Quantitative Approach
to
Managerial Decisions

The
QUANTITATIVE APPROACH
to
MANAGERIAL DECISIONS

LEONARD W. HEIN, PH.D., C.P.A.

Assistant Dean for Graduate Affairs
and
Professor of Accounting
School of Business and Economics
California State College at Los Angeles

PRENTICE-HALL, INC., Englewood Cliffs, New Jersey

Library of Congress Catalog Card Number: 67–10685

Printed in the United States of America—C

Current Printing (last digit):
10 9 8 7 6 5 4 3 2 1

PRENTICE-HALL INTERNATIONAL, INC., *London*
PRENTICE-HALL OF AUSTRALIA, PTY. LTD., *Sydney*
PRENTICE-HALL OF CANADA, LTD., *Toronto*
PRENTICE-HALL OF INDIA (PRIVATE) LTD., *New Delhi*
PRENTICE-HALL OF JAPAN, INC., *Tokyo*

To My Wife, Mildred

Preface

We are witnessing a romance, if not a marriage, between the traditional areas of mathematics and business management.

The mathematician has invaded, quite successfully in many instances, the area of the analysis of business problems. He has not been forced to carry on his courtship entirely outside the walls of the university schools of business. These schools have been quite receptive to the glamorous proposals of the mathematician, and have quite readily opened their gates to permit the romance to be carried on in a most cooperative atmosphere.

As with most romantic roads, this one has not been entirely smooth. The honeymooners are not infrequently rudely jostled as they wend their happy way.

The mathematician often does not understand nor appreciate the value of some of the more traditional approaches to the solution of business problems. He has, of course, a valid excuse in that the study in depth of the several disciplines may require more time than is available. The businessman and the professor of business administration similarly rarely have a thorough training in higher mathematics. There is bound to be some lack of communication.

Nevertheless, the mathematician has successfully carried his point. There is, indeed, much agitation to increase the depth of the mathematical requirements of the curriculum in schools of business. This has already borne fruit in many schools.

Many other disciplines are clamoring for similar consideration. Any adjustments made in specific curricula must result in compromise if the traditional length of the degree program is not to be increased. If new material is to be introduced, other areas of study very likely must be dropped. These are difficult decisions. They are not and should not be lightly made. The necessary adjustments will in all probability be made through an evolutionary rather than a revolutionary process.

If this be true, it will be some time before the elegant precision of the pure mathematical presentation will be within the comprehension of the usual student in schools of business. Mathematical symbology will mean little more than a series of "chicken scratches" to the mathematically unsophisticated.

Many of the presently developed analytical tools can be readily understood by the nonmathematician. In fact, it is extremely desirable that the business school graduate have a speaking acquaintance with many of these tools. Some of them are sufficiently simple and practical that he may himself apply them to the solution of problems that he encounters. Others, being more complex in nature, will require the services of professionals in the field.

This fact is not a valid argument against the study of these tools. Most people agree that the collection, analysis, and interpretation of accounting data should be carried on by professionals. Few have used this as an argument against teaching the principles of accounting to prospective business managers.

It is probably possible to present the discussion of these tools using a completely nonmathematical approach in the sense that only words and no symbols are used. This would, in my opinion, be a serious mistake. Here is a rare opportunity partially to bridge the gap between the language of the businessman and that of the mathematician. Therefore, the use of simple mathematical notation is gradually developed. Each segment of such notation is introduced where it is used, and it is explained in terms of everyday language wherever possible.

One concept of an ideal textbook is that it be completely self-contained, so that no assumption of prior knowledge is assumed. Such a textbook would be unwieldy indeed and perhaps undesirable in other respects. Nevertheless, the more completely self-explanatory a text is, other things being equal, the better. This text strives toward that goal. Certain minimal background achievements are presumed. The reader should have some knowledge of high school algebra. In college, he should have been exposed to at least the basic courses in accounting and statistics and be familiar with the basic terminology of economics. No other formal prerequisites are taken for granted in the explanations in the text.

Acknowledgments. No claim of originality, other than that of the form of presentation, is being made for the concepts developed in this book. Acknowledgment of the primary originators of each concept is given at the beginning of the chapter concerned. Many people other than the primary originators helped bring each technique to its present state of development. No attempt has been made to footnote each such contribution. The works of many of these developers are listed in the bibliography at the end of each chapter. Special mention is due to Mr. D. N. Petersen of the Northrop Corporation who read and constructively criticized Chapter 15. The author also acknowledges with thanks the comments and suggestions of Professor George M. Parks, Wharton School of Finance and Commerce, University of Pennsylvania and Professor William R. Beatty, College of Business, Rochester Institute of Technology. Very special mention is due my wife, Mildred, who spent many hours reading the text and whose many valuable suggestions were gratefully received. Naturally, I take full responsibility for any errors which are contained herein.

I wish to express my appreciation to Professor Dudley J. Cowden and his publisher, Prentice-Hall, Inc., and to Professor A. Hald and his publisher, John Wiley & Sons, Inc., for their kind permission to reproduce several of the tables contained in the appendices.

Leonard W. Hein

Contents

1
Managerial Decisions

2
Electronic Computers and Managerial Decisions

3
The Distribution Problem: I

7

The Simplex Method: II

8

The Learning Curve

9

Probability and Probability Distributions

10

The Poisson, the Gamma, and the Normal Distributions

11

The Monte Carlo Method

12

Waiting Lines

13
Quality Control Charts

14
Work Sampling

15
PACE—Performance and Cost Evaluation

16

PERT—Program Evaluation and Review Technique

17

CPM—The Critical Path Method

18

Line of Balance

List of Illustrations

The
Quantitative Approach
to
Managerial Decisions

1

Managerial Decisions

SEC. 1-1. MANAGERIAL VS. NONMANAGERIAL DECISIONS

What is a managerial decision? In a book dealing with the quantitative approach to managerial decision making, the definition of a managerial decision appears to be of distinct significance. Yet there is not complete agreement as to what distinguishes a manager from a worker, and hence a managerial from a nonmanagerial decision.

In a one-man business, the functions of manager and worker are merged, and the distinction between the two assumes little importance. As businesses grow, these functions tend to separate. Students of management have long been attempting to specify the strictly managerial tasks. Some have isolated a large number of classifications; others limit themselves to relatively few categories. There is general agreement that such functions as organizing, staffing, planning, and controlling are managerial. Yet few so-called managers devote themselves exclusively to these tasks. Many positions designated as *managerial* require that the incumbent perform nonmanagerial as well as managerial duties.

The head of a small engineering department would usually be regarded as a manager. It is quite likely, however, that a relatively small portion of his time is devoted to such duties as organizing, staffing, planning, or controlling. Very probably, he will-be spending the majority of his time performing functions similar to those in which his subordinate engineers are engaged.

A *managerial decision* is usually one made to attain or further the objectives of the business. The classical business objective is, of course, to maximize profits. A possibly better objective might be to maximize return on investment. These objectives may not necessarily be identical. The objective of profit maximization is postulated by economists because it

1

lends itself to a rational analysis. Both economists and business men agree that profit maximization is not the only business objective, and in fact, may not be the major one. Such objectives as business size (the largest in its field?), prestige, exclusiveness, and so forth, may well take precedence over profit maximization. Nevertheless, business decisions must be made with profits in mind. Without profits over an extended period of time, the business would cease to exist.

In the present state of the art (or science) of business management, profit maximization probably cannot be achieved. The larger the business structure and the more complex its organization, the more likely "sub-optimization" is to occur. *Suboptimization* is the optimization of a part of the organization at the expense of the whole. The optimum situation for a sales manager might be to have at his disposal a fully manned sales crew along with a completely stocked inventory, including every possible combination of color and size. Rarely would such a situation be likely to maximize profits.

Decisions designed to benefit one department tend toward suboptimization. The interdepartmental effect of decisions should be carefully analyzed. Ideally, the effect of each decision upon the entire business should be known. This would require an "input-output" model of the business such that, by varying any input or combination of inputs, the resulting effect upon the output could be obtained. No such model is presently available, nor is one likely to be in the foreseeable future. Although many of the concepts discussed in this book are a step in this direction, one should not infer that success has yet been achieved. A number of very useful tools have, nevertheless, been developed. In the hands of informed people, they can be quite effective; used by the inexperienced, they can be equally dangerous.

Some of the quantitative tools developed so far have as their objective the minimization of cost. The inference is that if costs are minimized, profits will be maximized. In many cases this inference is valid, and certainly cutting costs wherever possible is one of the safer managerial policies to follow. Yet if this policy is carried to its logical conclusion, costs can be cut to zero by going out of business. Profits, of course, will also be cut to zero. Profits are made by spending money. The better objective may be maximizing the return on the money spent, rather than minimizing such expenditures.

The head of the small engineering department might well operate his department at less cost if he acted as a part-time rather than a full-time manager. It is conceivable, however, that, by hiring more workers to perform his worker duties and therefore devoting his full time to managerial functions (assuming that he is an effective manager), he could increase the output of the department in a more than proportionate ratio to the increased cost.

SEC. 1-2. THE QUANTITATIVE APPROACH TO MANAGERIAL DECISIONS

The businessman is fond of saying that he is about to take a calculated risk when planning to embark on a new venture. If he were asked about the probabilities involved in the risk and how he had calculated them, he would, in all likelihood, be at a loss for a reply. His decision was based, rather, upon some form of intuitive judgment—an accumulation of past experiences and an ill-defined feeling for the current trends in the business world.

He plans to reduce his inventory because the "boom has run its course." Or he plans to increase his inventory because "purchase prices will be higher in the future." These judgments may or may not be valid. It has been said that the successful businessman is one who guesses right more than 50 per cent of the time. Unquestionably a large proportion of business decisions are based upon pure guesses—upon hunches.

Much recent research has been directed toward reducing to a minimum such guesswork in business decision making. The trend has been to express, wherever possible, the underlying business situation in mathematical quantities, and then to base the decision upon a mathematical process of optimization.

Many phases of business can easily be quantified. When a company must make a shipment to a customer from any one of several warehouses, the cost of the shipment from each warehouse can be calculated. If the company has a number of customers and a number of warehouses, a least-cost distribution pattern can be developed.

Other cases, although clearly quantifiable by nature, are not so easily quantified. Take, for example, the case of an inventory stockout. At least three conditions may result: (1) the customer will merely wait for future delivery; (2) the customer will buy this item from a competitor, but will be retained as a customer; (3) the customer will transfer all his business to a competitor. Clearly, there is always some cost to an inventory stockout. In case 1, the cost will be loss of the use of the profit on the sale for the waiting period—a calculable cost. In case 2, the cost will be loss of the profit on the sale—again a calculable cost. In case 3, the cost will be the profits on all the items that the customer would have bought in the future —a definite but imponderable value. Yet in planning inventory programs, the cost of an inventory stockout may have to be considered.

There are, of course, cases in which any quantities assigned must be purely subjective. The trend in manufacturing plants is to present a pleasing view to the public by attractively landscaping the grounds. In many cases the amount of the company's product sold locally is insignificant, and therefore customer good will is not involved. Yet managers regard such landscaping as a distinct asset. What value can be placed upon such an asset in order to estimate how much should be invested in landscaping? Business includes many such areas which are extremely difficult to quantify.

There has been, nevertheless, much success in assigning usable quantities to apparently unquantifiable situations. Much research is being devoted to this problem. A complete working model of a business would require that all business aspects be reduced to mathematical quantities. Such a development now appears to lie far in the future.

SEC. 1-3. DECISIONS IN THE FACE OF CERTAINTY, RISK, UNCERTAINTY, AND COMPETITIVE ACTION

Certainty

"The only things certain," goes the popular saying, "are death and taxes"; and the wit replies, "We may yet conquer death!" True, the absence of certainty about future events is the rule rather than the exception, and managerial decisions must be made in awareness that future conditions may vary widely from those contemplated when the decision is being made.

Nevertheless, many managerial decisions may be made in conditions approaching certainty. The distribution or transportation problem discussed in Sec. 1-2 is one such situation. It is possible to obtain the relevant facts for the problem—among them the types of transportation available, the costs per unit for each type from each source to each destination, and so forth. A number of the techniques to be considered are based upon the assumption of certainty or near-certainty.

Risk

One commonly stated function of the entrepreneur is to assume risk. Under this concept, the entrepreneur supplied the capital for the enterprise, and if it failed, the entrepreneur bore the loss.

The term *risk* took on a somewhat more technical meaning in the insurance business, where, through such means as the compilation of mortality tables, the total incidence of a class of events was computed with an accuracy approaching certainty—that is, with a comparatively small margin of error. Thus, the number of deaths per year per thousand members of a given occupational group is quite accurately known; hence, the probability that any individual member of that group will die may be directly derived. Intimately associated with this concept of risk is, therefore, the concept of known or precisely measured probabilities.

By extension, then, a decision in the face of risk may be a decision in the face of known probabilities. This concept differs markedly from that of certainty. The term *probability* implies that an event may or may not occur. The value of the probability associated with the event is a measure of the likelihood of the occurrence of that event.

Uncertainty

More prevalent than either conditions of certainty or risk are conditions of uncertainty. Uncertainty exists when the probabilities associated with the occurence or nonoccurrence of events are unknown. The more usual approach to the solution of such problems is an intuitive one. The solutions are based upon an important but rather nebulous thing called *experience*. When probabilities are associated with such events, the probabilities are usually derived subjectively, since no objective measures may be available. The subjective probabilities may therefore be highly variable, depending upon the inherent optimism or pessimism of the individual or even upon his current mood.

Competitive Action

Many managerial decisions must be made in the face of competitive action; that is, one of the factors to be considered is what competitors will do if certain steps are taken. Reducing prices, for example, will not result in an increased share of the market if competitors follow suit. Thus, rather complex strategies may be required to meet competition effectively.

There has been a considerable theoretical development in this area— generally referred to as the *theory of games*. The subject is, however, so complex that this development must be regarded as being in its rudimentary stages. There have been, to date relatively few practical applications of the theory to business situations.

SEC. 1-4. STATISTICAL DECISION THEORY

An important area of development in the making of business decisions lies in the field of *statistics*. Although statistical decision theory encompasses something more than theoretical statistics, the latter provides many of the background concepts used by the former.

Provided here is a relatively objective means for making decisions. The decision frequently takes the form of accepting or rejecting a hypothesis.

For example:

H_0: Green packaging has no influence on cigarette sales.
H_1: Green packaging influences cigarette sales.

The hypothesis H_0 is called the *null* or *no-difference* hypothesis, and H_1 is called the *alternate* hypothesis. Rejection of H_0 forces acceptance of H_1, and vice versa. Inherent in a decision of this nature is the possibility of error. Rejection of H_0 when H_0 is, in fact, true is called a *Type I* error. A Type I error may be controlled at any level set by the analyst. A typical level is at the 95 per cent confidence level, which means that a Type I error will be committed, on the average, 5 per cent of the time.

A second type of error (*Type II*) may also be committed, namely, accepting H_0 when H_0 is, in fact, false. Although a Type I error may be controlled at a specified level, a Type II error is less amenable to similar control. One can control the Type I error at the desired level, and then minimize the probability of committing a Type II error. Under certain circumstances, however, this probability may still be quite high.

SEC. 1-5. THE KIT OF QUANTITATIVE TOOLS

A number of quantitative tools or techniques have been developed which, under the proper circumstances, will significantly help the manager in his attempts to approach optimization in his decision making. Some of these tools were conceived as early as the 1920's, but the majority of them were developed either during or after World War II.

Many of the tools are based upon statistical or probabilistic concepts. Others take for granted that the basic facts are known with a reasonable degree of certainty. No attempt has been made to classify the tools using these concepts, since there appears to be little, if any, utility to such a classification.

The following chapters should be considered as merely an introduction to each of the tools treated. A definitive treatment of any one of them would require one or more volumes of this size.

DISCUSSION QUESTIONS

1-1. Name some of those tasks generally accepted as being managerial.
1-2. Are the usual duties of so-called managers solely managerial in nature?
1-3. Discuss possible and probable business objectives.

1-4. What is meant by *optimization? Suboptimization?*
1-5. Discuss the concept of the *calculated risk.*
1-6. What is meant by *decisions in the face of certainty?*
1-7. Describe the concept of *risk.*
1-8. What is meant by the term *uncertainty?* How does *uncertainty* differ from *risk?*
1-9. Discuss the concept of *decisions in the face of competitive action.*
1-10. What is *statistical decision theory?*
1-11. What is an *hypothesis?* A *null hypothesis?* An *alternate hypothesis?*
1-12. What is a *Type I error?* A *Type II error?*
1-13. Which type of error is easier to control?

BIBLIOGRAPHY

Bierman, Harold, Jr., "Probability, Statistical Decision Theory and Accounting," *The Accounting Review,* XXXVII (July, 1962), 400-405.

Bross, Irwin D. F., *Design for Decision.* New York: The Macmillan Company, 1953.

Hart, A. G., *Anticipations, Uncertainty, and Dynamic Planning.* New York: A. M. Kelly, 1951.

Jones, Manley H., *Executive Decision Making.* Homewood, Ill.: Richard D. Irwin, Inc., 1957.

Miller, David W., and Martin K. Starr, *Executive Decisions and Operations Research.* Englewood Cliffs, N. J.: Prentice-Hall, Inc., 1960, pp. 55-100.

Morris, William T., *Engineering Economy.* Homewood, Ill.: Richard D. Irwin, Inc., 1960, pp. 1-14.

Owens, Richard, *Introduction to Business Policy.* Homewood, Ill.: Richard D. Irwin, Inc., 1954, pp. 115-48.

Spencer, Milton H., and Louis Siegelman, *Managerial Economics.* Homewood, Ill.: Richard D. Irwin, Inc., 1959, pp. 3-24.

2

Electronic Computers and Managerial Decisions

SEC. 2-1. THE COMPUTER AS A DECISION MAKER

The trend in business management is to reduce all aspects of the business to arithmetical quantities and then to analyze these factors mathematically in the attempt to develop and maintain optimum business conditions. Although many business aspects still defy adequate quantification, much progress has been made. Since business operations are exceedingly complex, any adequate analysis of even presently available information requires the processing of unending quantities of data.

Mathematicians and other scientists have recently done much research on the development of mathematical models representing certain business conditions. Probably the major impetus for this development was the introduction of the high-speed, electronic computer. Many of the mathematical models developed would have been of small use if the computations had to be made by hand, for the results would have been obtained too late to be used for decision making; in fact, in many cases, hand processing could not have been accomplished at all.

Some idea of the speed of modern electronic computers may be obtained from the following comparisons: The first electronic computer, the ENNIAC, was developed in 1946. One of its tasks was to compute the trajectory of projectiles, which it could do in 30 seconds, half the time required for the flight of the projectile. It would take 2400 girls operating desk calculators to make the same calculations![1]

The first general-purpose, large-scale electronic computer was the Univac I, developed in 1951. It astounded the American public in 1952 by analyzing the trends in the Eisenhower election and early correctly predicting the results. The Univac I had a capacity many times greater than the ENNIAC. (Computer capacity may be measured with respect

[1]Eugene M. Grabbe (ed.), *Automation in Business and Industry* (New York: John Wiley & Sons, Inc., 1957), p. 217.

8

to many factors, such as input-output capability, internal operating speeds, repertoire of available commands or operating codes, and so forth. Univac I represented a great advance in most of these aspects.) Yet the super-scale computer, IBM Stretch, had announced internal speeds so fast that, in 24 hours, it could make the same computations as Univac I computing 24 hours a day, 365 days per year for the eight years following the Eisenhower election (1952 to 1960).[2] Such performance could not in practice be achieved because of input-output limitations. Present internal speeds permit approximately one and one-half *million* additions per second.

Many of the mathematical models so far developed are not intended to make managerial decisions directly, but to analyze the probable results of alternative decisions so that managers may select that result most nearly meeting their objectives. Other models are designed to obtain the optimum results under existing conditions.

A very useful managerial principle is that of management by exception. The manager first lays down guidelines which specify limits or norms. Then clerks investigate each detailed situation and compare it to the guidelines. Only the exceptional cases—those outside the limits—are submitted to management for consideration. This, of course, is decision making, but of a low order. It is a type of decision making to which electronic computers can be easily adapted, and here computers found early use in business data processing. The role of computers in decision making is being rapidly expanded. Entire refining plants have been placed under the supervision of computers, with product mix being varied as supply and demand factors change. The future of computers as decision makers is indeed bright; so bright, in fact, that many observers view the future role of computers with alarm, fearing lest their use go too far in replacing human beings.

Although it is sometimes necessary to employ electronic computers when utilizing many of the mathematical tools discussed in this book, understanding electronic computers is not a prerequisite to understanding the tools. Illustrative problems can readily be solved with paper and pencil methods. In fact, many of the smaller practical problems can be solved this way. Nevertheless, some familiarity with electronic computers is desirable as a basis for understanding how the tools may be applied to solve problems too complex for hand solution.

SEC. 2-2. ELECTRONIC COMPUTER HARDWARE

The mechanical and electronic components of an electronic computer are referred to as the electronic computer *hardware*. So-called electronic

[2]Graham Jones, "Trends in Computer Hardware," *Datamation*, 7 (January, 1961), 11.

computer software is discussed in Sec. 2-5. The hardware may be divided into five major components or types of components, namely, input unit, storage unit, arithmetic unit, control unit, and output unit. Individual computers can come equipped with one or several of each of these units, with the possible exception of the control unit, and some computers have several types of control units.

The relationship between these major components is shown in Figure 2-1. The solid lines show the major flows of information within the computer; the dotted lines extending from the control unit to each of the other units are control lines showing that all other units are under the direction of the control unit.

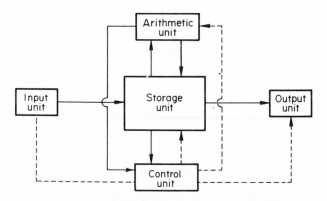

Fig. 2-1. The Major Components of an Electronic Computer

Information to be entered into the computer is usually on punched cards (Figure 2-2), punched paper tape, or magnetic tape. The latter is very similar to the magnetic tape of a home tape recorder. Input units that can read printed material are now available but are not yet in widespread use for typical data processing operations.

All information is normally entered into the computer through the input unit and placed directly in the storage unit. While in the storage unit, the information to be processed as data is indistinguishable in form from the information which is to instruct the computer in its operations. That is, both data and computer instructions are stored in the storage unit. Information to be used as data goes into the arithmetic unit to be processed. After processing, the data are usually returned to the storage unit. Information to be used as instructions for the computer goes into the control unit. Instructions usually tell the computer (1) to perform some arithmetic function, such as add, subtract, and so forth; (2) to make a logical decision, such as do one thing if A is greater than B, otherwise do

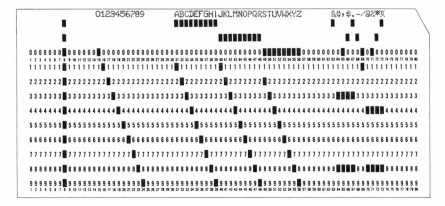

Fig. 2-2. Typical Punched Card

something else; (3) to bring information into or out of the computer. Notice that information can go from the arithmetic unit into the control unit to become an instruction. This is possible because data and instructions are both stored in the same general form and can therefore to some extent be used interchangeably. Information being brought out of the computer goes from the storage unit to the output unit.

SEC. 2-3. HOW THE COMPUTER PROCESSES DATA

In order to discuss how the computer processes data, a somewhat simplified hypothetical computer will be considered. This computer reads information from punched cards and as an output punches information into cards. It has a storage unit capable of storing 9000 alphanumerical characters. That is, each storage position may contain a numerical digit, a letter, or a special character, such as a punctuation mark. It is a fixed word-length computer with a nine-character word. A *computer word* may be defined as the amount of information which the computer treats as a unit of information. A word can be transferred intact; one word may be added to another, and so forth.

Computer operations may be roughly divided into three categories: (1) arithmetic operations, (2) logical operations, (3) data transfers. Some computers have as few as sixteen such operations, others may have operations numbering in the hundreds. Most computers can perform the four basic arithmetical operations—add, subtract, multiply, and divide. Logical operations usually take the form of comparisons or tests. Two numbers may be compared for magnitude: if the numbers are equal, perform one operation; if unequal, perform another. Data transfers involve the transfer of information into or out of the computer, from one place in storage to another, into or out of the arithmetic unit, and so forth.

Since the hypothetical computer has 9000 storage positions and a nine-character word length, it is capable of storing 1000 words. Each word location is identified by an address of three digits. The first address is 000 and the last is 999. Remember that either data or instructions can be stored at any of the 1000 addressable locations.

Assume that two numbers, 15 and 25, are to be added. Further assume that the 15 is stored in memory location 808 in the form 000000015 and the 25 is stored in location 926 in the form 000000025. The following computer program will cause the addition to be performed and the sum to be stored in location 758:

Location	Operation	Data Address	Instruction Address
000	RAD	808	001
001	ADD	926	002
002	STO	758	003
003	HLT	000	000

The location column merely indicates where in memory each instruction is located. Four instructions are needed, and they are stored in locations 000–003. Each instruction consists of nine characters (hence a computer word) and therefore can be stored at an addressable location.

To start the computer, the operator tells it to go to location 000 for its first instruction. Since the operator designated location 000 as containing an instruction, the computer transfers the nine characters, RAD808001, to the control unit. The control unit separates the instruction into three parts: (1) the operation code, (2) the data address, (3) the instruction address, thus:

Operation	Data Address	Instruction Address
RAD	808	001

It analyzes the operation code as to which operation to perform. The RAD tells the computer to reset the arithmetic unit to zeros and to then add into the arithmetic unit the number stored at the data address, location 808. The number 15 is stored at location 808, therefore the arithmetic unit now contains 000000015.

The first operation is completed, and the last three characters of the first instruction, 001, indicate the location of the next instruction. The nine characters at location 001, ADD926002, are automatically transferred to the control unit and are analyzed. The ADD indicates that a straight addition is to be performed (without resetting the arithmetic unit to zeros). Thus the contents of location 926 (the number 25) are added to the number in the arithmetic unit, which now contains 000000040. The next instruction in location 002 says to store the contents of the arithmetic unit in location 758. Location 758 now contains the desired sum, 000000040. The last instruction in location 003 stops the computer. Since every location must contain nine characters, the remaining six characters of this instruction were filled in with zeros.

SEC. 2-4. AN ILLUSTRATIVE COMPUTER PROBLEM

A more complex, but still very simple, computer problem will help to clarify many of these concepts. A company has 10,000 sets of three unequal, positive numbers. It wishes to list the smallest number in each set of three. That is, each set of three numbers is to be examined, the smallest number is then to be selected and listed.

Very complex data-processing problems are generally handled in three phases, namely, process analysis, detail flow charting, and computer coding. Although the simple problem selected for illustration could be coded directly into a computer program without such extensive analysis, the three phases will be presented.

The process flow chart is illustrated in Figure 2-3. It shows the flow of the work through the system as it passes from person to person or machine to machine. The first task is to keypunch each set of three numbers on a card. There will then be 10,000 cards in the input deck. The task of the computer is to select the smallest number of each set and punch it on a card. The output deck will also have 10,000 cards, but each card will now contain only one number. The information in the output deck is then listed on the printer.

The three numbers on the input deck may be referred to as *A*, *B*, and *C*, respectively. They will

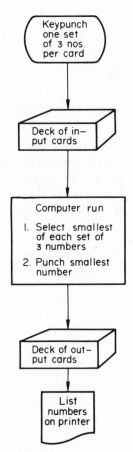

Fig. 2-3. Process Flow Chart

be punched into the card as follows (see Figure 2-2 for the available 80 columns of a punched card):

Number	Card Columns
A	1–10
B	11–20
C	21–30

The next step is to analyze the detailed operations to be carried on within the computer. This is most easily done by means of a detailed flow chart (Figure 2-4). No standardized symbols have been developed for detail flow charting. Each computer manufacturer has developed its own set of symbols. Those illustrated were developed by the Univac Division of Sperry Rand Corporation.

The first symbol (Start) designates the entrance point into the analysis.

The next symbol ① is a connector to which a return in the flow of information will occur. The [Read] indicates that the information from one

card is to be placed in storage. The next box (A: B) is a logical decision box and has two paths leading from it. If A is greater than ($>$) B, the flow goes to the right; if A is less than ($<$) B, the flow goes downward. If the flow goes to the right, then B is compared to C. Again two possible paths are available. If B is greater then ($>$) C, C is the smallest number. It is sent to output and punched on a card. The flow then goes back to

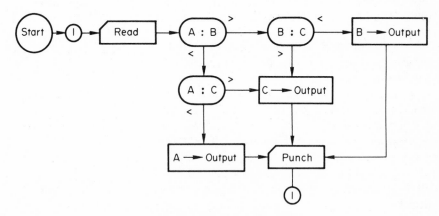

Fig. 2-4. Detailed Flow Chart

connector 1, and the information on the next card is read in. This cycle is repeated until all 10,000 sets of numbers have been analyzed. A typical speed at which this process could be performed is about 250 sets of numbers (cards) per minute. The limiting factor would be the speed of card punching, which is a mechanical (not electronic) process. (Trace each of the possible flow paths in Figure 2-4. A thorough understanding of this simple flow chart is highly desirable.)

The final step is to code the computer program, that is, to write the instructions for the computer. In writing the instructions, the detailed flow chart is carefully followed:

Location	Operation	Data Address	Instruction Address	Remarks
000	RDC	100	001	Read one set of numbers
001	RAD	100	002	
002	SUB	101	003	Compare A to B: if A < B, go to 010; if A > B, go to 004
003	BMI	010	004	
004	RAD	101	005	
005	SUB	102	006	Compare B to C: if B < C, go to 013; if B > C, go to 007
006	BMI	013	007	
007	RAD	101	008	C smallest
008	STO	200	009	Store in output area
009	PCH	200	000	Punch and return to 000
010	RAD	100	011	
011	SUB	102	012	Compare A to C: if A < C, go to 014; if A > C, go to 007
012	BMI	014	007	
013	RAD	101	008	B smallest
014	RAD	100	008	A smallest

Fourteen instructions are required for the program (in comparison to most practical programs, this is a very small number). The instruction in location 000 causes the computer to read (RCD) the information from the first card in the deck. The three numbers are placed in storage, A in 100, B in 101, and C in 102. The next three instructions compare A to B. This is done by subtracting (SUB) B from A and then testing the algebraic sign of the arithmetic unit. If the sign is positive, A is greater than B; if negative, B is greater than A.

The instruction in location 003 requires some explanation. It is called a *branch* or *logical instruction*. Notice that all the other instructions have a data address portion and an instruction address portion. The branch instruction has two instruction address portions. In this case, if the sign of the arithmetic unit is negative, the next instruction location is designated by the center three digits (010 in the case of the instruction in location 003). If the sign of the arithmetic unit is positive, then the location of the next instruction is designated by the last three digits (004 in this case).

If *A* is greater than *B*, the computer goes to location 004 and compares *B* to *C*. This comparison is performed in a fashion similar to that used previously. The branch instruction in location 006 again has two instruction addresses. If *B* is greater than *C*, *C* is the smallest number and is to be punched in a card. To do this, instructions 007 and 008 transfer *C* from location 101 to location 200, the punch-out area. Instruction 009 then causes *C* to be punched in a card and returns the program to location 000. The second card is read and the cycle starts over. (The reader should carefully trace the remaining segments of the program.)

SEC. 2-5. ELECTRONIC COMPUTER SOFTWARE

The computer programs so far discussed were coded in machine language. *Machine language* is a language intelligible to the computer. It is, however, difficult for the computer programmer to work in machine language. To help overcome this difficulty, a large number of programming aids, frequently referred to as *electronic computer software*, have been developed. These aids usually take the form of symbolic assembly programs, interpretive routines, compilers, and generators.

Symbolic assembly programs are designed primarily to permit the programmer to write in English language symbols rather than in machine language. The computer then converts the symbols into a machine language program. The program of Sec. 2-4, if written in a typical symbolic language, might appear as follows:

Location	Operation	Data Address	Instruction Address
START	RDC	A	
	RAD	A	
	SUB	B	
	BMI	BBIGA	ABIGB
ABIGB	RAD	B	
	SUB	C	
	BMI	CBIGB	BBIGC
BBIGC	RAD	C	STORE
STORE	STO	PUNCH	
	PCH	PUNCH	START
BBIGA	RAD	A	
	SUB	C	
	BMI	CBIGA	BBIGC
CBIGB	RAD	B	STORE
CBIGA	RAD	A	STORE

Notice how closely the symbols used follow normal English usage. Most symbolic assembly programs permit great latitude in selecting symbols. The usual restriction is in the maximum length permitted. Location and instruction addresses need be used only when the flow does not follow in sequence. Assembly programs may also perform other services for the programmer. Where some form of assembly program is available (and almost every computer has one or more assembly programs), few programmers code in machine language.

A more complex form of assembly program is known as a *compiler*. A compiler utilizes *macroinstructions*. One macroinstruction written by the programmer is converted into several (frequently many) machine language instructions by the compiler. Compilers may be machine oriented or problem oriented. A compiler is said to be *machine oriented* if the programmer must follow closely the pattern of the computer logic and machine language. It is said to be *problem oriented* if the programmer is permitted to write in the language and logic of the problem.

The output of an assembly program or a compiler is a machine language program. The programmer writes his program according to the rules of the assembler or compiler. His work is then processed on the computer under the supervision of the assembler or compiler, which then produces the machine language program. An *interpretive routine* permits the programmer to write in a nonmachine language, but it does not produce a machine language program as an intermediate product. Instead, the output of the interpretive routine is the results sought by the programmer—the problem solution. Interpretive routines are useful for one-shot programs. Because they are slow and inefficient, they are not suited to repetitive business data processing.

Generators produce specialized programs to fit the needs of the programmer. Examples of generators are sort generators and report generators. When the programmer desires to have the computer produce a certain type of report, he merely specifies the description of the report to the report generator, the number of columns required, the headings, and so forth. The report generator then produces a machine language program which will in turn produce the desired type of report.

The foregoing are a few examples of computer software. There are many other kinds, and much research is being done in producing better and more varied kinds of programming aids.

DISCUSSION QUESTIONS

2-1. What part have electronic computers played in the development of quantitative managerial techniques?

2-2. What is *management by exception?* What role can computers play in this concept?

2-3. What is meant by the term *electronic computer hardware?*

2-4. Name the major components of a computer and describe the function of each.

2-5. On what media is information usually stored in order to enter the information into the computer?

2-6. Describe the flow of information into and through the computer.

2-7. Distinguish between instructions and data *in* the computer.

2-8. Describe a computer instruction. What are the major functions of a computer instruction.

2-9. What is meant by the term *alphanumerical character*?

2-10. Define the term *computer word*.

2-11. What are the three main categories of computer operations?

2-12. What is an *addressable location*?

2-13. What is a *computer program*?

2-14. Describe the three stages of computer problem analysis.

2-15. Describe and state the purpose of a *process flow chart*.

2-16. Describe and state the purpose of a *detailed flow chart*.

2-17. Discuss in detail the functioning of a *branch instruction*.

2-18. What is meant by the term *electronic computer software*?

2-19. Describe and discuss the function of a *symbolic assembly program*.

2-20. What is a *compiler*?

2-21. What is a *macroinstruction*?

2-22. Discuss and distinguish between *machine-oriented* and *problem-oriented* compilers.

2-23. What is an *interpretive routine*?

2-24. Discuss the function of a *generator*.

PROBLEMS

2-1. Ten numbers are stored at locations 200–209. Write a computer program to add the 10 numbers and store the sum in location 300.

2-2. Five numbers are stored in locations 750–754. Write a program to find the average of the five numbers and store the average in location 800. The divide operation code is DVD.

2-3. There are 10 numbers in locations 400–409 and 1 number in location 500. Write a computer program to add the 10 numbers and then to compare the sum to the number in location 500. If the sum is greater than the number in location 500, place the sum in location 600. If the sum is less than the number in location 500, replace the number in location 500 with the sum.

2-4. The employee's gross pay is stored in location 300. If his year-to-date pay is equal to or less than $4800, his gross pay is subject to 3 5/8 per cent social security tax. If his prior year-to-date pay is in excess of $4800, his gross pay is not subject to any social security tax. Otherwise, part of his gross pay is subject to tax.

(a) Draw a detailed flow chart showing these relationships.

(b) Write a computer program to compute the social security tax. The multiply operation code is MPY. Store the amount of the social security tax in location 305.

2-5. An employee is paid either his base pay or his piecework pay, whichever is higher. The employees' names are listed in card columns 1–27, their base pay in columns 28–36, and their piecework earnings in columns 37–45. In reading the information into the computer, the names will be read into locations 100, 101, and 102, the base pay into location 103, and the piecework into location 104. Information to be printed out must be in locations 301–309. All nine words are printed at once by a WRT instruction. The words in 301–309 have all been preset to blanks. Write a program to print out the employees' names and their correct pay.

2-6. Obtain an instruction manual for an existing computer and redo Problems 2-1 through 2-5 using the correct procedures for the computer selected.

2-7. Obtain an instruction manual for a symbolic programming system for the computer selected for Problem 2-6 and redo Problems 2-1 through 2-5 using the correct procedures for the symbolic system.

BIBLIOGRAPHY

Brooks, Frederick P., Jr., and Kenneth E. Iverson, *Automatic Data Processing.* New York: John Wiley & Sons, Inc., 1963.

Chapin, Ned, *An Introduction to Automatic Computers.* Princeton, N.J.: D. Van Nostrand Company, Inc., 1963.

Gotlieb, C.C., and J.N.P. Hume, *High-Speed Data Processing.* New York: McGraw-Hill Book Company, Inc., 1958.

Gregory, Robert H., and Richard L. Van Horn, *Automatic Data-Processing Systems.* Belmont, Calif.: Wadsworth Publishing Company, Inc., 1963.

Hein, Leonard W., *An Introduction to Electronic Data Processing for Business.* Princeton, N.J.: D. Van Nostrand Company, Inc., 1961.

Ledley, Robert S., *Programming and Utilizing Digital Computers.* New York: McGraw-Hill Book Company, Inc., 1962.

Martin, E. Wainright, Jr., *Electronic Data Processing—An Introduction.* Homewood, Ill.: Richard D. Irwin, Inc., 1961.

McCracken, Daniel D., Harold Weiss, and Tsai-Hwa Lee, *Programming Business Computers.* New York: John Wiley & Sons, Inc., 1959.

Schmidt, Richard, and William E. Meyers, *Electronic Business Data Processing.* New York: Holt, Rinehart, and Winston, 1963.

3

The Distribution Problem: I

SEC. 3-1.   THE BASIC PROBLEM TO BE SOLVED

The Apex Distributing Company is the distributor for a television receiver manufacturer. Apex owns three warehouses as follows:

Location	Sets in Stock
Los Angeles	100
Fresno	25
Las Vegas	75

It has the following orders for set deliveries:

Location	Orders
San Francisco	80
Boise	30
San Diego	90

Delivery costs from each warehouse to each customer are largely a function of mileage or distance. The per unit costs have been determined to be

	San Francisco	Boise	San Diego
Los Angeles	5	10	2
Fresno	3	7	5
Las Vegas	6	8	4

These deliveries could be made in very many ways, but the distributor would like to deliver the television sets in a way that would minimize his

20

delivery costs. Given this simple situation it would not be too difficult to arrive at the least-cost delivery pattern by inspection or by trial-and-error methods. If, however, Apex had 25 warehouses and 100 customers, then the complexity of the problem would make a trial-and-error solution extremely difficult if not impossible.

Such a problem is known as the *distribution* or *transportation* problem. A simplified approach to solving the distribution problem was originated by W.W. Cooper and A. Charnes and subsequently refined by others. The remainder of this chapter deals with this approach.

SEC. 3-2. SETTING UP THE DISTRIBUTION MATRIX

Note that Apex has 200 television sets on hand and has orders for exactly the same number. This happy situation may not be the usual one in business, but such an assumption simplifies somewhat the solution to the problem. (The slightly more complicated problem of unequal supply and demand conditions is treated in Chapter 4.)

The first step in solving the distribution problem is to set up a matrix (see Figure 3-1) with one row for each warehouse and one column for each customer, plus two extra rows and columns. Each row and column is labeled with the appropriate source and destination. The additional rows are labeled *to* and *demand*, and the additional columns, *from* and *supply*. The figures for the available supply (Los Angeles, 100; Fresno, 25; and Las Vegas, 75) are entered in the supply column. Similarly, the orders (San Francisco, 80; Boise, 30; and San Diego, 90) are entered in the de-

| | | −5 | −10 | −8 | |
	From \ To	San Francisco	Boise	San Diego	Supply
0	Los Angeles	−5 · 80	−10 · 20	−2 · (−6)	100
+3	Fresno	−3 · (+1)	−7 · 10	−5 · 15	25
+4	Las Vegas	−6 · (+5)	−8 · (+2)	−4 · 75	75
	Demand	80	30	90	200 / 200

Fig. 3-1. Matrix and Initial Feasible Solution

mand row. The 200's in the lower right-hand box indicate that supply equals demand. The figures in the demand row and the supply column are called *rim values*.

The matrix is now complete, and the next step is to obtain the *initial feasible solution*. To do this, the *northwest corner* method is used. The name is derived from map directions, the northwest corner being the upper left corner of the matrix. Place in the northwest corner square the smaller of the rim values for that row and column. The rim value for the row is 100 and for the column, 80. Therefore place 80 in the northwest corner square. This signifies that 80 sets are to be shipped from Los Angeles to San Francisco. Because the rim value of the column was less than that for the row, the next square to be filled is the one to the right of the square just filled. Los Angeles still has 20 sets available for allocation (100 − 80 = 20). Boise has ordered 30. Therefore, place the 20 in the Los Angeles–Boise square. The Los Angeles supply has now been completely allocated, thus another move to the right cannot be made. The next square to be filled is down, that is, Fresno-Boise square. Fresno has 25 sets available, and Boise has an unsatisfied order for 10 sets. Therefore, 10 sets of the Fresno supply will be allocated to Boise.

Another downward move cannot be made because Boise's demand has been completely filled. The next square to be filled is the Fresno–San Diego square. The remaining Fresno supply of 15 is used to fill part of the San Diego demand of 90. Thus 15 is placed in the Fresno–San Diego square, leaving San Diego with a remaining demand for 75 units. Las Vegas, however, has exactly 75 units unallocated, which are assigned in the Las Vegas–San Diego square.

It is readily apparent that this is a feasible solution, but no claim can yet be made that it is a least-cost solution. The cost of this delivery pattern can, nevertheless, be easily computed. The cost per unit shipment from Los Angeles to San Francisco is $5. This cost is inserted in the sub-square of the Los Angeles–San Francisco square. Each of the other per unit costs are also inserted in the appropriate sub-squares. The units to be shipped are then multiplied by their related costs and the products summed to obtain the total shipping cost:

Shipment	Units	× Unit Cost	= Shipping Cost
Los Angeles–San Francisco	80	5	400
Los Angeles–Boise	20	10	200
Fresno–Boise	10	7	70
Fresno–San Diego	15	5	75
Las Vegas–San Diego	75	4	300
Total shipping cost			1045

It is necessary to explain why the per unit shipping costs were inserted in the sub-squares as negative values. *The distribution method as described here maximizes the objective value sought.* (By making certain modifications in the procedures, the method can be used to minimize the objective value.) If the values in the sub-squares were per unit *profits* rather than costs, the $1045 would represent total profits on the sale of television receivers. The objective would then be to increase the profits above the $1045 figure; in fact, the objective would be to *maximize* that figure. Here, however, the sub-square figures represent cost, and the objective is to *minimize* total distribution costs. If the $1045 is a negative figure, then to maximize it will cause it to approach zero. (If two negative numbers are compared for magnitude, that number is the greater which is closer to zero.)

The next step is to ascertain whether the solution obtained is the optimum solution. An *optimum solution* is that solution which most nearly achieves the desired objective. In this case, the desired objective is to distribute the television sets at no (zero) cost. Since that objective cannot be achieved, the solution which brings the delivery costs closest to zero will be the optimum solution. The test for optimization requires two phases: (1) computation of row and column values, (2) computation of the values of unoccupied squares.

SEC. 3-3. COMPUTING ROW AND COLUMN VALUES

Computing the row and column values involves a simple problem in algebraic addition. In computing r (row) and c (column) values, *only occupied squares are considered.* The rule is

> The sum of the row value and the column value is equal to the value in the sub-square of an occupied square.

Computation of the r and c values for Figure 3-1 will illustrate this. A zero (any arbitrarily selected number may be used) is placed to the left of the row of the first occupied square (in this case, row 1). Following the rule:

$$0 + (-5) = -5.$$

Therefore the c value is -5, which is placed over the column concerned (in this case, column 1). The next occupied square to consider is row 1, column 2 (Los Angeles–Boise).

$$0 + (-10) = -10.$$

Place a -10 over column 2. The next r and c value to be determined must be row 2. Column 2 value $= -10$. Therefore,

$$-10 + (+3) = -7,$$

and row 2 value $= +3$. Similarly, column 3 value is computed as -8 and row 3 value as $+4$.

The following table shows the computations:

Occupied Square	r Value	$+ c$ Value	$=$ Sub-square Value
r_1c_1	0	-5	-5
r_1c_2	0	-10	-10
r_2c_2	$+3$	-10	-7
r_2c_3	$+3$	-8	-5
r_3c_3	$+4$	-8	-4

Notice that once the arbitrary zero is placed to the left of row 1, all r and c values are then determined and cannot vary. Notice also that a specific pattern must be followed in computing the r and c values, going from a known r or c value to the unknown r or c value.

SEC. 3-4. EVALUATING UNOCCUPIED MATRIX POSITIONS

The evaluation of the unoccupied squares also utilizes the r and c values and the values in the sub-squares. This time, however,

The value in the sub-square is subtracted from the sum of the r and c values pertaining to the unoccupied square being evaluated.

In Figure 3-1, row 2, column 1 (Fresno–San Francisco) is unoccupied. To evaluate the square, sum the r and c values,

$$+3 + (-5) = -2,$$

and then subtract the value in the sub-square (-3):

$$-2 - (-3) = +1.$$

The value of unoccupied square r_2c_1 equals $+1$, and that value is placed in the space just under the sub-square. The values of each unoccupied square may be computed without regard to order, since all necessary data

(r, c, and sub-square values) are available. The following table shows the computation of the values of the remaining unoccupied squares:

Square	r Value $+$ c Value $=$ Sum of r and c $-$ Sub-square Value $=$ Unoccupied Square Value				
r_2c_1	$+3$	-5	-2	-3	$+1$
r_3c_1	$+4$	-5	-1	-6	$+5$
r_3c_2	$+4$	-10	-6	-8	$+2$
r_1c_3	0	-8	-8	-2	-6

SEC. 3-5. MOVING TOWARD THE OPTIMUM POSITION

After the unoccupied squares have been evaluated, the signs of the values indicate whether optimization has been achieved. The signs have the following significance:

1. A negative value in an unoccupied square indicates that a better solution can be had by moving units into the unoccupied square.
2. A positive value in an occupied square indicates that a poorer solution will result if units are moved into that square.
3. A zero value in an unoccupied square indicates that another solution of equal total value is available by moving units into the zero value square.

A glance at Figure 3-1 reveals that an improved solution can be had by moving into only one of the unoccupied squares (r_1c_3); all other unoccupied squares have positive values and a move into any of those squares would result in a poorer solution. It will frequently be found that there will be more than one square with a negative value (for example, see Figure 3-4). Although a move into any of the negatively valued squares would result in an improvement, *a move into the most negative square will result in the greatest improvement.* The square selected to be moved into is indicated by placing a plus ($+$) sign in it, in this case in square r_1c_3 in Figure 3-2. The plus signifies that units are to be added to square r_1c_3. But if units are added to r_1c_3, then the same number of units must be subtracted from either square r_2c_3 or square r_3c_3; otherwise San Diego will get more television sets than it has ordered. A minus ($-$) sign is placed in square r_2c_3 to indicate the necessary reduction in units. (As will be seen presently, it would not do to place the minus in r_3c_3.) This is called *maintaining the rim values*, since the sum of the units in each column and in each row must always equal the respective rim values.

Evidently, if the units in r_2c_3 are reduced below 15, then the sum of the units in row 2 will not equal 25. Therefore, units must be added in some square in row 2. It would appear that either of the two available

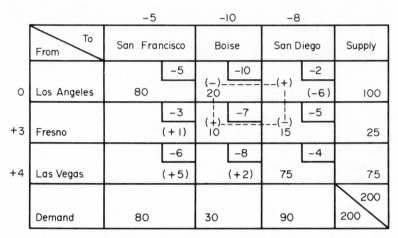

Fig. 3-2. Moving Toward the Optimum Condition

squares (r_2c_1 or r_2c_2) would do. However,

> The number of occupied squares must always equal the number of rows plus the number of columns minus one ($r + c - 1$).

In this problem there are three rows and three columns. Thus there can be only

$$3 + 3 - 1 = 5$$

occupied squares. To maintain the required $r + c - 1$ condition, one for-

From \ To		San Francisco (−5)		Boise (−10)		San Diego (−2)	Supply
0	Los Angeles	−5 / 80		−10 / (−)−−−5	−(+)	−2 / 15	100
+3	Fresno	−3 / (+1)		−7 / 25		−5 / (+6)	25
−2	Las Vegas	−6 / (−1)		−8 / (+)−−−(−4)	−(½)	−4 / 75	75
	Demand	80		30		90	200 / 200

Fig. 3-3. Second Iteration of the Distribution Problem

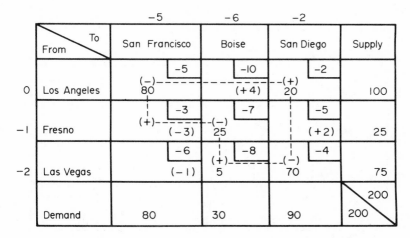

Fig. 3-4. Third Iteration of the Distribution Problem

merly unoccupied square is to be occupied, one formerly occupied square is to become unoccupied, and *all other movements must take place in occupied squares*. Therefore, the compensating plus sign for row 2 must be placed in square $r_2 c_2$ (Figure 3-2). The same reasoning requires that a minus sign be placed in square $r_1 c_2$. The dotted lines indicate the squares affected.

The next question is, how many units should be moved to square $r_1 c_3$? The answer is, as many as possible, for if money will be saved by moving one unit, it is clear that more money will be saved if more units are transferred. The limiting factor is the *smallest unit value in the squares in which the minus signs were just placed*. In Figure 3-2, this is square $r_2 c_3$ which contains a -15. All squares containing plus or minus signs are adjusted by the value 15, adding or subtracting as the signs indicate. The resulting new solution is shown in Figure 3-3. The evaluation of the total cost of this solution is

Shipment	Units	× Unit Cost	= Shipping Cost
Los Angels–San Francisco	80	5	400
Los Angeles–Boise	5	10	50
Los Angeles–San Diego	15	2	30
Fresno–Boise	25	7	175
Las Vegas–San Diego	75	4	300
Total shipping cost			955

The total shipping cost for the delivery pattern for iteration 2 is $955, or $90 under the $1045 of the pattern of the initial feasible solution. Iteration 2 must now be tested for optimization. The process is identical to

From \ To	San Francisco (−5)	Boise (−6)	San Diego (−2)	Supply
Los Angeles (0)	−5 (−)‑55	−10 (+4)	−2 (+)‑45	100
Fresno (+2)	−3 25	−7 (+3)	−5 (+5)	25
Las Vegas (−2)	−6 (+)‑(−1)	−8 30	−4 (−)‑45	75
Demand	80	30	90	200 / 200

Fig. 3-5. Fourth Iteration of the Distribution Problem

that used in iteration 1. ALL r and c values must be recomputed; ALL unoccupied square values must be recomputed. In some cases, some of the recomputed values will be the same as in the preceding iteration, but such will not always be the case. The r and c values and the unoccupied square values for iteration 2 are shown in Figure 3-3; the new move positions are also shown. This problem, as set up, requires five iterations to optimize. Iterations 3, 4, and 5 are shown in Figures 3-4, 3-5, and 3-6, respectively. Since iteration 5 has no negative values in the unoccupied squares, it represents the optimum solution. Notice (Figure 3-4) that the movement of units may require a more complex arrangement than merely a

From \ To	San Francisco (−5)	Boise (−7)	San Diego (−2)	Supply
Los Angeles (0)	−5 10	−10 (+3)	−2 90	100
Fresno (+2)	−3 25	−7 (+2)	−5 (+2)	25
Las Vegas (−1)	−6 45	−8 30	−4 (+1)	75
Demand	80	30	90	200 / 200

Fig. 3-6. Fifth Iteration and Optimum Solution

rectangular pattern affecting adjacent squares. The progression through the five iterations is shown by the following:

Iteration	Total Cost	Savings over Previous Iteration
1	1045	—
2	955	90
3	935	20
4	860	75
5	815	45

SEC. 3-6. SUMMARY OF STEPS OF THE DISTRIBUTION METHOD

1. Lay out the matrix, allowing one column for each destination and two designated *from* and *supply*, and one row for each source and two designated *to* and *demand*. (One additional column and/or row may be required for unequal demand and supply conditions. See Chapter 4.)

2. Obtain the initial feasible solution by using the northwest corner method.

3. Obtain row and column values using the formula: $r + c =$ value in the sub-square.

4. Evaluate unoccupied squares by using the formula: $r + c -$ (value in the sub-square).

5. Test for optimization. Move to the most negative unoccupied square.

6. Repeat steps 3-5 until all unoccupied squares have positive values.

DISCUSSION QUESTIONS

3-1. Discuss the basic problem to which the distribution method applies. Are there other types of problems which could be solved by the same method?

3-2. Describe how to set up the distribution matrix. What is the significance of the *supply column* and the *demand row*?

3-3. Discuss the concept of the *initial feasible solution*. Explain the *northwest corner* approach. Would a southeast corner do just as well? Northeast?

3-4. What is meant by the term *rim values*?

3-5. Explain how to evaluate a given solution.

3-6. The per unit costs were entered in the sub-squares as negative values. Explain the reasoning behind this. How would you handle per unit profit figures?

3-7. Explain how to compute row and column values.

3-8. How are the unoccupied squares evaluated? Discuss the significance of these evaluations.

3-9. Describe the method of moving toward the optimum position. How is the amount of the move determined?

3-10. The distribution method is known as an *iterative* process. In this context describe what is meant by an iteration of the distribution method.

3-11. What is the rule pertaining to the number of occupied squares? Is this a hard-and-fast or a flexible rule?

3-12. What is the test for optimization?

PROBLEMS

3-1. The A Company has three warehouses and three customers as follows:

Warehouses	Capacity	Customers	Demand
Chicago	30	Bangor	10
New Orleans	90	Baltimore	100
New York	40	Miami	50

Shipping Costs:

	Bangor	Baltimore	Miami
Chicago	50	32	61
New Orleans	80	52	35
New York	20	9	58

Required:
a. The least-cost shipping schedule.
b. The evaluation of each iteration.

3-2. The A Company, of Problem 3-1, has increased its New York capacity to 70 units and has obtained a customer in Louisville for the additional 30 units. The shipping costs involved are

	Louisville
Chicago	14
New Orleans	33
New York	34

Required:
a. The least-cost shipping schedule.
b. The evaluation of each iteration.

3-3. The B Company has three factories and three customers as follows:

Factories	Capacity	Customers	Demand
Omaha	75	Wichita	50
Dallas	80	Albuquerque	100
Phoenix	35	Denver	40

The B Company can make the following per unit profits:

Place Manufactured	Place Sold	Profit per Unit
Omaha	Wichita	38
Omaha	Albuquerque	14
Omaha	Denver	26
Dallas	Wichita	34
Dallas	Albuquerque	23
Dallas	Denver	17
Phoenix	Wichita	5
Phoenix	Albuquerque	33
Phoenix	Denver	21

Required:
  a. The maximum-profit distribution schedule.
  b. The evaluation of each iteration.

3-4. The B Company, of Problem 3-3, has increased its Omaha capacity to 95 units and has obtained a customer in Kansas City for the additional 20 units. The additional profit per unit figures are

Place Manufactured	Place Sold	Profit per Unit
Omaha	Kansas City	8
Dallas	Kansas City	10
Phoenix	Kansas City	20

Required:
  a. The maximum-profit distribution schedule.
  b. The evaluation of each iteration.

3-5. The C Company has three factories and three customers as follows:

Factory	Capacity	Production Cost per Unit
Detroit	85	50
Chicago	45	30
Cleveland	75	40

Customer	Demand	Selling Price
Wichita	100	100
Houston	80	110
Memphis	25	105

Shipping Costs:

	Wichita	Houston	Memphis
Detroit	43	57	33
Chicago	30	49	25
Cleveland	44	58	33

Required:
   a. The maximum-profit distribution schedule.
   b. The evaluation of each iteration.

3-6. The C Company, of Problem 3-5, has increased its Chicago capacity to 85 units and has obtained a customer in Denver for the additional 40 units. The selling price per unit in Denver is $125 and the shipping costs from Detroit, Chicago, and Cleveland are $60, $47, and $64, respectively.

Required:
   a. The maximum-profit distribution schedule.
   b. The evaluation of each iteration.

BIBLIOGRAPHY

See end of Chapter 4.

4

The Distribution Problem: II

SEC. 4-1. THE MORE COMPLEX DISTRIBUTION PROBLEM

The Apex Distributing Company in Chapter 3 had available 100 television receivers and had orders for exactly the same number of sets. Such a condition would probably be the exception rather than the rule. In the more usual situation, the company either has more orders than it can fill or its available supply exceeds its orders. In either case (barring other factors which must be considered), the company will seek the least-cost distribution pattern. In the case of the excess of orders over available supply, factors other than cost may be controlling, since one or more customers will not receive the full quantity ordered. If these factors can be quantified, the quantities may be treated as costs and added to any other cost figures to be placed in the sub-squares. If the factors cannot be quantified, the distribution method may still be applicable. One such application is considered in Sec. 4-3.

For illustration of the unequal supply-demand situation, the Apex Distributing Company in the period subsequent to that of Chapter 3 has more orders than it has stock on hand:

Warehouses	Sets in Stock	Customers	Orders
Los Angeles	100	San Francisco	105
Fresno	25	Boise	30
Las Vegas	75	San Diego	90
	200		225

The per unit shipping costs remain the same. Obviously, at least one order will not be fully shipped. Two questions require answering: (1) Which customer(s) will not receive a full order? (2) What is the least-cost distribution pattern?

SEC. 4-2. HANDLING UNEQUAL SUPPLY-DEMAND CONDITIONS

Figure 4-1 shows the second shipping problem of the Apex Distributing Company set up in a matrix as described in Chapter 3. A glance at the lower, right-hand square reveals that the 200 sets in stock are not equal to the orders for 225 sets. The distribution method, however, will not function unless the figures in that square are equal—in other words, unless supply equals demand. Therefore an adjustment must be made to the matrix in order to achieve the required condition. This is done by increasing the available supply by adding a row (designated *dummy*, representing a fictitious supplier) as shown in Figure 4-2. If supply exceeds demand, an extra column for a dummy customer would be provided. The northwest corner method is then used to obtain the initial feasible solution. The costs are entered in the sub-squares as usual.

But, what costs should be entered in the sub-squares pertaining to the dummy supplier? A rational answer would appear to be zeros, since the dummy supplier will make no shipments, and therefore no costs will be incurred. A second argument in favor of the use of zeros is that when an iteration is evaluated, any units appearing in the dummy row will be multiplied by a zero cost factor, and hence will have no effect upon the evaluation. Mathematically, however, the only necessary consideration is that the cost values in the dummy row be equal. The equality of these values signifies indifference as to which customer's order(s) will be short. The insertion of plus (say, $+10$'s) or minus (say, -10's) figures in each sub-square of the dummy row will have no effect upon the resulting distribution pattern. The reader is urged to solve the illustrative problem using (1) zeros in the dummy row, (2) $+10$'s in the dummy row, (3) -10's

To From	San Francisco	Boise	San Diego	Supply
Los Angeles				100
Fresno				25
Las Vegas				75
Demand	105	30	90	225 / 200

Fig. 4-1. Unbalanced Supply-Demand Condition

	To / From	San Francisco	Boise	San Diego	Supply
		−5	−9	−5	
0	Los Angeles	−5 100	−10 (+1)	−2 (−3)	100
+2	Fresno	−3 5	−7 20	−5 (+2)	25
+1	Las Vegas	−6 (+2)	−8 (−)----(+) 10	−4 65	75
+5	Dummy	0 (0)	0 (+)----(−) (−5)	0 25	25
	Demand	105	30	90	225 / 225

Fig. 4-2. The Use of a Dummy Supplier

in the dummy row as an empirical test of this statement. Figure 4-2 shows the completed first iteration, including the test for optimization. This particular problem (as set up) requires five iterations to optimize (see Figure 4-3 for the fifth and optimum iteration). The reader is urged to carry the problem through the intervening iterations.

	To / From	San Francisco	Boise	San Diego	Supply
		−5	−7	−2	
0	Los Angeles	−5 10	−10 (+3)	−2 90	100
+2	Fresno	−3 25	−7 (+2)	−5 (+2)	25
−1	Las Vegas	−6 70	−8 5	−4 (+1)	75
+7	Dummy	0 (+2)	0 25	0 (+5)	25
	Demand	105	30	90	225 / 225

Fig. 4-3. Iteration 5, Optimum Solution

SEC. 4-3. PROHIBITED SHIPMENT-RECEIPT COMBINATIONS

There are occasions when a given shipment-receipt route must be prohibited. Such a condition is more usual when the distribution method is used to solve scheduling problems other than transportation problems (see discussion of this type of problem in Sec. 4-5). As an illustration, presume that, in the preceding problem, no shipment can be made between Las Vegas and Boise. There are a number of ways to handle this situation, two of which will be discussed here. The first method lends itself to mathematical manipulation; therefore a modification of it may be used if the problem is to be solved on an electronic computer. The second method has distinct advantages if the solution is to be obtained by hand computation.

By the first method, a $-M$ cost is assigned to the prohibited square. The M stands for a value which is greater than any other value except another M. The standard procedures of the distribution method are then carried out, beginning with the northwest corner approach. However, in computing the r, c, and unoccupied square values, the M's are treated as an algebraic unknown. Thus a row, column, or unoccupied square value may appear as $-M$; $+M$; $3 + (-M)$; $(-M) + (-5)$; $M + (-2)$; $M + 6$; and so forth. Remember that magnitude has significance in choosing the unoccupied square into which to move—a $(-M) + (-3)$ is more negative than a $(-M) + (-1)$, even though the $-M$'s are very negative numbers.

From \ To		San Francisco -5	Boise -9	San Diego $+M-5$	Supply
0	Los Angeles	-5 100	-10 $(+1)$	-2 $(+M-3)$	100
$+2$	Fresno	-3 5	-7 20	-5 $(+M+2)$	25
$-M+9$	Las Vegas	-6 $(-M+10)$	$-M$ $(-)$ 10	-4 $(+)$ 65	75
$-M+5$	Dummy	0 $(-M)$	0 $(+)$ $(-M-4)$	0 $(-)$ 25	25
	Demand	105	30	90	225 / 225

Fig. 4-4. Use of $-M$'s

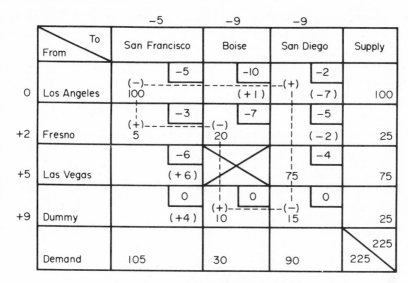

Fig. 4-5. Prohibited Shipment-Receipt Route

The use of the M's is shown in Figure 4-4. Since $(-M) + (-4)$ is more negative than either $(-M) + 10$ or $-M$, the Dummy-Boise square is selected as the square into which to move units. Notice that the square with the $-M$ cost is vacated immediately.

The second method for handling prohibited shipment-receipt routes is merely to block out the prohibited square. This is shown in Figure 4-5. Again, the northwest corner approach is used. After 20 units have been entered in the Fresno-Boise square, however, the next square to be filled would normally be that one which is now prohibited. This square is skipped, and 10 units are entered in the Dummy-Boise square. Proceeding to the right, the remaining Dummy supply of 15 units is entered in the Dummy–San Diego square. Then enter the Las Vegas supply of 75 units in the Las Vegas–San Diego square, and the initial feasible solution is completed. The procedures for computing the r, c, and unoccupied square values and for making moves remain the same.

SEC. 4-4. THE DEGENERATE CONDITION

The distribution method requires that the number of occupied squares be equal to the number of rows plus the number of columns minus one ($r + c - 1$). It is possible for a feasible solution to occur with fewer than $r + c - 1$ occupied squares. This condition is known as *degeneracy*. It is then impossible to calculate all of the row and column values, since $r + c - 1$ squares must be occupied for all r and c values to be determined after the arbitrary evaluation of one row or column.

The degenerate condition can be illustrated by changing the preceding figures as follows:

Warehouses	Sets in Stock	Customers	Demand
Los Angeles	100	San Francisco	95
Fresno	25	Boise	30
Las Vegas	75	San Diego	75

The only change is that orders from San Diego have been reduced from 90 to 75. Figure 4-6 shows the first iteration completed including the test

		−5	−8	−5	
	From \ To	San Francisco	Boise	San Diego	Supply
0	Los Angeles	−5 100	−10 (+1)	−2 (−3)	100
+2	Fresno	−3 5	−7 20	−5 (+2)	25
+1	Las Vegas	−6 (+2)	−8 (−) 10	−4 (+) 65	75
+5	Dummy	0 (0)	0 (+) (−5)	0 (−) 10	10
	Demand	105	30	75	210 \ 210

Fig. 4-6. Illustration of Degenerate Condition

for optimization. Notice that the pattern of unit movements has two negative squares, each of which contains ten units. On the next iteration, these *two* squares will be unoccupied. Since only one new square will be occupied, the number of occupied squares will equal $r + c - 2$.

There are several possible ways to handle a degenerate condition. One of the simpler ways is by inserting a zero unit value in one of the squares which were just vacated. Although this square will contain no effective unit value, it will be treated as an occupied square when computing the r, c, and unoccupied square values. The second iteration is shown in Figure 4-7. Notice that in this case the movement of unit values involves only shifting the zero unit value from the Dummy–San Diego square to the Los Angeles–San Diego square.

Since two squares were vacated, the question arises as to which to select for the insertion of the zero unit value. In many cases it makes little difference. In this case, optimization occurs in five iterations if the zero is placed in the Dummy–San Diego square and in four iterations if placed in the Las Vegas–Boise square. In other cases, a wrong selection may result in *cycling*. That is, instead of each iteration proceeding toward the optimum solution, some iterations will move away from the optimum, with solution patterns being repeated in a cycling process. In the event that cycling occurs, the iteration in which the zero unit value was introduced must be repeated, with the zero unit value being inserted in the other possible location. Notice that more than one zero unit value may be

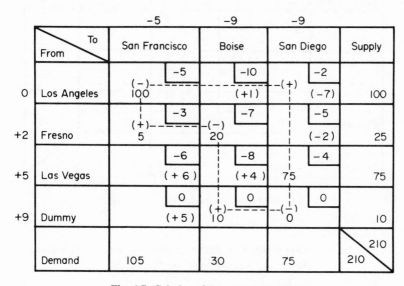

Fig. 4-7. Solution of Degenerate Condition

required. In those cases where minus signs are placed in more than two squares (and in large problems there may be many such squares), should several of the squares have equal unit value, then the number of occupied squares may be even less than $r + c - 2$.

The tendency to cycle may be eliminated by the following method:

1. Fill in with zeros sufficient of the squares which were vacated by the most recent move to bring the number occupied up to $r + c - 1$.
2. Evaluate the remaining unoccupied squares.
3. If the most negatively valued unoccupied square is one of those vacated in the last move, shift one of the zero unit values to that square.

4. Repeat 2 and 3 until the most negatively valued unoccupied square is a square other than one vacated during the last movement of units.

5. Proceed with the subsequent iterations.

Degeneracy can occur in the initial feasible solution when the available supply of one supplier exactly equals the demand of one customer. This is illustated in Figure 4-8. A zero unit value is inserted in the manner just discussed.

From \ To	San Francisco		Boise		San Diego		Supply
		−5		−10		−2	
Los Angeles	100		0				100
		−3		−7		−5	
Fresno			25				25
		−6		−8		−4	
Las Vegas			5		70		75
		0		0		0	
Dummy					10		10
							210
Demand	100		30		80		210

Fig. 4-8. Degeneracy in the Initial Feasible Solution

SEC. 4-5. APPLYING THE DISTRIBUTION METHOD TO OTHER THAN TRANSPORTATION PROBLEMS

The distribution method may be used to solve many problems other than those involving the transportation of goods. The method applies generally to the assignment of sources to objects when the items involved can be considered in terms of units. Some examples of this more extended application are assigning men to tasks, assigning jobs to machines, scheduling production to shifts and days, and so forth. Inherent in each of these assignment prolems is the existence of a large number of possible patterns in which the major objective may be accomplished. In the transportation problem, the major objective is to deliver the goods from the sources to the destinations. The secondary objective is usually (but not necessarily) to achieve the major objective with the least possible cost, or in such a way as to result in the largest possible profit.

The assignment of jobs to machines may be used as an example. Jobs J_1, J_2, and J_3 may be made on any of machines M_1, M_2, or M_3. Machine M_2 requires half the operating time of M_1, and machine M_3 requires twice the time of M_1. Machine and labor costs are

Machine	Cost per Hour
M_1	$2.00
M_2	3.00
M_3	1.50

If, however, J_1 is performed on M_2, extra labor costs of $2 per hour are incurred, and if J_3 is performed on M_3, extra labor costs of $1 are incurred. Unit production times (in hours) per machine for each job are

	J_1	J_2	J_3
M_1	0.5	0.125	0.25
M_2	0.25	0.0625	0.125
M_3	1.0	0.25	0.5

Machine times available are

Machine	Hours
M_1	10
M_2	20
M_3	30

Job requirments in units are

Job	Units
J_1	30
J_2	72
J_3	60

In order to apply the distribution method to this problem, the rim values and the values in the sub-squares must refer to the same type of units. Here all units may be stated in terms of M_1 hours. Machine M_2 has 20 hours available but can do twice the work of M_1. Therefore the equivalent M_1 hours are 40. Similarly, M_3 has 30 hours available but can do only half the work of M_1. Hence M_3 has 15 equivalent M_1 hours.

The job units also must be expressed in terms of M_1 hours. J_1 requires 30 units and takes 0.5 hour per unit, hence requiring 15 M_1 hours. Similarly, J_2 requires 0.125 × 72 or 9 M_1 hours, and J_3 requires 0.25 × 60 = 15 M_1 hours.

The costs to be placed in the sub-squares must be costs per M_1 hour.

First the costs per unit are computed by multiplying the cost per hour by the required time per unit. The extra cost of $2 per hour for J_1 on M_2 and of $1 per hour for J_3 on M_3 must be included. Thus the cost per hour of M_1 is $2 and the time per unit of J_1 on M_1 is 0.5. Hence,

$$\$2 \times 0.5 = \$1.00.$$

The costs per unit are

	J_1	J_2	J_3
M_1	$2.0 \times 0.5 = 1.00$	$2.0 \times 0.125 = 0.25$	$2.0 \times 0.25 = 0.50$
M_2	$5.0 \times 0.25 = 1.25$	$3.0 \times 0.0625 = 0.1875$	$3.0 \times 0.125 = 0.375$
M_3	$1.5 \times 1.0 = 1.50$	$1.5 \times 0.25 = 0.375$	$2.5 \times 0.5 = 1.25$

Then the costs per unit are multiplied by the number of units that can be produced in 1 M_1 hour. It takes 0.5 hour to produce one unit of J_1 on M_1. In 1 hour, M_1 can produce $1 \div 0.5 = 2$ units. The units per M_1 hour are

Job	Time per Unit on M_1	Units per M_1 Hour
J_1	0.5	2
J_2	0.125	8
J_3	0.25	4

The costs per M_1 hour are then obtained by multiplying the job per unit costs by the units per M_1 hour:

	J_1	J_2	J_3
M_1	$1.00 \times 2 = 2.00$	$0.25 \times 8 = 2.00$	$0.50 \times 4 = 2.00$
M_2	$1.25 \times 2 = 2.50$	$0.1875 \times 8 = 1.50$	$0.375 \times 4 = 1.50$
M_3	$1.50 \times 2 = 3.00$	$0.375 \times 8 = 3.00$	$1.25 \times 4 = 5.00$

Since there is more machine time than job time, a dummy job must be provided. The manipulations to arrive at the optimum solution then follow the standard pattern. The initial feasible solution is shown in Figure 4-9. In this case, the initial feasible solution also turns out to be the optimum solution, since the evaluations of the unoccupied squares are all positive.

Note, however, that the assigned values shown in Figure 4-9 are still in terms of M_1 hours, and must be reconverted into units. To convert J_1 units to M_1 hours, the units (30) were multiplied by the M_1 per unit time (0.5). To reconvert to units, the 10 M_1 hours (the amount of J_1 to be produced on M_1) are divided by 0.5. Thus,

		−2.00	−1.00	−1.00	+0.50	
From \ To		J_1	J_2	J_3	Dummy	Supply
0	M_1	−2.00 / 10	−2.00 / (+1.00)	−2.00 / (+1.00)	0 / (+0.50)	10
−0.50	M_2	−2.50 / 5	−1.50 / 9	−1.50 / 15	0 / 11	40
−0.50	M_3	−3.00 / (+0.50)	−3.00 / (+1.50)	−5.00 / (+3.50)	0 / 15	15
	Demand	15	9	15	26	65 / 65

Fig. 4-9. The Job Assignment Problem—First Iteration and Optimum Solution

$$10 \div 0.5 = 20,$$

or 20 J_1 units are to be produced on M_1. Some J_1 units are to be produced on M_2, in fact 5 M_1 hours worth:

$$5 \div 0.5 = 10.$$

Thus the 30 J_1 units will be produced 20 on M_1 and 10 on M_2. J_2 is to be produced solely on M_2. The conversion factor is 0.125:

$$9 \div 0.125 = 72 \text{ units.}$$

J_3 also is to be produced solely on M_2, the conversion factor being 0.25:

$$15 \div 0.25 = 60 \text{ units.}$$

The final schedule is as follows:

		Units		
Job	M_1	M_2	M_3	Total Units
J_1	20	10		30
J_2		72		72
J_3		60		60

M_2 will have 11 M_1 equivalent idle hours or:

$$11 \times 0.5 = 5.5$$

M_2 idle hours. M_3 will be completely free, having available its original 30 hours.

DISCUSSION QUESTIONS

4-1. Describe how to handle the unequal supply-demand situation.

4-2. Explain in precise terms why a *dummy supplier* or *customer* may at times be required in order to apply the distribution method successfully.

4-3. What costs should be assigned to the dummy row or column? Support your conclusion with adequate reasoning.

4-4. What is the significance of equal cost values assigned to a row or column?

4-5. Describe how to handle prohibited shipment-receipt combinations. What meaning is attached to M?

4-6. What is meant by degeneracy?

4-7. Describe the method of handling a degenerate condition.

4-8. What is meant by *cycling*? How would you correct this condition?

4-9. Discuss the distribution method in relation to problems other than the transportation problem.

PROBLEMS

4-1. Solve Problem 3-1, but change the Miami demand to 70 units.

4-2. Solve Problem 3-3, but change the Phoenix supply to 70 units.

4-3. Solve Problem 4-2, but add the restriction that no shipments may be made from Dallas to Albuquerque.

4-4. Solve Problem 4-1, but add the requirement that Bangor must receive its full order.

4-5. Solve Problem 4-2, but change the Denver demand to 25.

4-6. Company B has four machines (M_1, M_2, M_3, and M_4) and five jobs (J_1, J_2, J_3, J_4, and J_5). In each given week, 160 units of J_1, 48 units of J_2, 14 units of J_3, 140 units of J_4, and 180 units of J_5 are to be produced. M_2 is twice as fast as M_1, M_3 is 0.8 times as fast as M_1, and M_4 is 1.5 times as fast as M_1. M_1 time costs $2 per hour; M_2, $2.50; M_3, $1; and M_4, $2.25. Extra labor costs by job and machine are

	J_1	J_2	J_3	J_4	J_5
M_1	–0–	–0–	1.50	1.00	0.50
M_2	2.00	–0–	–0–	0.50	–0–
M_3	–0–	1.00	1.00	1.00	1.00
M_4	–0–	1.75	0.25	–0–	0.75

The hours required to produce one unit of each job on M_1 are

Job	J_1	J_2	J_3	J_4	J_5
Hours	0.125	0.5	1.0	0.25	0.2

The following machine times are available:

Machine	M_1	M_2	M_3	M_4
Hours	20	30	15	26

Required: The least-cost job assignment schedule.

BIBLIOGRAPHY

Bierman, Harold, Jr., Lawrence E. Fouraker, and Robert K. Jaedicke, *Quantitative Analysis for Business Decisions.* Homewood, Ill.: Richard D. Irwin, Inc., 1961, p. 242–58.

Charnes, A., and W. W. Cooper, "The Stepping Stone Method of Explaining Linear Programming Calculations," *Management Science*, 1 (October, 1954), 49–69.

Churchman, C. West, Russell L. Ackoff, and E. Leonard Arnoff, *Introduction to Operations Research.* New York: John Wiley & Sons, Inc., 1957, p. 279–98.

Metzger, Robert W., *Elementary Mathematical Programming.* New York: John Wiley & Sons, Inc., 1958, p. 6–58.

Reinfeld, Nyles V., and William R. Vogel, *Mathematical Programming.* Englewood Cliffs, N. J.: Prentice-Hall, Inc., 1958, p. 11-70.

Sasieni, Maurice, Arthur Yaspan, and Lawrence Friedman, *Operations Research—Methods and Problems.* New York: John Wiley & Sons, Inc., 1959, p. 194–220.

Vazsonyi, Andrew, *Scientific Programming in Business and Industry.* New York: John Wiley & Sons, Inc., 1958, p. 20–52.

5

Graphical Approach
to Linear Programming

The Oakdale Furniture Company specializes in the manufacture of tables and chairs. Both tables and chairs must be worked in Department I, roughing; Department II, finishing; and Department III, painting. Department I has available 100 man hours per week, Department II has 77, and Department III has 80. Each table requires 10 man hours in Department I, 7 in Department II, and 2 in Department III. Similarly, each chair requires 2 hours in Department I, 3 hours in Department II, and 4 hours in Department III. Net profit on the sale of each table is $12 and on each chair, $3.

This is a problem in production scheduling or in product mix. The question to be answered is, How many tables and how many chairs should be manufactured each week? The answer is dependent upon the objective selected, and the correct objective is not necessarily self-evident. The classical objective would be to maximize weekly profits. At least two other feasible objectives could be stated: (1) the competitive situation for domination of the market could be such that maximum units of production might be the prime objective; (2) maximum utilization of facilities, particularly of employees, could also be of interest. As will be seen, these three objectives are not necessarily compatible.

The following table shows the relationships involved in the problem:

	Departments			
	I	II	III	Profit per Unit
Tables, hours per unit	10	7	2	$12
Chairs, hours per unit	2	3	4	$ 3
Total hours available	100	77	80	

SEC. 5-2. SETTING UP THE EQUATIONS AND/OR INEQUALITIES

Let T represent the number of tables and C the number of chairs manufactured per week. Then 10 times T ($10T$) is the total time spent manufacturing tables in Department I; $7T$, in Department II; and $2T$, in Department III. Similarly, $2C$, $3C$, and $4C$ represent the time spent making chairs in Departments I, II, and III respectively. Since Department I has available 100 man hours, the most time that can be spent making both tables and chairs in Department I is

$$10T + 2C = 100.$$

There is, however, no requirement that Department I work its full 100 man hours. It can work less. This fact is expressed by

$$10T + 2C \leq 100.$$

The sign $\leq$ is read "is equal to or less than." The situation in Departments II and III may be similarly expressed:

$$\text{Dept. II:} \ \ 7T + 3C \leq 77,$$

$$\text{Dept. III:} \ \ 2T + 4C \leq 80.$$

Only one other relationship need be set forth—that relating to achieving the objective. This relationship is usually referred to as the *objective function*. Three objectives have been considered as possibilities: (1) to maximize profits, (2) to maximize the number of units produced, (3) to maximize the utilization of man hours. Each of these can be expressed mathematically.

The profit per table is equal to $12. Therefore the total profit on tables sold is equal to 12 times T or $12T$. Similarly, the total profit on chairs equals $3C$, and

$$\text{Total profits} = 12T + 3C.$$

The objective, then, is to maximize this objective function, or to maximize the value $12T + 3C$. Since the number of tables produced is equal to T and the number of chairs is equal to C, then,

$$\text{Total units produced} = T + C,$$

and this objective function is to be maximized if the second objective is chosen.

To develop the objective function for maximizing the utilization of facilities (in this illustration the only facilities available are man hours), the time spent making tables in all three departments is summed

$$10T + 7T + 2T = 19T,$$

and the time spent making chairs is similarly summed

$$2C + 3C + 4C = 9C.$$

The total utilization of facilities (man hours) is then equal to

$$19T + 9C,$$

which function is to be maximized.

The following relationships have been developed:

Dept. I: $10T + 2C \leq 100$

Dept. II: $7T + 3C \leq 77$

Dept. III: $2T + 4C \leq 80$

Objective function I: Total profits $= 12T + 3C$

Objective function II: Total units produced $= T + C$

Objective function III: Total man hours used $= 19T + 9C$

SEC. 5-3.   THE SCHEDULING PROBLEM AND THE DISTRIBUTION METHOD

The application of the distribution method to the general assignment problem was discussed in Sec. 4-5. The scheduling problem being considered is, in effect, a problem in assigning production units to departments. The question arises, then, Is this problem amenable to solution by the distribution method? In order to answer this question effectively, it is necessary to convert the distribution method into its component equations and/or inequalities.

The distribution problem of Chapter 3 required a three by three matrix for solution; that is, it required three rows and three columns. Each of the nine positions was designated by row and column, namely, $r_1c_1, \ldots,$ r_3c_3. If the unit value placed in each of the nine squares is designated by $x_{11}, \ldots, x_{33}$, then each of these positions will be as shown in Figure 5-1. Notice that x_{11} and x_{12} are different variables, just as much as if they had been labeled x and y. The amount supplied by Los Angeles may be expressed by

$$x_{11} + x_{12} + x_{13} = 100.$$

This states that the total sent from Los Angeles to San Francisco, Boise, and San Diego together must be exactly equal to 100 units. Similarly, each of the other suppliers can be formulated:

$$\text{Fresno:} \quad x_{21} + x_{22} + x_{23} = 25,$$
$$\text{Las Vegas:} \quad x_{31} + x_{32} + x_{33} = 75.$$

The orders can be expressed in the same manner:

$$\text{San Francisco:} \quad x_{11} + x_{21} + x_{31} = 80,$$
$$\text{Boise:} \quad x_{12} + x_{22} + x_{32} = 30,$$
$$\text{San Diego:} \quad x_{13} + x_{23} + x_{33} = 75.$$

From \ To	San Francisco	Boise	San Diego	Supply
Los Angeles	-5 x_{11}	-10 x_{12}	-2 x_{13}	100
Fresno	-3 x_{21}	-7 x_{22}	-5 x_{23}	25
Las Vegas	-6 x_{31}	-8 x_{32}	-4 x_{33}	75
Supply	80	30	90	200 / 200

Fig. 5-1. Designation of Positions in Distribution Matrix

The objective function can also be set up using the data in Figure 5-1. The cost of a shipment from Los Angeles to San Francisco is equal to the cost per unit (C_{11}) times the number of units shipped (x_{11}). C_{11} is known and is \$5; x_{11} is a variable not yet determined. Therefore the cost of the Los Angeles—San Francisco shipment is $5x_{11}$. If no units are shipped, then $x_{11} = 0$, and the cost of the shipment is zero. Thus the objective function is

$$5x_{11} + 3x_{12} + 2x_{13}$$
$$+ 3x_{21} + 7x_{22} + 5x_{23}$$
$$+ 6x_{31} + 8x_{32} + 4x_{33}.$$

The objective was to minimize this objective function. Since the distribution method (as described) is a maximization process, the objective function was multiplied by a -1, and then maximized; thus,

$$- 5x_{11} - 3x_{12} - 2x_{13}$$
$$- 3x_{21} - 7x_{22} - 5x_{23}$$
$$- 6x_{31} - 8x_{32} - 4x_{33}.$$

The negative coefficients of the objective function variables were placed in the sub-squares of the distribution matrix.

The equations and the objective functions of the two problems can now be compared:

The scheduling problem:

$$10T + 2C \leq 100$$
$$7T + 3C \leq 77$$
$$2T + 4C \leq 80.$$

Maximize profit function: $12T + 3C$.
The distribution problem:

$$x_{11} + x_{12} + x_{13} = 100$$
$$x_{21} + x_{22} + x_{23} = 25$$
$$x_{31} + x_{32} + x_{33} = 75$$
$$x_{11} + x_{21} + x_{31} = 80$$
$$x_{12} + x_{22} + x_{32} = 30$$
$$x_{13} + x_{23} + x_{33} = 75.$$

Maximize the negative cost function:

$$- 5x_{11} - 3x_{12} - 2x_{13}$$
$$- 3x_{21} - 7x_{22} - 5x_{23}$$
$$- 6x_{31} - 8x_{31} - 4x_{33}.$$

One major difference in the two systems is immediately apparent. The coefficient of every variable in the system of equations of the distribution problem is equal to one. The scheduling problem inequalities have coefficients of varying values, all (coincidentally in this case) of some value other than one. A requirement of the distribution method is that the underlying system of equations and/or inequalities have every coefficient equal to one. Therefore this particular scheduling problem, as set up, cannot be solved by using the distribution method. The fact that the one system consists of equations and the other of inequalities is not significant in this case, because, for computation, the inequalities are changed into equations. In the case of the distribution problem, this was done by the use of dummy suppliers or dummy customers as the case might be. Another technique for changing the inequalities into equations is discussed in Sec. 6-3 and 7-2.

Further, observe that each variable in the distribution method appears exactly twice in the system of equations (or inequalities). This condition must always exist for the problem to be solved by the distribution method. In the present problem, both the variables, T and C, appear three times. This problem, therefore, fails to pass both the coefficient test and the test of the number of times the variables appear.

SEC. 5-4. GRAPHING THE LINEAR INEQUALITIES

Note that every variable in all the inequalities of both the scheduling problem and the distribution problem has an exponent (power) of one. Equations which have all variables with exponents of one are called *linear* equations, because these equations, when graphed, form a straight line. Problem solving based upon systems of linear equations or linear inequalities is referred to as *linear programming*. Thus the distribution method is a linear-programming technique, as is the simplex method treated in Chapters 6 and 7. Simple linear programming problems can be easily and swiftly solved by graphing the underlying system of equations and inequalities, and then applying the objective function in such a way as to achieve the objective (maximization or minimization as the case may be).

The first step in graphing the inequalities of the scheduling problem is to convert them temporarily into equations:

$$10T + 2C = 100$$
$$7T + 3C = 77$$
$$2T + 4C = 80.$$

Then a system of coordinate axes is laid out on graph paper as shown in Figure 5-2. The axes are labeled with the variables, in this case T and C. To scale the graph, the range of each of the variables at the axes must be known. If $C = 0$ in each of the three equations, then,

I: $10T = 100,$ $T = 10$

II: $7T = 77,$ $T = 11$

III: $2T = 80,$ $T = 40.$

If $T = 0$, then,

I: $2C = 100$, $C = 50$

II: $3C = 77$, $C = 25\dfrac{2}{3}$

III: $4C = 80$, $C = 20$.

The pertinent range of T on the T axis (when $C = 0$) is therefore from 10 through 40, and the range for C on the C axis (when $T = 0$) is from 20 through 50. Appropriate scale values are chosen to bring these ranges within the working area of the graph (Figure 5-2).

In most linear programming problems, one of the basic requirements is that each of the variables must not be negative. That is, in this case, $T \geq 0$ and $C \geq 0$. The sign $\geq$ is read "is equal to or greater than." This concept appears to be quite reasonable when it is realized that it would be impossible to make a negative number of tables or chairs. The C axis in Figure 5-2 is the graph of the equation $T = 0$. Thus, when $T = 0$, any value of C will fall on the C axis. The entire space above the C axis represents the inequality $T > 0$. The sign $>$ is read "is greater than." Therefore, any point on the line $T = 0$, or any point in the area above the line $T = 0$ will satisfy the inequality $T \geq 0$.

An inequality with a "greater than" component is called a *requirement*. It is required that T be at least equal to zero. All the area below the C

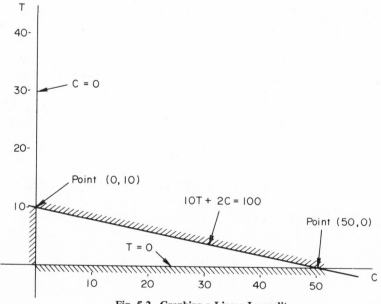

Fig. 5-2. Graphing a Linear Inequality

axis is forbidden territory. This fact is so designated by placing fringe lines below the C axis (Figure 5-2).

By similar reasoning, the T axis represents the line $C = 0$, and that line and all the area to the right represent the inequality $C \geq 0$. Fringe lines are placed to the left of the T axis to indicate that area as unacceptable for a solution.

In graphing any straight line, only two points need be identified, and the line is then drawn through the two points. The two required points for equation $10T + 2C = 100$ are found by first letting $C = 0$ and then letting $T = 0$. When $C = 0$, $10T = 100$, and $T = 10$. The point $C = 0$, $T = 10$ is located on the T axis (Figure 5-2). This point is referred to mathematically as $(0, 10)$. When $T = 0$, $2C = 100$, $C = 50$. The point $C = 50$, $T = 0$ $(50, 0)$ is located on the C axis. The line connecting the two points represents the equation $10T + 2C = 100$.

The problem, however, contained the inequality $10T + 2C \leq 100$. This time, all the area below (and including) the line is within the acceptable solution. That portion above the line is excluded by again using the fringe marks. An inequality with a "less than" component is called a *restriction*. Notice that a requirement prevents the solution from being *smaller* than certain values, and a restriction prevents it from being *larger* than certain values.

SEC. 5-5. GRAPHING THE SCHEDULING PROBLEM

The graph of the inequalities of the scheduling problem is shown in Figure 5–3. Any point within the area bounded by the fringe lines will provide a solution meeting all the restrictions and requirements of the problem. There are, of course, an infinite number of points within this area; therefore there are an infinite number of feasible solutions to this problem.

What is being sought, however, is that solution which will maximize some objective. One such objective in this case is the profit function, $12T + 3C$. The equation is

$$12T + 3C = P,$$

where P stands for profits. But P can take on any one of many possible values. Therefore, the equation $12T + 3C = P$ will not graph as one line, but as a family of lines, depending upon the value of P. A few lines from this family of lines is shown in Figure 5-4. Note especially that all the lines are parallel to each other.

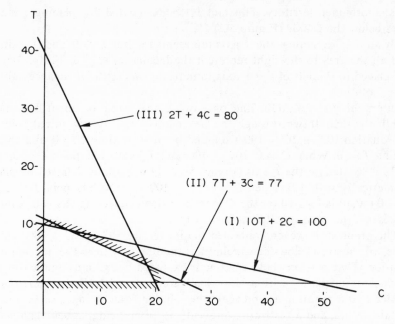

Fig. 5-3. Graph of the Inequalities of the Scheduling Problem

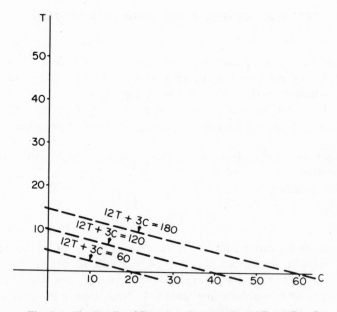

Fig. 5-4. The Family of Equations Representing $12T + 3C = P$

Returning to Figure 5-3, of the infinite number of points making up the acceptable solution area, that point is sought which lies farthest from the origin and which will also satisfy the objective function. Since every equation in the family of objective equations has the same slope (that is, they are parallel to each other), the technique is to keep extending the series of parallel lines away from the origin until only one point on the objective function line lies within the acceptable solution area. If there is a unique optimum solution to the problem, this point will be an intersection of two of the graphed lines (including the axes as possible points of intersection). It is also possible that there may be an infinite number of optimum solutions. This would occur when the slope of the objective function is equal to the slope of one of the restricting lines.

The solution to the scheduling problem is shown in Figure 5-5. The objective function line reaching farthest from the origin is shown by the dotted line. Only one point on the objective function line is within the acceptable area of solution—at the intersection of lines I and II. Lines are then drawn vertically to each axis. The points at which these lines intersect the axes represent the number of tables (T axis) and chairs (C axis) to be scheduled for production each week.

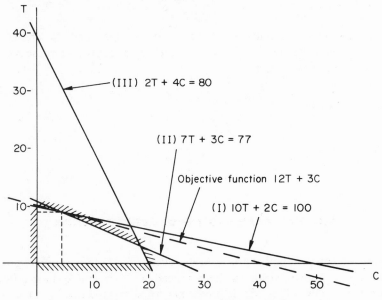

Fig. 5-5. Solution to Scheduling Problem

The numbers of each can be read roughly directly from the graph. Since the solution is the point of intersection of two linear equations, that point can be found by simultaneously solving these equations:

$$\text{I:} \quad 10T + 2C = 100$$
$$\text{II:} \quad 7T + 3C = 77.$$

First multiply Eq. I by 3 and Eq. II by 2:

$$\text{Ia:} \quad 30T + 6C = 300$$
$$\text{IIa:} \quad 14T + 6C = 154.$$

Subtract IIa from Ia.

$$16T = 146$$
$$T = \frac{73}{8} = 9\frac{1}{8}$$

Substitute $T = \frac{73}{8}$ in I

$$5 \cdot \frac{73}{8} + 2C = 100$$
$$C = \frac{35}{8} = 4\frac{3}{8}.$$

Thus the optimum solution is to schedule $9\frac{1}{8}$ tables and $4\frac{3}{8}$ chairs per week. The profit per week may be computed by substituting these values into the objective function:

$$\text{profits} = 12T + 3C$$
$$= 12 \cdot \frac{73}{8} + 3 \cdot \frac{35}{8}$$
$$= \$122\frac{5}{8} \text{ per week.}$$

SEC. 5-6. CHANGING THE OBJECTIVE FUNCTION

Three objective functions have been developed, (1) to maximize profits $(12T + 3C)$, (2) to maximize units produced $(T + C)$, and (3) to maximize man hours used $(19T + 9C)$. If profits are to be maximized, $9\frac{1}{8}$ tables and $4\frac{3}{8}$ chairs per week will be produced. If, however, it is desired to maximize the number of units produced, both the product mix and the profits are likely to change. In this case, the objective function,

$$\text{total units produced} = T + C,$$

will graph as a family of lines each with a 45° negative slope. (A line has a negative slope if it slopes downward and to the right.) The new objective function is shown graphed in Figure 5-6. The solution is now at the intersection of Eq. II and III. Solving these two equations:

$$\text{II:} \qquad 7T + 3C = 77$$
$$\text{III:} \qquad 2T + 4C = 80$$

$$\text{Multiply II by 4; IIa:} \qquad 28T + 12C = 308$$
$$\text{Multiply III by 3; IIIa:} \qquad 6T + 12C = 240$$
$$\text{Subtract IIIa from IIa:} \qquad 22T \qquad\;\; = 68$$

$$T = \frac{34}{11} = 3\frac{1}{11}$$

Substitute $T = 34/11$ in III:

$$2 \cdot \frac{34}{11} + 4C = 80$$

$$C = \frac{203}{11} = 18\frac{5}{11}$$

Therefore, the largest number of units that can be produced per week are $3\frac{1}{11}$ tables and $18\frac{5}{11}$ chairs or $21\frac{6}{11}$ units. This compares to $9\frac{1}{8}$ tables

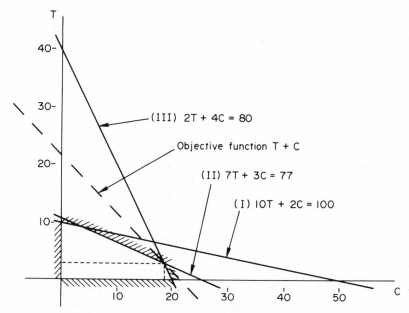

Fig 5-6. Change in Objective Function

plus $4\frac{3}{8}$ chairs or $13\frac{1}{2}$ units if profits are to be maximized. If the maximum number of units are produced, the weekly profits will be

$$\text{profits} = 12T + 3C$$

$$= 12 \cdot \frac{34}{11} + 3 \cdot \frac{203}{11}$$

$$= \$92\frac{5}{11} \text{ per week.}$$

By changing the objective from the maximization of profits to the maximization of units produced, the number of units produced will be increased by $8^1/_{22}$ units, but profits will be reduced by $\$30^{15}/_{88}$ per week.

The solution of the third objective function, the maximum utilization of man hours, is left as an exercise for the reader.

DISCUSSION QUESTIONS

5-1. Discuss the concept of inequalities and their relationship to equations. Define the signs $>$, $\geq$, $<$, $\leq$.

5-2. What is meant by the term *objective function?*

5-3. Explain why the scheduling problem illustrated in the chapter was not amenable to solution by the distribution method.

5-4. Explain the meaning of the subscripts in the terms $x_{11}, \ldots, x_{33}$.

5-5. What is the derivation of the figures placed in the sub-squares of the distribution method?

5-6. What is meant by the term *linear programming?*

5-7. Describe the technique of graphing a *linear inequality.*

5-8. What is meant by the term *requirement?*

5-9. What is meant by the term *restriction?*

5-10. Explain why some problems may have an infinite number of possible or feasible solutions.

5-11. Explain the technique of graphing the objective function. What is meant by the term *family of equations?*

5-12. The illustration in the text pertained to a process of maximization. Explain how the same techniques could be applied to problems requiring minimization. (Hint: Think in terms of the relationship of the objective function to the origin.)

5-13. Once the point on the graph indicating the solution has been found, explain (1) how to read the solution from the graph and (2) how to find the exact mathematical solution to the problem.

5-14. Where on the graph is an optimum point usually located? Explain what effect upon the optimum point may result from changing the objective function.

5-15. Under what circumstances may there be an infinite number of optimum solutions instead of unique optimum solution?

5-16. Can the illustrative problem of Chapter 3 be solved by the graphical method? If you believe that it cannot, then explain why.

PROBLEMS

5-1. Using the graphical method, *maximize* the function $19x + 9y$, subject to the following:

$$4x + 9y \leq 180$$
$$19x + 70y \leq 1330$$
$$5x + 7y \leq 175$$
$$5x + 3y \leq 150.$$

5-2. Solve Problem 5-1 by maximizing the function $19x + 45y$.

5-3. Solve Problem 5-1 by maximizing the function $4x + 7y$.

5-4. Solve Problem 5-1 by maximizing the functiou $5x + 6y$.

5-5. Solve Problem 5-1 by maximizing the function $2x + y$.

5-6. Using the graphical method, *minimize* the function $2x + 3y$, subject to the following:

$$35x + 5y \geq 175$$
$$5x + 3y \geq 75$$
$$x + 2y \geq 30$$
$$x + 10y \geq 50.$$

5-7. Solve Problem 5-6 minimizing the function $10x + y$.

5-8. Solve Problem 5-6 minimizing the function $5x + 2y$.

5-9. Solve Problem 5-6 minimizing the function $3x + 10y$.

5-10. Solve Problem 5-6 minimizing the function $2x + 25y$.

5-11. Assume that only four nutrients for cattle have been isolated, namely, A, B,C, and D. The Department of Agriculture pamphlet specifies that the minimum daily requirements per animal are A, 5 lb; B, 7 lb; C, 6 lb; and D, 6 lb. Only two feeds, corn and alfalfa, are available. The analyses of corn and alfalfa are

	Corn (per cent)	Alfalfa (per cent)
A	10	50
B	45	15
C	25	15
D	20	20

Corn costs 2 cents and alfalfa 1 cent per lb. Derive the least-cost feeding program.

BIBLIOGRAPHY

Bierman, Harold, Jr., Lawrence E. Fouraker, and Robert K, Jaedicke, *Quantitative Analysis for Business Decisions.* Homewood, III.: Richard D. Irwin, Inc., 1961, pp. 239-40.

Churchman, C. West, Russel L. Ackoff, and E. Leonard Arnoff, *Introduction to Operations Research.* New York: John Wiley & Sons, Inc., 1957, pp. 330-34.

Flagle, Charles D., William H. Huggins, and Robert H. Roy, *Operations Research and Systems Engineering.* Baltimore: The Johns Hopkins Press, 1960, pp. 371-78.

Metzger, Robert W., *Elementary Mathematical Programming.* New York: John Wiley & Sons, Inc., 1958, pp. 82-87.

Reinfeld, Nyles V., and William R.Vogel, *Mathematical Programming.* Englewood Cliffs, N. J.: Prentice-Hall, Inc., 1958, pp. 120-30.

Vazsonyi, Andrew, *Scientific Programming in Business and Industry.* New York: John Wiley & Sons, Inc., 1958, pp. 171-93.

6

The Simplex Method: I

SEC. 6-1. STATEMENT OF THE PROBLEM TO BE SOLVED

The Oakdale Furniture Company of Chapter 5 desires to expand its furniture line. In addition to tables and chairs, it wishes to manufacture a high kitchen stool. The stools, like the tables and chairs, must be processed in all three of Oakdale's departments, Department I, roughing (1 hour per stool), Department II, finishing (2 hours per stool), and Department III, painting (1 hour per stool). Each stool will sell for a net profit of $1. All other conditions will remain the same as before the addition of the stools to the product line. These relationships are

	Department			
	I	II	III	Profit per Unit
Tables (hours per unit)	10	7	2	$12
Chairs (hours per unit)	2	3	4	$ 3
Stools (hours per unit)	1	2	1	$ 1
Total hours available	100	77	80	

SEC. 6-2. DEVELOPING THE SYSTEM OF INEQUALITIES

The reasoning applied to developing the inequalities in Sec. 5-2 applies equally here. A new variable must be added, say S, for the number of stools made, and S, $2S$, and S then stand for the time spent making stools in Departments I, II, and III, respectively. The inequalities representing the conditions in each department are:

$$\text{(I)} \quad 10T + 2C + S \leq 100$$
$$\text{(II)} \quad 7T + 3C + 2S \leq 77$$
$$\text{(III)} \quad 2T + 4C + S \leq 80,$$

and of course, $T \geq 0, C \geq 0$, and $S \geq 0$.

Once again, any one of a number of objectives can be sought. In this case, the management wishes to know what the effect on profits would be. The total profits made will equal the sum of the profits made on tables, chairs, and stools. Therefore, the profit function is

$$\text{profits} = 12T + 3C + S,$$

and this objective function is to be maximized.

The problem under consideration is very similar to that discussed in Chapter 5. The question then arises: Can this problem be solved by the graphical method? The answer is that it can, but with some difficulty. The reason is quite simple. The problem of Chapter 5 had two variables, T and C. Two variable drawings can be made in two-dimensional space—on a sheet of paper, for example. The present problem has three variables, T, C, and S. This must be drawn in three-dimensional space. Such a drawing can be accomplished with some degree of satisfaction on a two-dimensional sheet of paper, but it is frequently quite difficult to visualize the relationships. Should a fourth variable be added, the difficulties of graphical presentation are increased manyfold.

A method of solving multivariable linear problems with coefficients other than one was developed by G. B. Dantzig and has since been further improved by a number of other people. This is known as the *simplex* method, and is discussed in the remainder of this chapter.

SEC. 6-3. THE SIMPLEX TABLEAU

There are several ways of setting up the simplex tableau, all of which have the same general result. The one chosen for illustration is, it is believed, one of the easier to present and to understand.

The first step is to convert the inequalities to equations. The first inequality in the system is

(a) $\qquad 10T + 2C + S \leq 100.$

It is easy to see that a possible equation can be

(b) $\qquad 10T + 2C + S = 100,$

and such an equation would, of course, satisfy the original inequality (a). However, there are times that

(c) $10T + 2C + S < 100,$

and (b) would not satisfy this condition. To compensate for the amount that the sum on the left side of (c) is less than 100, another variable is added to the left side of (b), thus,

(d) $10T + 2C + S + W_1 = 100.$

Then if $10T + 2C + S = 100$, $W_1 = 0$. If $10T + 2C + S < 100$, W_1 is equal to the difference. Therefore, W_1 can range from 0 to 100 ($0 \leq W_1 \leq 100$), depending upon the value of $10T + 2C + S$. W_1 is referred to as a *slack variable*, because it takes up any slack between the left and right sides of the inequality when converting it to an equation. The system converted to equations is

(e) $10T + 2C + \ S + W_1 = 100$
(f) $7T + 3C + 2S + W_2 = \ \ 77$
(g) $2T + 4C + \ S + W_3 = \ \ 80.$

The inequalities $T \geq 0, C \geq 0, S \geq 0$ need not be converted to equations. In fact, the condition that all variables must be equal to, or greater than, zero is basic to both the distribution and simplex method. The condition must exist, but no further attention need be given to these inequalities. Notice that the W_1, W_2, and W_3 are three different variables just as much as if they were labeled x, y, and z.

The initial tableau is shown in Figure 6-1. To set up the tableau, first list horizontally *all* the variables contained in the problem, including the slack variables. In this problem, there are six such variables, T, C, S, W_1, W_2, and W_3. Then in a column to the left of the leftmost variable, list the constants appearing on the right-hand side of the equations. In a similar fashion, list vertically the coefficients under their respective variables. Note that each of the slack variables appears in only one equation. The coefficient of each of these variables in the other equations is zero. Since the value of $0W_1$ is zero, adding this to Eq. (f) and (g) has no effect on these equations.

The rightmost three columns (in this case containing the slack variables) are called the *identity*. Notice that the identity contains all zeros except a diagonal column of plus ones. *The identity must always have this square form, with all zeros and a diagonal of plus ones.* The size of the square is equal to the number of equations in the system.

Constant Column	12 T	3 C	1 S	0 W_1	0 W_2	0 W_3	Objective row Variable row
100	10	2	1	1	0	0	Equation Coefficients
77	7	3	2	0	1	0	
80	2	4	1	0	0	1	

Identity

Fig. 6-1. Setting Up Simplex Tableau

The values in the objective row in Figure 6–1 require further explanation. The objective function for maximizing profits was given as

$$\text{profits} = 12T + 3C + S.$$

But the objective function for the simplex must contain *every* variable in the system, including any slack or other variables added. Therefore, the objective function must also contain the variables W_1, W_2, and W_3. Before adding these variables to the objective function, some coefficient must be assigned to them.

In each simplex problem, the slack variables will have some (probably significant) meaning, but they will change meaning from problem to problem. In the present problem, in Eq. (e), the $10T + 2C + S$ represent the utilization of man hours in Department I. Hence, W_1 represents unused man hours in that department. Similarly, W_2 and W_3 represent unused man hours in Departments II and III respectively. The coefficient may represent the *cost* of unused man hours. For the first illustration, it will be presumed that unused man hours have no cost. Therefore the coefficients assigned will be zeros and the objective function becomes

$$\text{profits} = 12T + 3C + S + 0W_1 + 0W_2 + 0W_3.$$

The coefficients of the variables of the objective function are then placed above the respective variables in the simplex tableau (see Figure 6-1).

Three more steps are required to complete the first tableau: (1) deriving the first feasible solution, (2) setting up the check column, (3) computing the index row. These are shown in Figure 6-2.

In deriving the first feasible solution, all variables other than those in the identity are set equal to zero. Hence those variables in the identity will have the values of the constants in each equation. This is signified by placing the variables in a column (called the *variable column*) to the left of the constant column (Figure 6-2). Variables in the variable column are equal to the corresponding values in the constant column. Thus,

$$W_1 = 100$$
$$W_2 = \ \ 77$$
$$W_3 = \ \ 80.$$

Since T, C, and S must all be equal to, or greater than, zero, they must all be equal to zero if the slack variables have the foregoing values. The objective function coefficients of the slack variables are placed in a column (called the *objective column*) to the left of the variable column.

Objective Column	Variable Column		12 T	3 C	1 S	0 W_1	0 W_2	0 W_3	Ck
0	W_1	100	10	2	1	1	0	0	114←
0	W_2	77	7	3	2	0	1	0	90
0	W_3	80	2	4	1	0	0	1	88
		0	−12 ↑	−3	−1	0	0	0	−16 Index row

Fig. 6-2. Completing the First Tableau

A check column is placed to the right of the identity. To compute the check figures, merely sum all the values in the row which lie to the right of the variable column. Thus the check figure for the first row is found by adding $100 + 10 + 2 + 1 + 1 + 0 + 0 = 114$. The other values in the check column were computed in a similar manner.

The remaining item to complete the first tableau is computing the bottom row of figures, called the *index row*.

The index row figure is equal to the sum of the products of the column values and the objective column values, less the objective row value for that column.

To compute the first and second index row figures:

First Index Figure			Second Index Figure		
Objective Column	Constant Column	Product	Objective Column	T Column	Product
0 × 100 =		0	0 × 10 =		0
0 × 77 =		0	0 × 7 =		0
0 × 80 =		0	0 × 2 =		0
Sum of products		0			0
Less objective row value		0			12
Index figure		0			−12

The other index row figures are similarly computed, except that for the check column, which is the sum of the other index figures.

Several points about the simplex tableau may now be noted. Each tableau, if correctly assembled and computed, represents a feasible solution to the problem. A tableau represents an optimum solution if, with the exception of the constant column value and the check column value, there are no negative values in the index row. Only those variables in the variable column can be nonzero. In the illustrative problem, there are six variables, but only three equations. Therefore, in every iteration there will be at least three variables equal to zero. More than the minimum number of variables can be equal to zero, since there can be zeros in the constant column. But the values in the constant column *never* may be negative. The values in the constant column represent the values of the corresponding variables in the variable column. But all variables in the simplex must be equal to, or greater than, zero. A negative figure in the constant column indicates some kind of error, either in setting up the problem or in moving from one iteration to the next.

The figure at the intersection of the constant column and the index row represents the value of the objective function. For the initial solution, the values of the variables are $T = 0, C = 0, S = 0, W_1 = 100, W_2 = 77,$ and $W_3 = 80$. Substituting these values into the objective function:

$$\text{profits} = 12T + 3C + S + 0W_1 + 0W_2 + 0W_3$$
$$= 12 \cdot 0 + 3 \cdot 0 + 1 \cdot 0 + 0 \cdot 100 + 0 \cdot 77 + 0 \cdot 80$$
$$= 0.$$

Each of the remaining figures in the index row signifies the amount of change in the objective function which would occur if one unit of the variable in that column were introduced into the solution. If the index row figure is negative, the change will be an increase, and if positive, a decrease. For this reason, variables with negative index row values are brought into the solution, as will be seen in Sec. 6-4.

SEC. 6-4. THE SECOND TABLEAU

A negative value in the index row (except in the constant or check columns) indicates that the solution is not an optimum one, but can be improved. In Figure 6-2, there are three such negative values, in the T, C, and S columns. This indicates that the solution can be improved by moving into the solution any one of these variables. If, however, a variable is transferred from the zero group (those not in the variable column) to the nonzero group (those in the variable column), then one of the nonzero variables must be transferred to the zero group. While moving into the solution *any* of the variables T, C, or S will improve the results, the greatest improvement will occur by selecting that variable with the most negative index value. In this case, the value is -12, and the variable is T. This selection is indicated by placing an arrow under the T column. The column selected is referred to as the *pivot column*.

The next step is to select that variable which is to be taken out of the solution.

To make that selection, the constant column values are divided by the pivot column values, and the row with the smallest positive quotient selected. Note that only positive, nonzero quotients are considered.

Constant Column	÷	Pivot Column	=	Quotient
100		10		10
77		7		11
80		2		40

The W_1 row has the smallest positive quotient, and is selected as indicated by the arrow. The row selected is called the *pivot row*, and the figure at the intersection of the pivot column and pivot row is the *pivot number*. The pivot number is circled.

All information for calculating the second iteration is now available. The first step is to set up the objective and variable columns. Except for the pivot row, these columns are merely copied from the preceding iteration (Figure 6-3). The items from the pivot row are replaced with those from the pivot column. In this case 0 W_1 goes out, and 12 T comes in. Notice that the objective row value is brought into the solution along with the variable.

The next step is to replace the pivot row. *Each value in the pivot row is divided by the pivot number to obtain the corresponding value in the new iteration.* Thus,

Pivot row values	100	2	1	1	0	0	114
Pivot number	10	10	10	10	10	10	10
New iteration value	10	1/5	1/10	1/10	0	0	57/5

All values in the row, except that in the check column, are summed. If the arithmetic is correct, the sum should equal the value in the check column. This new row will be referred to as the *replacement row*.

Every other value in the new iteration may be computed with the formula:

New value = value replaced − (row value in pivot column

× corresponding replacement row value)

12			12	3	1	0	0	0	
			T	C	S	W_1	W_2	W_3	CK
12	T	10	1	1/5	1/10	1/10	0	0	57/5
0	W_2	7	0	8/5	13/10	−7/10	1	0	51/5←
0	W_3	60	0	18/5	4/5	−1/5	0	1	326/5
		120	0	−3/5	1/5	6/5	0	0	604/5

Fig. 6-3. The Second Iteration

For the W_2 row, these computations are

Value Replaced	−	Product of Row Value in Pivot Column and Replacement Row Value	=	New Value
77		7 × 10 = 70		7
7		7 × 1 = 7		0
3		7 × 1/5 = 7/5		8/5
2		7 × 1/10 = 7/10		13/10
0		7 × 1/10 = 7/10		−7/10
1		7 × 0 = 0		1
0		7 × 0 = 0		0
88		7 × 57/5 = 399/5		57/5

The new values for the W_3 and index row are similarly computed. After each set of new row values has been computed, the values should be summed and compared to the check column. *Never proceed until each row passes the check test.* The completed second iteration is shown in Figure 6-3. (Check out each figure in this iteration.)

Notice the meaning of the various values in this iteration. $T = 10$, therefore 10 tables would be produced. C and S are equal to zero, hence no chairs or stools would be made. $W_1 = 0$. This means there would be no idle hours in Department I. On the other hand, $W_2 = 7$ and $W_3 = 60$, meaning that there would be 7 idle hours in Department II and 60 in Department III. The figure 120 at the intersection of the constant column and the index row represents a profit of $120 for this production schedule. The index value of $−3/5$ for the C column indicates that more profits would be made by manufacturing some chairs, that is, by bringing variable C into the solution.

The third and optimum iteration is shown in Figure 6-4. The process to derive the third iteration in identical to that used to derive the second iteration. The steps to be followed are detailed in Sec. 6-6.

The optimum solution gives some important information to the managers of the Oakdale Furniture Company. It shows that, given the production and profit figures for kitchen stools, the company's profits will be reduced if any of its production facilities are devoted to the manufacture of stools. It further shows that maximum profits will be obtained by sched-

			12	3	1	0	0	0	
			T	C	S	W_1	W_2	W_3	CK
12	T	73/8	1	0	−1/16	3/16	−1/8	0	81/8
3	C	35/8	0	1	13/16	−7/16	5/8	0	51/8
0	W_3	177/4	0	0	−17/8	11/8	−9/4	1	169/4
		981/8	0	0	15/16	15/16	3/8	0	999/8

Fig. 6-4. The Third Iteration and Optimum Solution

uling for production 73/8 or 9 1/8 tables and 35/8 or 4 3/8 chairs per week. This will result in a profit of 981/8 or $122 5/8 per week. Department III will have 177/4 or 44 1/4 unused man hours per week.

Note that the schedule for table and chair production and the resulting weekly net profits as derived by the simplex method are identical to that obtained from the graphical solution. As long as the variable C did not enter into the solution, the recommended solution for the three-variable problem was not different from that for the two-variable problem.

SEC. 6-5. CHANGING THE OBJECTIVE FUNCTION

The managers of the Oakdale Furniture Company were interested in obtaining two further pieces of information: (1) what would be the product mix if the company were to produce the maximum possible number of units; (2) what would the product mix be if maximum use of facilities were the objective.

The objective for the maximum number of units would be

$$\text{total units produced} = T + C + S + 0W_1 + 0W_2 + 0W_3.$$

Zeros were again selected as coefficients for the slack variables because idle time should have no effect when computing total units. If the objective is maximizing units produced, then the objective in relation to idle time is one of indifference. This indifference is designated in the objective function by the zero coefficients. The first iteration for this problem is

			1	1	1	0	0	0	
			T	C	S	W_1	W_2	W_3	CK
0	W_1	100	10	2	1	1	0	0	114←
0	W_2	77	7	3	2	0	1	0	90
0	W_3	80	2	4	1	0	0	1	88
		0	−1	−1	−1	0	0	0	−3

Fig. 6-5. First Iteration, Maximum Units Objective

presented in Figure 6-5. (Obtaining the optimum values is left as an exercise for the reader.) Since the index values for columns T, C, and S are all -1, the leftmost was arbitrarily chosen as the pivot column.

A different approach from that used in the graphical method may be used in developing the objective function for the maximum use of facilities. Since idle time is to be minimized, a negative idle time function may be used. That is, maximizing negative idle hours, will, in effect, minimize idle hours expended.

$$\text{negative unused man hours} = 0T + 0C + 0S - W_1 - W_2 - W_3.$$

This function shows an indifference to the units of T, C, or S produced, but seeks to maximize the negative values of W_1, W_2, and W_3. Remember that zero is the limit for the maximum size of a negative number. Should some idle time be necessary, the equality of the coefficients of the slack variables (all -1's) indicates indifference as to which department will have idle time. The first iteration is shown in Figure 6-6. Notice that the

			0	0	0	-1	-1	-1	
			T	C	S	W_1	W_2	W_3	CK
-1	W_1	100	10	2	1	1	0	0	114←
-1	W_2	77	7	3	2	0	1	0	90
-1	W_3	80	2	4	1	0	0	1	88
		-257	-19	-11	-4	0	0	0	-291

Fig. 6-6. First Iteration, Minimum Idle Time Objective

objective column for the initial feasible solution contains -1's instead of the 0's of the previous illustrations. The interpretation of the -257 at the intersection of the constant column and the index row is, with this solution, there would be 257 unused man hours.

SEC. 6-6. RÉSUMÉ OF THE SIMPLEX METHOD

1. Convert the inequalities of the system to equations by adding or subtracting slack variables.
2. Provide for the identity by supplying each equation of the system with a variable whose coefficient is 1, and whose coefficient in each of the other equations is zero. The slack variable when added (in an $\leq$ situation) supplies this. Otherwise use an artificial variable (see Sec. 7-2).
3. Derive the objective function, using every variable, including all slack and

artificial variables. Assign coefficients to the slack and artificial variables to achieve the results desired:

   a. Negative coefficients tend to minimize these variables.

   b. Positive coefficients tend to maximize them.

   c. Equal coefficients show indifference between the variables.

   d. $-M$ coefficients will force the variables out of the solution (sec Sec. 7-2).

4. Set up the first simplex tableau:

   a. List horizontally every variable in the system, placing the identity variables to the right.

   b. List the coefficients from the equations under the respective variables. Use a zero coefficient for any variables not appearing in a given equation.

   c. In a column to the left of the coefficients, list the constants (the right-hand values of the equations).

   d. Set up the initial feasible solution:

     (1) List the variables from the identity in a column to the left of the constant column. Each variable should be in the row in which it has a coefficient of 1.

     (2) List the objective coefficients of these variables in a column to the left of the constant column.

   e. Compute the index row using the formula: The index row value is equal to the sum of the products of the column values and the objective column values, less the objective row value of the column being computed.

   f. Compute the check column figures: The value in the check column is the sum af all the row values excluding the objective column.

5. Derive the second iteration:

   a. Select the pivot column by placing an arrow at the column with the most negative index figure, excluding the constant and check columns.

   b. Select the pivot row by placing an arrow at that row with the smallest positive quotient of the constant figure divided by the pivot column figure.

   c. Circle the pivot number at the intersection of the pivot column and the pivot row.

   d. Set up the second tableau:

     (1) Copy the objective and variable columns except those figures in the pivot row.

     (2) Replace the objective and variable figures in the pivot row with those from the pivot column.

     (3) Replace the pivot row by dividing each figure in it with the pivot number.

     (4) Replace all other figures in the first tableau by using the formula: Old number $-$ (old pivot column number for row $\times$ replacement row number for that column).

     (5) Test accuracy of arithmetic by summing all row values except objective and check values, and comparing the sum to the check figure.

   e. Test for optimum condition. Negative index figures, except constant and check figures, indicate a nonoptimum solution. If nonoptimum, repeat all steps under 5.

DISCUSSION QUESTIONS

6-1. Discuss the pros and cons of using the graphical method for solving the illustrative problem in the chapter.

6-2. What is a *slack variable*? How is it used in the simplex method?

6-3. Explain how those equations expressing the fact that all variables must be equal to, or greater than, zero are treated in the simplex method.

6-4. What is the *identity*? Describe its form and explain how that form is obtained.

6-5. How must the *objective function* of the graphical method be expanded for use in the simplex method?

6-6. Explain the method of assigning coefficients to the slack variables in the objective function. (Be explicit in discussing the expected effect of the various possible choices.)

6-7. What is the approach to obtaining the *initial feasible solution*?

6-8. Explain the function and use of the *check column*.

6-9. What is the rule for deriving the *index row* in the initial iteration? In the other iterations?

6-10. What values may be attached to each variable in any given solution? State explicitly how to derive these values from the simplex tableau.

6-11. What is the test for optimization in the simplex method?

6-12. Why is a negative value in the constant column (other than in the index row) never permitted?

6-13. What is the significance of the figure at the intersection of the constant column and the index row?

6-14. What is the *pivot column*? How is it selected?

6-15. What is the *pivot row*? How is it selected?

6-16. What is the *pivot number*?

6-17. Explain the construction of the objective and variable columns in the new (after the first) iteration.

6-18. What is the rule for deriving the replacement row for the pivot row?

6-19. How are all other figures in the new iterations derived?

PROBLEMS

6-1. Maximize $2x + 3y + 2z$
subject to

$$x + 8y + 4z \leq 80$$
$$3x - 4y + z \leq 120$$

and $x \geq 0,\ y \geq 0,\ z \geq 0.$

6-2. Derive the optimun values for the illustrative problem, using the objective to maximize total units produced.

6-3. Derive the optimum solution for the illustrative problem, using the objective to minimize unused man hours.

6-4. Solve Problem 5-1 using the simplex method.

6-5. Maximize $5x + 4y$
   subject to

$$4x + 8y \leq 15$$
$$10x + 6y \leq 25$$
$$25x + y \leq 19$$
$$x + 30y \leq 5$$

and $\qquad x \geq 0, \; y \geq 0.$

6-6. Maximize $10x + 2y + 15z$
   subject to

$$30x + 15y + 3z \leq 40$$
$$3x + 18y + 25z \leq 25$$
$$2x + 8y + 10z \leq 50$$
$$5x + 16y + 20z \leq 35$$

and $\qquad x \geq 0, \; y \geq 0, \; z \geq 0.$

6-7. Given $\qquad x + 30y \leq 18$
$$5x + 15y \leq 30$$
$$10x + 5y \leq 20$$
$$x + 10y \leq 40$$

and $\qquad x \geq 0, \; y \geq 0.$

(a) Maximize $x + 2y$, subject to the preceding four inequalities.

(b) Find the redundant equation, eliminate it, and maximize $x + 2y$, subject to the remaining inequalities.

(c) Compare the solutions.

BIBLIOGRAPHY

See bibliography at the end of Chapter 7.

7

The Simplex Method: II

A nutrition or diet problem was presented for graphical solution in Chapter 5 (Problem 5-11). This problem can also be solved by the simplex method, but to do so requires some additional consideration. The problem follows:

Assume that only four nutrients for cattle have been isolated, namely, A, B, C, and D. The Department of Agriculture pamphlet specifies that the minimum daily requirements (MDR) per animal are A, 5 lb; B, 7 lb; C, 6 lb; D, 6 lb. Only two feeds, corn and alfalfa, are available. The analyses of corn and alfalfa are

	Corn (per cent)	Alfalfa (per cent)
A	10	50
B	45	15
C	25	15
D	20	20

Corn costs 2 cents and alfalfa 1 cent per lb. Derive the least-cost feeding program.

By adding a third available feed, silage, the problem becomes much more difficult to solve graphically, making the simplex method a more attractive approach to the solution. Silage contains 25 per cent A, 10 per cent B, 15 per cent C, and 50 per cent D. It costs one-half as much per pound as does alfalfa, or $\frac{1}{2}$ cent per lb. Assume further that a later publication of the Department of Agriculture recommends that the MDR of 6 lb per day of nutrient D be changed to *exactly* 6 lb; since both under- and over-feeding of nutrient D appear to have undesirable effects upon the cattle.

SEC. 7-2. HANDLING EQUATIONS, APPROXIMATIONS, AND GREATER THAN INEQUALITIES

In setting up the diet problem, a block arrangement of data similar to that used in Chapters 5 and 6 is helpful:

	Percentage			
	Corn	Alfalfa	Silage	MDR
A	10	50	25	5
B	45	15	10	7
C	25	15	15	6
D	20	20	50	6

Let

$X =$ lb corn per animal per day

$Y =$ lb alfalfa per animal per day

$Z =$ lb silage per animal per day.

Then

$A \quad 0.10X + 0.50Y + 0.25Z \geq 5$

$B \quad 0.45X + 0.15Y + 0.10Z \geq 7$

$C \quad 0.25X + 0.15Y + 0.15Z \geq 6$

$D \quad 0.20X + 0.20Y + 0.50Z = 6.$

Note that the percentages have been converted to decimals:

$$10\% = 0.10.$$

Minimum daily requirements are expressed using an equal to, or greater than, inequality, since intake of these nutrients may exceed the MDR. Therefore the inequalities expressing the relationships for nutrients A, B, and C use the $\geq$ sign. Since the specifications for D have been changed from an MDR situation to an exact intake, the relationship for D is expressed by using the $=$ sign.

It will be recalled that all inequalities must be converted into equations in order to use the simplex method. In Chapter 6, less than, or equal to, inequalities were considered. To convert this type of inequality, a slack variable was added to the left side. To convert the *greater than*, or equal to, inequality, the slack variable must be subtracted instead of added. The first inequality will serve as an example:

(a) $\qquad 0.10X + 0.50Y + 0.25Z \geq 5.$

Under certain conditions, (a) can become

(b) $\qquad 0.10X + 0.50Y + 0.25Z = 5.$

Under other conditions, (a) can become

(c) $\qquad\qquad 0.10X + 0.50Y + 0.25Z > 5.$

Therefore, to take care of the possible excess of the left side of (c) over 5, a slack variable is *subtracted* from the left side of (b); thus,

(d) $\qquad\qquad 0.10X + 0.50Y + 0.25Z - W_1 = 5.$

It will be further recalled that each equation for the simplex must contain at least one variable with a coefficient of *plus one*, and this same variable in every other equation in the system must have a coefficient of *zero*. No variable in (d) has a coefficient of plus one; therefore, some further adjustment to (d) must be made in order to provide for the identity requirements. To supply the needed plus one for the identity, a so-called *artificial variable* is added to the left side of (d):

(e) $\qquad\qquad 0.10X + 0.50Y + 0.25Z - W_1 + U_1 = 5.$

More will be said later about manipulating the artificial variable, but it should be clear that *in any usable solution*, the value of the artificial variable *must* be zero, since the sum of the other four components *must* be equal to 5.

The problem statement for nutrient D,

(f) $\qquad\qquad 0.20X + 0.20Y + 0.50Z = 6,$

is already in the form of an equation. It suffers from the same deficiency as did the converted equation (d) for nutrient A with respect to the requirements for the identity. An artificial variable is added to equations in the same manner as to greater than inequalities.

The system converted for application of the simplex method is

$$
\begin{aligned}
A \quad & 0.10X + 0.50Y + 0.25Z - W_1 + U_1 = 5 \\
B \quad & 0.45X + 0.15Y + 0.10Z - W_2 + U_2 = 7 \\
C \quad & 0.25X + 0.15Y + 0.15Z - W_3 + U_3 = 6 \\
D \quad & 0.20X + 0.20Y + 0.50Z \quad\;\; + U_4 = 6.
\end{aligned}
$$

The objective function must now be derived. The function for the original system before conversion may be stated;

$$\text{pounds of feed per animal per day} = 2X + Y + \tfrac{1}{2}Z$$

which is to be minimized. Since the simplex method, as described, is a maximization process, the objective function is multiplied by -1 to obtain

$$\text{pounds of feed (expressed as a negative)} = -2X - Y - \tfrac{1}{2}Z.$$

This function is to be maximized.

It will be recalled that the objective function as it is applied to the simplex method must contain every variable in the system, including any slack variables added or subtracted and any artificial variables added. Each variable must have a coefficient which will achieve the objective desired, namely, (1) positive coefficients tend toward the maximization of the variable, (2) negative coefficients tend toward the minimization of the variable, (3) zero coefficients are neutral, and have no effect in computing the value of the objective function, (4) indifference between variables is expressed by equal coefficients.

An analysis of the W's in the system reveals that they represent amounts of the nutrients in excess of MDR. The cattleman is indifferent as to whether his cattle get any or how much excess nutrients. He wants to be certain that they get at least the MDR, and to get this at the least cost. If zero coefficients are assigned to the W's, these objectives will be achieved, since the zeros are neutral, tending toward neither maximization nor minimization, and the equal coefficients for all the W's express indifference between them.

It was stated previously that the artificial variables (the U's), in any usable solution, must be equal to zero. The coefficients of the artificial variables in the objective function during the operation of the simplex method must force this to occur. There are four artificial variables in the problem under consideration, a total of ten variables, and a system of four equations. There will therefore be at least six variables in any iteration of the simplex which will be equal to zero. The coefficients chosen must assure that four of these six, in the optimum iteration, are the U's. This may be achieved by assigning $-M$'s as coefficients, where M stands for a number larger than any other number except another M.

The completed objective function, then, is

$$\text{pounds of feed (as a negative)} = -2X - Y - \tfrac{1}{2}Z + 0W_1 + 0W_2 + 0W_3$$
$$- MU_1 - MU_2 - MU_3 - MU_4.$$

The first iteration is shown in Figure 7-1. The decimals have been converted to fractions. This will permit the check column to be an exact rather than an approximate check. The M's are handled algebraically in a manner similar to that discussed in Sec. 4-3. Notice that the initial

		−2 X	−1 Y	−1/2 Z	0 W₁	0 W₂	0 W₃	−M U₁	−M U₂	−M U₃	−M U₄	Ck
−M	U_1	5	1/10	1/2	1/4	−1	0	0	1	0	0	0	117/20
−M	U_2	7	9/20	3/20	1/10	0	−1	0	0	1	0	0	77/10
−M	U_3	6	1/4	3/20	3/20	0	0	−1	0	0	1	0	131/20
−M	U_4	6	1/5	1/5	1/2	0	0	0	0	0	0	1	69/10 ←
		−24M	(2 − M)	(1 − M)	(1/2 − M) ↑	M	M	M	0	0	0	0	(7/2 − 24M)

Fig. 7-1. First Iteration of Diet Problem

		0 X	0 Y	0 Z	0 W₁	0 W₂	0 W₃	−1 U₁	−1 U₂	−1 U₃	−1 U₄	CK
−1	U_1	5	1/10	1/2	1/4	−1	0	0	1	0	0	0	117/20
−1	U_2	7	9/20	3/20	1/10	0	−1	0	0	1	0	0	77/10
−1	U_3	6	1/4	3/20	3/20	0	0	−1	0	0	1	0	131/20
−1	U_4	6	1/5	1/5	1/2	0	0	0	0	0	0	1	79/10 ←
		−24	−1	−1	−1 ↑	1	1	1	0	0	0	0	−24

Fig. 7-2. Use of Dummy Objective Function

solution has the artificial variables meeting the total value of the equations—all other variables are equal to zero. Although this provides a mathematically acceptable solution, it does not provide a feasible solution in any practical sense. No solution will be feasible until all artificial variables are equal to zero. The simplex method, as set up in Figure 7-1, immediately proceeds to force these artificial variables out of the solution, although it will take one iteration to force out each artificial variable. (Derivation of the optimum solution is left as an exercise for the reader.)

Approximations

Assume that the Department of Agriculture communication had stated that the daily consumption per animal of nutrient D should be *approximately* 6 lb rather than *exactly* 6 lb. The mathematical presentation would then be

(g) $$0.20X + 0.20Y + 0.50Z \doteq 6.$$

The $\doteq$ sign is read "is approximately equal to." Again, the following equation would, under certain conditions, satisfy the approximation:

(h) $$0.20X + 0.20Y + 0.50Z = 6.$$

At other times these two conditions may exist

(i) $$0.20X + 0.20Y + 0.50Z > 6$$

(j)   and $$0.20X + 0.20Y + 0.50Z < 6.$$

To take care of (i), a slack variable is subtracted from the left side of (h), and to take care of (j), one is also added to obtain:

(k) $$0.20X + 0.20Y + 0.50Z - W_4 + W_5 = 6.$$

The W_5, moreover, meets all the requirements for use in the identity, so no artificial variable need be added. Equation (k) is ready for use in the simplex tableau.

The next question to be answered is, What coefficients should be assigned to W_4 and W_5 in the objective function? An *approximation* means that the left-hand sum should be as close to being equal to the right-hand constant as possible, but the left-hand sum may either exceed or be less than the constant. Therefore, the objective is to minimize both W_4 and W_5, but be indifferent as to their relative values. This can be accomplished by assigning coefficients of -1 to both W_4 and W_5.

SEC. 7-3. USING A DUMMY OBJECTIVE FUNCTION

Using the $-M$'s in the objective function makes it necessary to perform some simple but tedious algebraic manipulations. Some of these can be eliminated by substituting a dummy objective function for the objective function as developed to meet the requirements of the problem. One of the immediate mathematical objectives is to force the artificial variables out of the solution. This can be accomplished in one iteration per artificial variable by using an objective function with the coefficients of the artificial variables equal to -1, and all other coefficients equal to zero. The dummy objective for Figure 7-1 is

$$0X + 0Y + 0Z + 0W_1 + 0W_2 + 0W_3 - U_1 - U_2 - U_3 - U_4.$$

The initial iteration using this objective is shown in Figure 7-2. The process is carried to an optimum iteration; that is, when there are no negative index values. At that time, the dummy objective is replaced with the original objective function. This means that the objective column must also be replaced. The index row in the optimum iteration obtained with the dummy objective is struck out and replaced by recomputing the index row using the original objective function. The process may still be at an optimum (no negative values in the recomputed index row). If not, as many more iterations are performed as are necessary, but now using the original objective function. Note that, in recomputing the index row, the values in the objective column must be replaced by the original objective coefficients for the variables in the variable column at that time.

In some few cases, the optimum iteration will be derived before all the artificial variables have been driven out of the solution. It is possible to proceed using the dummy objective, but the process is somewhat complex. The simpler procedure, probably, is to discard the dummy objective method and solve the problem using the original objective function.

SEC. 7-4. ELIMINATING REDUNDANT CONSTRAINTS

The time and effort required to solve a simplex problem rise greatly with the number of constraints and the number of variables in the system. The term *constraint* is used here to include inequalities, equations, and approximations. There are occasions when some constraints in a given system have no effect on the solution of the problem; yet their presence in the system requires just as much manipulation as they would if they were necessary to derive the solution.

A simple example of this condition is

$$x \geq 10 \qquad x \geq 5.$$

Clearly, if any acceptable solution requires that x be equal to, or greater than, 10, an additional requirement that x be equal to, or greater than 5, can have no effect upon the solution. Such an inequality may merely be dropped from the system with the beneficial result that the amount of mathematical manipulation is greatly decreased.

Not all redundant constraints are as easy to spot as in the preceding illustration; some experience is helpful in seeing occasions where redundancies exist. The following illustrates a common type of redundancy:

(I)	$2x + y \geq 30$
(II)	$4x + 9y \geq 180$
(III)	$3x + 11y \geq 165$
(IV)	$2x + 7y \geq 70$
and	$x \geq 0;\ y \geq 0.$

These requirements are graphed in Figure 7-3. The area inside the fringed lines is unacceptable solution area. This area is bounded by inequalities (I), (II), and (III). No part of inequality (IV) lies within the acceptable

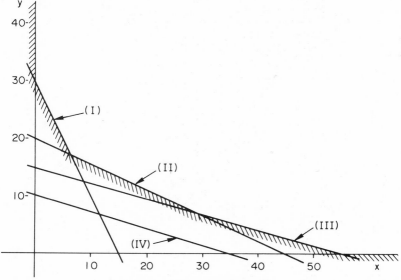

Fig. 7-3. A Redundant Constraint

area of solution. Therefore (IV) can be dropped from the system, with no ill effects, and with the saving of much computational labor.

This same concept may be extended to systems with three or more variables. Consider the following requirements:

(A) $4x + 3y + 6z \geq 120$

(B) $10x + 7y + 16z \geq 250$

and $x \geq 0; \; y \geq 0; \; z \geq 0.$

These requirements are graphed in Figure 7-4. Only that portion of space away from the origin and outside *Plane A* is available for solution. The entire *Plane B* lies inside the unacceptable area, and hence is redundant.

This type of redundancy may be discovered by computing the axis in-

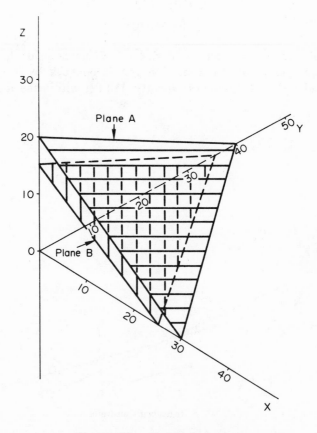

Fig. 7-4. Three-Variable Redundancy

tercepts for each variable. Merely set all other variables in the constraint equal to zero:

	A	B
When $y = 0$ and $z = 0$, $x =$	30	25
When $x = 0$ and $z = 0$, $y =$	40	35 5/7
When $x = 0$ and $y = 0$, $z =$	20	15 5/8

Since every axis intercept of (A) is greater than every corresponding axis intercept of (B), the planes do not intersect in the area of acceptable solutions. Constraints (A) and (B) are greater than conditions, which makes (B) redundant. If they had been less than conditions, (A) would have been redundant. If one had been greater than and the other less than, it is possible that neither would be redundant.

SEC. 7-5. THE DUAL PROBLEM

The simplex problems as set up so far in the discussions represent a class of the simplex known as the *primal problem*. The primal problem results from those primary relationships normally observed when analyzing the basic facts presented. For every primal problem there is a related *dual problem*. The dual problem can be easily set up from the primal. If desired, however, the dual also can be set up from the original data without first setting up the primal problem.

The optimum solution to the dual problem, in terms of the evaluation of the objective function, is *identical* to that of the primal problem. The dual problem may have more or fewer constraints than the primal, and it may have more or fewer variables. If the dual has fewer constraints or variables, less work may be required to solve it; hence, from that standpoint, the dual may be a more desirable approach.

To illustrate the setting up of the dual problem, the initial problem described in Sec. 7-1 will be used. The constraints and objective function are

$$0.10X + 0.50Y \geq 5$$
$$0.45X + 0.15Y \geq 7$$
$$0.25X + 0.15Y \geq 6$$
$$0.20X + 0.20Y \geq 6.$$

Minimize the cost function $2X + Y$.
The first and optimum iterations for the primal problem are shown in Figure 7-5. This is a four by ten matrix—four equations and ten variables.

(a) First Iteration

		-2 x	-1 Y	0 W_1	0 W_2	0 W_3	0 W_4	-M U_1	-M U_2	-M U_3	-M U_4	Ck
-M	U_1	5	1/10	1/2	-1	0	0	0	1	0	0	0	28/5
-M	U_2	7	9/20	3/20	0	-1	0	0	0	1	0	0	38/5
-M	U_3	6	1/4	3/20	0	0	-1	0	0	0	1	0	32/5
-M	U_4	6	1/5	1/5	0	0	0	-1	0	0	0	1	32/5
		-24M	(2 − M)	(1 − M)	M	M	M	M	0	0	0	0	(3 − 22M)

(b) Optimum Iteration

		-2 x	-1 Y	0 W_1	0 W_2	0 W_3	0 W_4	-M U_1	-M U_2	-M U_3	-M U_4	Ck
-1	Y	95/3	0	1	0	25/3	-15	0	0	-25/3	15	0	98/3
-2	x	5	1	0	0	-5	5	0	0	5	-5	0	6
0	W_4	4/3	0	0	0	2/3	-2	1	0	-2/3	2	-1	4/3
0	W_1	34/3	0	0	1	11/3	-7	0	-1	-11/3	7	0	34/3
		-125/3	0	0	0	5/3	5	0	M	(M − 5/3)	(M − 5)	M	(4M − 125/3)

Fig. 7-5. First and Optimum Iterations of Primal Problem

84

The interpretation of the optimum solution is: Feed 5 lb of corn and 31 $\frac{2}{3}$ lb of alfalfa per animal per day. The cost will be 125/3 or 41 $\frac{2}{3}$ cents per animal per day. The 125/3 is negative because the original objective function was multiplied by -1. Each animal will get an excess over the MDR of nutrient A of 11 1/3 lb and of nutrient D of 1 1/3 lb.

To set up the dual problem from the primal, choose new variables, one for each constraint in the primal. There are four constraints, therefore Q, R, S, and T are acceptable (these could have been T_1, T_2, T_3, and T_4, or any other similar set of four different variables). Next list the new variables in a vertical column and the coefficients of the primal constraints and of the primal objective function in rows aligned with the new variables, placing the objective coefficients at the bottom; thus,

	X	Y	Constant
Q	0.10	0.50	5
R	0.45	0.15	7
S	0.25	0.15	6
T	0.20	0.20	6
Primal objective	2	1	

Reading down, starting with the first column of figures, construct the constraints for the dual:

$$0.10Q + 0.45R + 0.25S + 0.20T \leq 2$$
$$0.50Q + 0.15R + 0.15S + 0.20T \leq 1.$$

Maximize $5Q + 7R + 6S + 6T.$

The inequality signs for the dual constraints are the opposite of those for the primal. In this case, the primal contained equal to or greater than inequalities, therefore the dual constraints are equal to or less than. The objective function is constructed from the constant column of the primal by reading down in the same manner as the constraints were formed. The objective is, however, reversed from the primal. In this case, the primal objective function was to be minimized; therefore, the objective function of the dual is to be maximized.

The dual system and objective function as converted for application to the simplex are

$$0.10Q + 0.45R + 0.25S + 0.20T + V_1 = 2$$
$$0.50Q + 0.15R + 0.15S + 0.20T + V_2 = 1.$$

Maximize the function

$$5Q + 7R + 6S + 6T + 0V_1 + 0V_2.$$

This will form a two by six simplex matrix—appreciably smaller than the four by ten matrix of the primal, and hence solvable with a great reduction in labor expended. The first and optimum iterations of the dual are shown in Figure 7-6. The decimals have been converted to fractions.

The conversion from dual solution to primal solution is quite simple. The following is an extraction from the optimum dual solution (from Figure 7-6) showing only the variable and index rows:

Q	R	S	T	V_1	V_2
$\dfrac{125}{3}$	$\dfrac{34}{3}$	0	0	$\dfrac{4}{3}$	5	$\dfrac{95}{3}$

Now cross out each of the variables and replace the slack variables of the dual with the variables of the primal and the variables of the dual with the slack variables of the primal; thus,

W_1	W_2	W_3	W_4	X	Y
Q	R	S	T	V_1	V_2
$\dfrac{125}{3}$	$\dfrac{34}{3}$	0	0	$\dfrac{4}{3}$	5	$\dfrac{95}{3}$

The solution of the primal is: $X = 5$, $Y = 95/3$, $W_1 = 34/3$, $W_2 = 0$, $W_3 = 0$, and $W_4 = 4/3$. Inspection of the optimum solution of the primal (Figure 7-5) will verify these values.

			5	7	6	6	0	0	
			Q	R	S	T	V_1	V_2	CK
0	V_1	2	1/10	9/20	1/4	1/5	1	0	4
0	V_2	1	1/2	3/20	3/20	1/5	0	1	3
		0	−5	−7	−6	−6	0	0	−24

(a) First Iteration

			5	7	6	6	0	0	
			Q	R	S	T	V_1	V_2	CK
7	R	5/3	−11/3	1	0	−2/3	5	−25/3	−5
6	S	5	7	0	1	2	−5	15	25
		125/3	34/3	0	0	4/3	5	95/3	273/3

(b) Optimum Iteration

Fig. 7-6. First and Optimum Iterations of the Dual Problem

A similar transition may be made from the primal solution to the dual solution. The variable and index rows of the optimum primal solution (from Figure 7-5) are

	X	Y	W_1	W_2	W_3	W_4	U_1	U_2	U_3	U_4
$-125/3$	0	0	0	5/3	5	0	M	$(M-5/3)$	$(M-5)$	M

Again substituting the variables of the dual for the slack variables of the primal and the slack variables of the dual for the variables of the primal:

	V_1	V_2	Q	R	S	T				
	X	Y	W_1	W_2	W_3	W_4	U_1	U_2	U_3	U_4
$-125/3$	0	0	0	5/3	5	0	M	$(M-5/3)$	$(M-5)$	M

Hence: $R = 5/3$, $S = 5$, $Q = T = V_1 = V_2 = 0$. There are, of course, no equivalents for the U's.

Remember, the index row figures, other than that in the constant column, represent the change in the objective function that would result in the introduction of one unit of the variable from the column under consideration (see Sec. 6-3). The relationship between the variables of the primal and dual, then, becomes readily apparent. The variables (nonslack) of the dual are equal to the marginal values in the slack variables of the primal, and hence may be viewed as "opportunity profits" which would result if that constraint were relaxed by one unit. The slack variables of the dual are equal to the marginal values of the nonslack variables in the primal, and hence represent the change in the objective function which would result from the introduction of one unit of that variable into the solution of the problem.

DISCUSSION QUESTIONS

7-1. Explain how to convert greater-than inequalities for use with the simplex.

7-2. What is meant by an *artificial variable*? Why are these variables sometimes used with the simplex method?

7-3. How are equations converted for use with the simplex?

7-4. What method is used in the simplex to force artificial variables out of the solution?

7-5. What is an *approximation*? How are approximations handled in the simplex method?

7-6. How are the $-M$'s handled in solving the simplex?

7-7. Describe a technique for eliminating some of the computations involving the $-M$'s.

7-8. What is a *dummy objective*? How is it used and what is it supposed to accomplish?

7-9. What is meant by a *redundant constraint*? Illustrate such a condition.

7-10. Describe the *dual problem*.
7-11. Explain how to derive the dual tableau from the primal problem.
7-12. Explain the relationship of the inequality signs in the primal and dual.
7-13. How do the objectives of the dual and primal differ?
7-14. Under what circumstances might it be preferable to solve the dual rather than the primal?
7-15. Explain how to derive the primal solution from the dual and vice versa.

7-1. a. Solve the primal simplex problem: Minimize the function $x + y$ subject to

$$3x + 2y \geq 5,$$
$$x + 6y \geq 3,$$
and
$$x \geq 0, y \geq 0.$$

    b. Analyze the solution.
    c. Solve the dual problem.
    d. Analyze the solution.

7-2. a. Solve the primal simplex problem: Minimize the function $2x + y + 3z$ subject to

$$5x - 4y + 3z \geq 18,$$
$$2x + 3y + z \geq 7,$$
and
$$x \geq 0, y \geq 0, z \geq 0.$$

    b. Analyze the solution.
    c. Solve the dual problem.
    d. Analyze the solution.

7-3. Using the simplex method:
    a. Solve the primal problem of Problem 5-6.
    b. Obtain the solution to the dual directly from the primal.
    c. Verify the solution obtained in (b) by setting up and solving the dual.

7-4. Maximize the function $2x + y + 3z$ subject to

$$5x - 4y + 3z \leq 18$$
$$2x - 3y + z \leq 7$$
$$x + y + z = 25$$
and
$$x \geq 0, y \geq 0, z \geq 0.$$

7-5. Maximize the function $x + y$ subject to

$$4x + 5y \leq 200$$
$$x + 4y \geq 40$$
$$2x + 3y \doteq 90$$
and
$$x \geq 0, y \geq 0.$$

7-6. An oil refinery wishes its premium oil to have at least minimum amounts of components A, B, and C—10 per cent A, 20 per cent B, and 12 per cent C. It has available three different grades of crude oil. Texas crude has 15 per cent A, 10 per cent B, and 9 per cent C, and costs $2 per barrel. Pennsylvania crude has 18 per cent A, 25 per cent B, and 3 per cent C, and costs $2.50 per barrel. California crude has 10 per cent A, 15 per cent B, and 30 per cent C, and costs $1.80 per barrel. Derive the least-cost mix for the oil, using the simplex primal problem, and explain the meaning of the solution. Also solve the dual problem and explain that solution.

7-7. Solve the primal problem of the illustrative problem of Sec. 7-1.

BIBLIOGRAPHY

Bierman, Harold, Jr., Lawrence E. Fouraker, and Robert K. Jaedicke, *Quantitative Analysis for Business Decisions*. Homewood, Ill.: Richard D. Irwin, Inc., 1961, pp. 198-224.

Churchman, C. West, Russell L. Ackoff, and E. Leonard Arnoff, *Introduction to Operations Research*. New York: John Wiley & Sons, Inc., 1957, pp. 304-325.

Glicksman, A. M., *Linear Programming and the Theory of Games*. New York: John Wiley & Sons, Inc., 1963.

Metzger, Robert W., *Elementary Mathematical Programming*. New York: John Wiley & Sons, Inc., 1958, pp. 59-118.

Naylor, Thomas H., and Eugene T. Byrne, *Linear Programming, Methods and Cases*. Belmont, Calif.: Wadsworth Publishing Company, Inc., 1963.

Sasieni, Maurice, Arthur Yaspan, and Lawrence Friedman, *Operations Research, Methods and Problems*. New York: John Wiley & Sons, Inc., 1959, pp. 225-36.

Vazsonyi, Andrew, *Scientific Programming in Business and Industry*. New York: John Wiley & Sons, Inc., 1958, pp. 99-146.

8

The Learning Curve

SEC. 8-1. THE BASIC PROBLEM TO BE SOLVED

The West Coast Aircraft Corporation wishes to respond to a request for bids issued by the United States Air Force. The contract under consideration is for 250 Air Force T-7000 Combat Trainers. Sealed bids only are to be accepted, and the contract is to be awarded to the lowest responsible bidder.

It is of paramount importance to the West Coast Aircraft Corporation to receive this contract. Their principal operations are devoted to governmental contract work. They, of course, must make an acceptable profit on this contract (as on all others, on the average), if received, in order to stay in business. Because all other bidders will base their bids upon efficient methods of producing the aircraft and minimal acceptable profits, the West Coast Aircraft Corporation must not exceed these factors in order to remain competitive. The corporation already has some experience in producing the T-7000. It had the Air Force contract to produce the prototype. The Air Force was sufficiently satisfied with its tests of the prototype to decide to order 250 planes.

The corporation has kept accurate records of its costs in building the prototype. The total costs came to $125,000, of which $25,000 were for materials. The remaining $100,000 were for direct labor and overhead.

On first consideration, it would appear that the computation of the contract bid is simple arithmetic. The corporation feels that the minimum profit rate that it can accept is 25 per cent of the selling price. Therefore the $125,000 cost is 75 per cent of the required price:

$$\text{Selling price} = \frac{\$125,000}{0.75} = \$166,667.$$

The contract bid would then be $166, 667 \times 250$ or $41, 666, 750.

Is it likely that the West Coast Aircraft Corporation's bid will be the low bid? A further question might be, If the corporation is the only bidder, will the Air Force award the contract to it? Some possible answers to these questions will be developed in the remainder of the chapter.

SEC. 8-2. THE EFFECTS OF LEARNING ON PRODUCTION

Anyone who has constructed two or more relatively complex and similar objects is well aware that the time required to construct the second was appreciably less than the time required to construct the first.

Officials and consultants in the aircraft industry during and after World War II also were aware of this fact. They decided to study the effects of learning on the rate of production of aircraft. They discovered some interesting and useful facts and relationships. They found that the learning process continued indefinitely, almost no matter how long the production series ran. More important, perhaps, their analysis revealed that the rate of learning was measurable and fairly constant. As a result, they were able to draw graphs to represent the effects of learning on the rate of production.

It soon became evident that the rate of learning in the aircraft industry was approximately 80 per cent in the following sense: Given any specific point in the production series, say, 100 planes completed, the *accumulated average* time per unit is 80 per cent of the *accumulated average* time per unit at *one-half* that point in the production series. In this case the one-half point would be 50 planes.

There is, of course, nothing magic about the 80 per cent figure. This was the rate experienced in the aircraft industry. A little reflection will reveal that the limiting values are 100 per cent and 50 per cent. If *no* learning occurs, the *accumulated average* time per unit does not change. This would be a 100 per cent rate; that is, given any specific point in the series, the accumulated average time per unit is 100 per cent of that at any earlier point in the series. (It is conceivable, but presumably improbable, that negative learning, or unlearning could occur.) If the 50 per cent rate were the effective rate, the following impossible condition would result. The average accumulated time for the first unit equals 100 per cent. If the average accumulated time for the first two units is to equal 50 per cent, then the production time for the second unit must be equal to zero. Thus,

$$\frac{100 + 0}{50} = 50.$$

Therefore the 50 per cent rate is the upper limit of learning—a limit which can never be reached.

Reference to Figure 8-1 will clarify some of these concepts. The vertical scale represents *average accumulated time per unit* expressed in terms of per cent. The horizontal scale represents total number of units produced. Notice that the horizontal scale starts at 1 and not at 0.

The average accumulated time per unit for one unit is, of course, 100 per cent. In the case of the plane contract, this would have a dollar value of $100, 000. The material component of the cost of producing the aircraft naturally would not be subject to the same learning concepts as would the time elements of the construction. Overhead may logically be included because overhead is, generally speaking, a function of both time and space in which space is held constant, with time acting as the variable element.

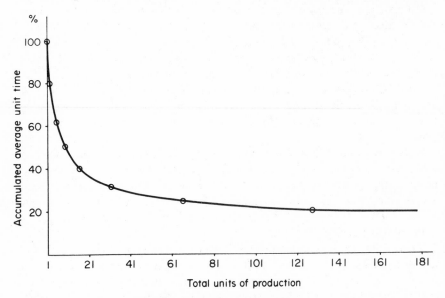

Fig. 8-1. The 80% Learning Curve

If the production of one unit is doubled, total production equals two units. Therefore, the next point on Figure 8-1 is plotted above point 2 on the horizontal scale. The vertical distanceat point 2 is equal to the rate of learning under consideration. In this case, an 80 per cent rate has been postulated. Thus, the height of the point plotted at two units of production is 80 per cent of 100 per cent or 80 per cent.

Doubling two units of production gives four units as the next point to be plotted. The accumulated average unit time at four units 80 per cent of what it was at two units. Therefore, the height at four units is 80 per cent of 80 per cent or 64 per cent. Thus the first nine points will be:

Units Produced	Accumulated Average Time per Unit (%)
1	100.00
2	80.00
4	64.00
8	51.20
16	40.96
32	32.77
64	26.21
128	20.97
256	16.78

Considering once more the corporation's bid, it would evidently not be the low bidder if its competitors were aware of the effects of learning upon production as historically experienced in the airframe industry. In actuality, it is likely that only one of the 250 planes to be built would cost $100,000 for the direct labor and overhead components. The *average* costs (assuming for the moment a production run of 256 units) would be only 16.78 per cent of this figure or $16,780. The bid on this basis would be

Direct labor and overhead ($16,780 × 256)	$4,295,680
Materials ($25,000 × 256)	6,400,000
Total cost	$10,695,680
Profit	3,565,225
Bid price ($10,695,680 ÷ 0.75)	$14,260,905

Under the original method considered, the bid price for a 256-unit order would have been $166,667 × 256 or $42,666,752. This would have resulted in an excess (over minimum) profit of $28,405,847.

The resulting profit rate, based upon selling price, would have been

Selling price	$42,666,752
Cost	10,695,680
Profit	$31,971,072

Profit rate ($31,971,072 ÷ $42,666,752) = 74.93%. Clearly, a profit rate of 74.93 per cent would not be acceptable to a governmental contracting agency.

SEC. 8-3. THE CONSTRUCTION OF THE LEARNING CURVE

The points plotted on Figure 8-1 have been connected with a smooth line. If this line had been accurately constructed, the effects of learning on production could be ascertained at points other than those obtained by doubling the number of units starting with the first. The West Coast

Aircraft Corporation wishes to bid on an order for 250 planes. The closest point plotted is for 256 units. It would therefore be highly desirable if a formula for the curve could be developed so as to permit accurate construction of the curve.

Inspection of the curve of Figure 8-1 reveals that it starts high at the left, drops off rapidly at first, and then continues to drop off but at a decreasing rate. If we let Y stand for the vertical height of any point and X stand for the distance out from the point marked 1, then it can readily be seen that if we let A equal the height of the graph at point 1, the following equation will hold for point 1:

$$Y = \frac{A}{X}.$$

Substituting in this equation $A = 100$ and $X = 1$; then,

$$Y = \frac{100}{1} = 100.$$

This fits the graph as drawn.

In order to make the equation hold true for the second point of the curve, the following must hold true:

$$Y = \frac{A}{X}; \qquad Y = \frac{100}{2} = 80.$$

It is apparent that $100 \div 2$ is not equal to 80, but is equal to 50. Therefore some adjustment must be made to the equation.

Whatever adjustment is made to the equation must be made without disturbing its validity at point 1. The following may be tried:

$$Y = \frac{A}{x^b}.$$

Of course, no matter what value is attached to b, the value of x^b when $X = 1$ will still be 1, since 1 to any power is still 1.

The problem, then, is to obtain some value for b so that

$$Y = \frac{A}{x^b}; \qquad Y = \frac{100}{2^b} = 80,$$

We now have the equation,

$$\frac{100}{2^b} = 80,$$

with b as the only unknown. To solve this equation, we first cross-multiply to obtain

$$80 \times 2^b = 100, \quad \text{or} \quad 2^b = \frac{100}{80} = 1.25.$$

This equation may be solved as follows: Take the logarithm of each side (see Appendix A for a discussion of logarithms). The equation then becomes

$$b \log 2 = \log 1.25; \qquad b = \frac{\log 1.25}{\log 2}$$

By using log tables to find the logarithms of 1.25 and 2, the solution becomes

$$b = \frac{0.0969}{0.3010} = 0.322.$$

Similarly, the following must hold true for $X = 4$:

$$Y = \frac{A}{X^b}; \qquad Y = \frac{100}{4^b} = 64.$$

Again, the equation becomes

$$64 \times 4^b = 100; \qquad 4^b = \frac{100}{64} = 1.56.$$

Taking the logarithm of each side, it becomes

$$b \log 4 = \log 1.56; \qquad b = \frac{\log 1.56}{\log 4}.$$

Obtaining the logs of 1.56 and 4 from the log tables, this becomes

$$b = \frac{0.1931}{0.6021} = 0.322.$$

We may check the third point for corroboration.

$$Y = \frac{A}{X^b}; \qquad Y = \frac{100}{8^b} = 51.2$$

$$51.2 \times 8^b = 100; \qquad 8^b = \frac{100}{51.2} = 1.95$$

$$b \log 8 = \log 1.95; \qquad b = \frac{\log 1.95}{\log 8}$$

$$b = \frac{0.2900}{0.9031} = 0.322.$$

Therefore, the equation of the 80 per cent learning curve appears to be

$$Y = \frac{A}{X^{0.322}}.$$

Since $1/X^{0.322}$ may be written $X^{-0.322}$, the equation will frequently be written

$$Y = AX^{-0.322}.$$

As a final check, let us compute point $X = 256$.

$$Y = \frac{A}{X^{0.322}}; \qquad Y = \frac{100}{256^{0.322}}.$$

Again, this may be solved by logarithms as follows:

$$\log Y = \log 100 - 0.322 \log 256$$
$$\log Y = 2.0000 - 0.322\,(2.4082)$$
$$\log Y = 2.0000 - 0.7754 = 1.2246$$
$$Y = \text{antilog of } 1.2246 = 16.78 \text{ per cent.}$$

This is the same value computed in Sec. 8-2.

Any point on the curve can be computed in this manner. If sufficient points are computed, the curve can be quite accurately graphed.

There remains the problem of the bid price on the 250-plane contract. This merely involves solving the equation for $X = 250$:

$$Y = \frac{A}{X^{0.322}}; \qquad Y = \frac{100}{250^{0.322}}.$$

The process is identical to the foregoing:

$$\log Y = \log 100 - 0.322 \log 250$$
$$\log Y = 2.0000 - 0.322\,(2.3979)$$

$$\log Y = 2.0000 - 0.7721 = 1.2279$$
$$Y = \text{antilog of } 1.2279 = 16.90 \text{ per cent.}$$

The contract bid price would therefore be

Direct labor and overhead (250 × $16,900)	$4,225,000
Materials (250 × $25,000)	6,250,000
Total costs	$10,475,000
Profit	3,491,667
Selling price ($10,475,000 ÷ 0.75)	$13,966,667

Once again, the comparison with the original estimate of $41,666,750 is quite startling.

SEC. 8-4. STRAIGHTENING OUT THE LEARNING CURVE

The learning curve in the form presented in Figure 8-1 is quite useful. Nevertheless it has some readily apparent disadvantages. Should it be desired to read the accumulated average time per unit directly from the curve, the curve must be very accurately plotted to render the required accuracy.

In Sec. 5-4, the concept of the straight-line graph was discussed. Any equation with two variables which are to the first power will graph as a straight line. The 80 per cent learning curve equation does not graph as a straight line because the variable X is not to the first power. The equation can be transformed into a linear (first-power) equation by taking the logarithm of each side:

$$Y = \frac{A}{X^{0.322}}$$
$$\log Y = \log A - \log X^{0.322}$$
$$\log Y = \log A - 0.322 \log X.$$

We now have an equation in the standard linear form, $y = a + bx$.

That this equation will graph as a straight line is demonstrated in Figure 8-2. Here, the vertical scale represents the logarithm of the accumulated average time per unit expressed in terms of per cent, and the horizontal scale represents the logarithm of the total units produced. The points to be plotted may be derived as follows:

Total Units (X)	Log X	Accumulated Average Time per Unit (Y)	Log Y
1	0.0000	100.00	2.0000
2	0.3010	80.00	1.9031
4	0.6021	64.00	1.8062
8	0.9031	51.20	1.7093
16	1.2041	40.96	1.6124
32	1.5051	32.77	1.5155
64	1.8062	26.21	1.4185
128	2.1072	20.97	1.3215
256	2.4082	16.78	1.2247

Since two points determine a straight line, it is unnecessary to compute more than two of the foregoing points. The points selected should be as far apart as possible. This will permit the positioning of the line with great accuracy.

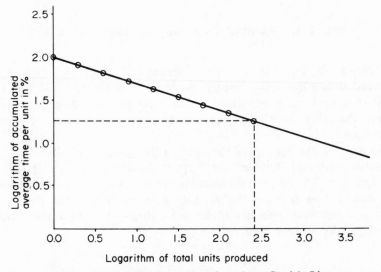

Fig. 8-2. The Learning Curve Transformed to a Straight Line

Figure 8-2 can be used to estimate the percentage of learning for the 250-plane order. It will first be necessary to find the log of 250, which is 2.3979. We then go to point 2.3979 on the horizontal scale of the graph. A line is drawn vertically to intersect the line of the learning curve. At this intersection a line is drawn horizontally to intersect the vertical scale. The reading here represents the logarithm of the per cent of learning at 250 units. The logarithm is approximately 1.23. The antilog of logarithm 1.23. is 16.98, or 16.98 per cent learning. This compares very favorably with the 16.90 per cent computed from the formula. Naturally, the larger the scale of the graph, the more accurate will be the readings.

SEC. 8-5.   USING LOG-LOG PAPER TO GRAPH THE LEARNING CURVE

There still remain several unsatisfactory features about the graph of Figure 8-2, even though it is a definite improvement over the graph of Figure 8-1. The major one of these is that the absolute values cannot be read directly from the graph. Instead, the number of units must first be converted to a logarithm, and then the percentage of learning converted from a logarithm.

Graph paper is available which has both of its scales laid out in values of the logarithms of the numbers instead of the numbers themselves. Since the logarithm of zero is minus infinity, and the logarithm of one is zero, it is necessary to have the scale start at other than zero, say, one. The following table shows how the differences between the logarithms decrease as the numbers increase

Number	Logarithm	Difference
1	0.0000	
2	0.3010	0.3010
3	0.4771	0.1761
4	0.6021	0.1250
5	0.6990	0.0969
6	0.7782	0.0792
7	0.8451	0.0669
8	0.9031	0.0580
9	0.9542	0.0511
10	1.0000	0.0458
11	1.0414	0.0414
12	1.0792	0.0378
13	1.1139	0.0347
14	1.1461	0.0322
15	1.1761	0.0300

These decreasing differences are reflected in the decreasing spaces of the logarithmic scale as shown in the accompanying drawing:

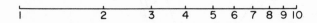

By comparison, an arithmetic scale has equal spacing.

Figure 8-3 shows the learning curve graphed on the log-log graph paper. The central line represents the accumulated average unit time learning curve. Again, only two points are required to locate the line. There is no difference between the line of Figure 8-2 and that of Figure 8-3. If the scales were matched, then the lines could be superimposed. In effect, the

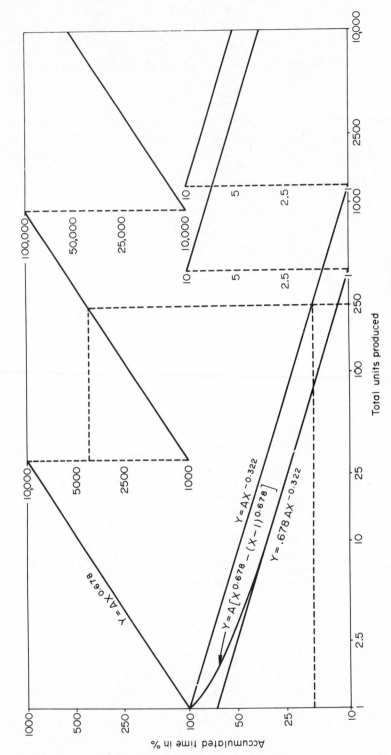

Fig. 8-3. The Three 80% Learning Curves Using Log-Log Graph Paper

use of logarithmic scales on the graph paper is the equivalent of looking up the logarithm of a given number in the log tables and then graphing that logarithm on an arithmetic scale. Note that each succeeding cycle of the 10 logarithmic values is equal to 10 times that of the preceding cycle. If the first cycle is assigned the values of 1 to 10, then the second cycle starts at 10 and ends at 100. Similarly, the third cycle would start at 100 and end at 1000.

Since each scale is of the same physical size, merely renumbered to fit the 10 times rule, the device shown on Figure 8-3 can be used when the line runs off the top or bottom of the graph. At the point of runoff, a vertical line is drawn back to the starting point. In the case of runoff at the bottom of the graph, the value assigned to the top line is equal to the value assigned to the bottom line of the preceding segment. In this case, that value is 10 per cent. The value assigned to the bottom of the new segment is $\frac{1}{10}$ of that of the top—in this case 1 per cent. This technique can be used used as many times as desired as the graph proceeds to the right. At each adjustment, the new values assigned are changed by a factor of 10. That is, where the first scale reads from 1 to 10, the new one will read either from 10 to 100 or from 0.1 to 1.

Now the problem of locating the learning percentage for the 250-unit order is considerably simplified, since it can be read directly from the graph. This time the 250-unit point is located on the horizontal scale as shown. A vertical line is drawn to the learning curve, and a horizontal line from this point on the learning curve to the vertical scale. The learning percentage is read directly from the vertical scale as 16.9 per cent.

SEC. 8-6. THE TOTAL PRODUCTION TIME LEARNING CURVE

The analyst may be more interested in total time of production for a given number of units than he is in the accumulated average time. Total time is easily computed by multiplying accumulated average time by the number of units. We did that to obtain the total time figures for the 250- and 256-unit estimates.

A learning curve representing total time of production can be easily constructed by the same method. Figure 8-4 shows the total production time curve and the accumulated average curve. A smaller vertical scale was used because of the rapidly rising characteristic of the total production time curve.

The various points on the curve were computed as follows:

No. of Units	Accumulated Average Time per Unit (%)	Total Production Time (%)
1	100.00	100.00
2	80.00	160.00
4	64.00	256.00
8	51.20	409.60
16	40.96	653.36
32	32.77	1048.64
64	26.21	1677.44
128	20.97	2684.16
256	16.78	4295.68

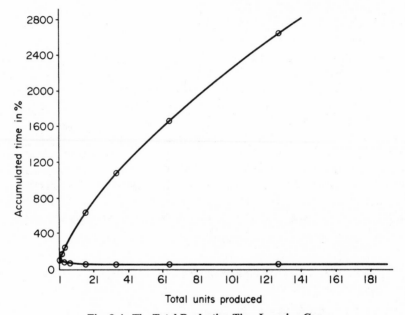

Fig. 8-4. The Total Production Time Learning Curve

It is possible to develop an equation for the total production time curve using a technique similar to that used for the accumulated average time curve. Here, however, the curve rises as it moves to the right. The curve will therefore take the form,

$$Y = AX^c.$$

Again, when X equals 1, Y equals A or 100 per cent. The problem is to ascertain the value of c.

For $X = 2$, the equation becomes:

$$Y = AX^c; \qquad 160 = 100 \times 2^c$$

$$2^c = \frac{160}{100} = 1.60$$

$$c \log 2 = \log 1.60$$

$$c = \frac{\log 1.60}{\log 2} = \frac{0.2041}{0.3010} = 0.678.$$

For $X = 8$, the equation becomes

$$Y = AX^c; \qquad 409.6 = 100 \times 8^c$$

$$8^c = \frac{409.6}{100} = 4.096$$

$$c \log 8 = \log 4.096$$

$$c = \frac{\log 4.096}{\log 8} = \frac{0.6124}{0.9031} = 0.678.$$

Therefore the equation of the total production time curve is

$$Y = AX^{0.678}.$$

Notice that the sum of the exponents of the accumulated average time curve and the total production time curve $(0.322 + 0.678)$ is equal to 1. This fact may be proved quite simply. Each point on the total production time curve was obtained by multiplying the corresponding Y value on the accumulated average unit time curve by the number of units, X. Thus the equation for Y in the total production time curve is

$$Y = \frac{A}{X^b} \cdot X$$

$$= \frac{AX}{X^b}$$

$$= AX^{(1-b)},$$

and

$$c = 1 - b$$

or

$$c + b = 1.$$

We may now apply this to solve the 250-unit problem:

$$Y = AX^{0.678}; \qquad Y = 100 \cdot 250^{0.678}.$$

Solving with logarithms,

$$\log Y = \log 100 + 0.678 \log 250$$
$$\log Y = 2.0000 + 0.678 \cdot 2.3979$$
$$\log Y = 2.0000 + 1.6258 = 3.6258$$
$$Y = \text{antilog of } 3.6258 = 4{,}225.$$

Therefore, the production percentage at 250 units is 4,225 per cent. Thus the total labor and overhead cost would be 42.25 × \$100,000 or \$4,225,000; the same figure which was obtained by the accumulated average time method.

The total production time learning curve graphed on arithmetic graph paper has all the disadvantages discussed under the accumulated average time learning curve. Plotting this curve on log-log graph paper will straighten it out in the same manner. This is shown as the upper line on Figure 8-3. Once again we employ the fact that the logarithmic scale cycles are repetitive in size but change by a factor of 10. Each time the vertical scale is reevaluated accordingly.

The total production time percentage of the first item can now be read directly from the curve for any given number of units in the production series. For the 250-unit series, a vertical line is raised from the point 250 on the horizontal scale to the total production time curve and then a horizontal line carried over to the appropriate vertical scale. The reading obtained is approximately 4200 per cent. Of course, the larger the scale of the graph, the more accurate will be the reading obtained.

SEC. 8-7. THE INDIVIDUAL UNIT TIME LEARNING CURVE

Some analysts (for example, supervisors desiring to compare the progress of their employees against the learning standard) will be interested in knowing the time required for individual units in the production series.

This information can be obtained indirectly from the total production learning curve. The time required to produce the two-hundred and fiftieth unit is the total time required to produce 250 units minus the total time required to produce 249 units. This may be expressed in terms of our previous equations as follows:

$$\text{unit production time} = Y = AX^{0.678} - A(X - 1)^{0.678}.$$

Factoring out the A, this becomes

$$Y = A[X^{0.678} - (X - 1)^{0.678}]. \tag{1}$$

We may graph this curve in a manner similar to that used for the preceding curves. This time, however, we shall proceed immediately to the log-log graph paper.

In order to develop the points to be graphed, Eq. (1) must be solved for the various points. For point 1, $X = 1$, and $X - 1 = 0$:

$$Y = A[X^{0.678} - (X - 1)^{0.678}]; \qquad Y = 100(1^{0.678} - 0^{0.678})$$
$$Y = 100.$$

For point 2, $X = 2$, and $X - 1 = 1$:

$$Y = 100(2^{0.678} - 1^{0.678}).$$

Of course, $1^{0.678}$ equals 1. To obtain $2^{0.678}$, we must use logarithms:

$$2^{0.678} = \text{antilog of } 0.678 \log 2$$
$$= \text{antilog of } 0.678 \times 0.3010$$
$$= \text{antilog of } 0.2041$$
$$= 1.60$$

Therefore $Y = 100(1.60 - 1) = 60$.

Using the same technique, the points shown in columns (1) and (2) of Figure 8-5 may be developed. These points are plotted on Figure 8-3 (the lower curved line) and connected with a smooth curve. Notice that the use of log-log graph paper straightened out the accumulated average time curve and the accumulated total time curve, but the individual unit time curve still remains curvilinear. Notice further that beyond the 10-unit point the curve becomes almost a straight line.

Reference to Figure 8-5, column (3) will help explain this phenomenon. Unit 2 is 60 per cent of unit 1. As production doubles to 4 units, unit 4 is 75.6 per cent of unit 2. Each doubling of production brings the percentage reduction of time closer to the 80 per cent value, making the slope of the individual unit time curve *approach* that of the accumulated average unit time curve. The word "approach" is significant, because the 80 per cent value is never quite reached. The 80.0— figures in column (3) are rounded up from slightly lower values. For the purpose of drawing the curve, however, the 80 per cent figure is closely approximated from about the unit-10 point on.

A line with an 80 per cent slope (that is, one parallel to the accumulated average unit time curve) can be drawn in such a way that the individual unit time curve is asymptotic to it. An *asymptote* is a line which a curve continues to approach, but never quite reaches, except at infinity. An equation to represent the asymptote may be developed as follows.

The exponent of X in the accumulated average unit time curve $Y = AX^{-0.322}$ represents the slope of that curve. Therefore, since the slopes are the same, the asymptote will have as part of its equation the term $X^{-0.322}$.

Unit (X) (1)	Individual Unit Time (2)	% Unit 2X is of Unit X (3)	Accumulated Average Unit Time (4)	Column (2) ÷ Column (4) (5)
1	100.00	60.0	100.00	1.000
2	60.00	75.6	80.00	0.750
4	45.36	78.2	64.00	0.709
8	35.45	79.1	51.20	0.692
16	28.04	79.6	40.96	0.684
32	22.32	79.8	32.77	0.682
64	17.81	79.9	26.21	0.680
128	14.23	80.0—	20.97	0.679
256	11.38	80.0—	16.78	0.678+
512	9.10	80.0—	13.42	0.678+
1024	7.28	80.0—	10.74	0.678+
2048	5.82	80.0—	8.59	0.678+
4096	4.66	80.0—	6.87	0.678+
8192	3.72		5.50	0.678+

Fig. 8-5. Data the Unit Time Curve

It is evident from inspection of Figure 8-3 that the Y values of the two equations are different. Since the form of the two equations should be similar, and since term $X^{-0.322}$ is the same for both, then A must have a different value for the asymptote.

Column (4) of Figure 8-5 represents the accumulated average unit times for the corresponding units of column (1). Column (5) represents the values in column (2) divided by the values in column (4). Column (5) may be said to represent A, but for the straight line of the asymptote, A is a constant. As we go down column (5), however, we approach the value of 0.678. This is the exponent of X in the accumulated total time curve and also one minus the absolute value (0.322) of the exponent of the accumulated unit time curve. The formula for the asymptote of the individual unit time curve is therefore,

$$Y = 0.678AX^{-0.322}.$$

SEC. 8-8. ASCERTAINING THE RATE OF LEARNING

In Sec. 8-1 we mentioned that there is nothing magical about the 80 per cent figure that has been used as an illustration. The rate of learning experienced under specific conditions can lie anywhere between the 50 per cent and the 100 per cent limits. In order to ascertain the rate of learning, some production data must be available for analysis.

Assume that the following figures are available: Accumulated direct labor hours at unit 10 were 350 and accumulated direct labor hours at unit 50 were 700.

The equation for the accumulated total time curve is

$$Y = AX^c.$$

Solving this for A, we get

$$A = \frac{Y}{X^c}.$$

The observed data may now be substituted so that

$$A = \frac{350}{10^c} \quad \text{and} \quad A = \frac{700}{50^c}.$$

Then, of course,

$$\frac{350}{10^c} = \frac{700}{50^c}.$$

We may then multiply both sides of the equation by $50^c/350$, and it becomes

$$\frac{50^c}{10^c} = \frac{700}{350}.$$

The $50^c/10^c$ may be written $(50/10)^c$ which equals 5^c. Therefore,

$$5^c = 2.$$

This may be solved by the logarithm method discussed previously.

$$c \log 5 = \log 2$$

$$c = \frac{\log 2}{\log 5} = \frac{0.30103}{0.69897} = 0.4307.$$

A may be found by substituting c in the equation:

$$A = \frac{350}{10^c} = \frac{350}{10^{0.4307}}.$$

Again using logs, this becomes

$$\log A = \log 350 - 0.4307 \log 10$$
$$= 2.54407 - 0.4307 \times 1.00000$$

$$= 2.11337$$

$$A = \text{antilog of } 2.11337 = 129.83.$$

The equation for the accumulated total time curve is

$$Y = 129.83X^{0.4307}.$$

In order to ascertain the rate of learning, the accumulated average unit time curve may be used. It will be recalled that the accumulated average unit time at any point on this curve is the learning rate times the accumulated average unit time at the one-half point. In this case we have the data at point-50 units. We must compute the data for point-25 units. The equation for the accumulated average unit time curve is

$$Y = \frac{A}{X^b},$$

where $b = 1 - c$. In this case, $b = 1 - 0.4307 = 0.5693$. Therefore the equation is

$$Y = \frac{129.83}{X^{0.5693}}.$$

We wish to solve for $X = 25$.

$$\log Y = \log 129.83 - 0.5693 \log 25$$

$$= 2.11337 - 0.5693 \times 1.39794$$

$$= 2.11337 - 0.79585 = 1.31752$$

$$Y = \text{antilog of } 1.31752 = 20.74$$

The accumulated average unit time at 50 units equals $700 \div 50 = 14$. The learning rate therefore equals $14 \div 20.74 = 67.5$ per cent.

SEC. 8-9. USING THE LEARNING CURVES

As with any tool of management, the learning curve should be used with caution and supplemented with good judgment. A company desiring to put the learning curve to practical use should employ it on an experimental basis along with current procedures in order to gain experience and confidence.

The learning curve is a regression line and therefore brings with it the difficulties as well as the benefits of regression analysis. Users of regression analysis are painfully aware that, even when the coefficient of determination is extremely high, individual observations tend to fall around, rather than on, the regression line. Users of the learning curve also must cope with this problem. As experience is gained, standard error figures may be computed and confidence limits determined. It would be fruitless to attempt to correct a merely random deviation from the projected curve.

Even more difficult is the problem of exactly what segment of the production process to include in that portion which is considered subject to learning. Many users feel that only direct labor of a type which is largely devoted to hand rather than machine operation should be included. In this category, the assembly type of operation, such as airframe assembly, is especially noteworthy. Machine operations in which production rates are controlled more by machine speeds and capacities than by the skills of the worker clearly are less subject to the learning process.

The learning curve concept is, however, applicable to group operations. Reductions in unit production time are caused by many things other than the learning of the direct workers. Development of new assembly methods, new jigs, new processes all tend to contribute. Determining what to include and what to exclude requires considerable study and experience. During the experimental period, the learning curve should be computed using many bases. Those areas in which little if any learning appears to occur should be excluded at least temporarily until it can be determined whether learning should be but is not occurring.

One area to be excluded from the application of the learning-curve technique is that of the continuing production run. This does not imply that this type of production is not subject to learning. If, however, hundreds of thousands or millions of these units have already been produced, then more hundreds of thousands or millions must be produced before appreciable learning may be measured. Remember that the rate is constant at each *doubling* of production units. Before this extremely large number of units is produced, many factors, such as design, model, and so forth, may have changed so as to obscure any learning trend which might exist.

Major changes which occur during a given production run must naturally be taken into account. If costs rather than time units are being considered, changes, such as in labor rates, will alter the results. Many of these changes would be observed and allowed for as a result of the normal, common-sense operations of the managers. It is well, nevertheless, to develop procedures so that any relevant changes in the trend line are made as the changes in the underlying data occur. Employing tools, such as the learning curve, sometimes tends to induce a feeling of perhaps false confidence so that the user may suffer from a semihypnotic blindness to changes in the basic data.

SEC. 8-10. APPLICATIONS OF THE LEARNING CURVE TECHNIQUE

The illustrations used in this chapter refer to the airframe industry where the pioneering work in the learning curve techniques was performed. The ideas developed are applicable in all industries where hand operations are important and production runs are not of the mass-production, continuous-run type.

The major illustration was that of bidding on contracts of the sealed-bid type. This, of course, is a pricing application and would be useful for establishing prices under other than bid conditions.

However, the co-event of selling is purchasing. The government as the purchaser would find the learning curve technique just as useful to determine whether fair and competitive bids had been received. Actually, various governmental agencies were very active in the development of the learning curve techniques. We may therefore answer the second question propounded at the end of Sec. 8-1 with a reasonably definite "no." It is very unlikely that the government would have accepted such a bid, even though that were the only bid. It would have had the cost data from the prototype. It would have computed reasonable-bid figures for the 250-plane order before opening up the bidding.

These concepts are just as useful to private industry in its purchases from suppliers and subcontractors. Arrangements can be made with suppliers so that prices rendering reasonable or agreed-upon profits may be computed after the supplier has proceeded far enough in his production schedule to permit estimation of the rate of learning, and therefore of average costs for the entire production run.

Make-or-buy decisions in the face of firm price quotations from suppliers may also be made. The manufacturer can compute his average costs over the entire production run and compare this figure with the firm price submitted by the supplier.

Potential uses of the learning curve are continually being uncovered in the areas of planning and controlling various phases of business operations. Accuracy in developing the learning curve and judgment in applying it are the two major requisites for success. (For more information on the various possible applications see the bibliography at the end of this chapter.)

DISCUSSION QUESTIONS

8-1. State the basic concepts underlying the relationships involved in the learning curve.

8-2. State specifically what is meant by the term 80 per cent *learning curve.* Exactly how would this differ from a 90 per cent learning curve?

8-3. What is meant by *accumulated average unit time?*

8-4. What are the limiting percentages of learning curves? State the exact significances of these limits.

8-5. Why is it necessary to use logarithms in developing the exponent of X?

8-6. Explain why the learning curve is curvilinear when graphed on arithmetic graph paper and straight when graphed on log-log graph paper. Explain the relationship between the straight-line graph in Figure 8-2 and the straight-line graph in Figure 8-3.

8-7. Explain in detail the superiorities of the log-log graph of Figure 8-3 over the arithmetic graph of Figure 8-1.

8-8. Explain the method of numbering the scales of the log-log graph paper through several cycles of the scales.

8-9. Explain the difference between the *total production time* learning curve and the *accumulated average unit time* learning curve.

8-10. What is the relationship between the exponents of the *total production time* learning curve and the *accumulated average unit time* learning curve?

8-11. Explain how the *individual unit time* learning curve differs from the *total production time* learning curve and from the *accumulated average unit time* learning curve.

8-12. Why does the *individual unit time* learning curve not graph as a straight line on the log-log graph paper?

8-13. Explain how the learning *rate* may be ascertained from raw production data.

8-14. Discuss some precautions which should be observed when using the learning curve technique.

8-15. Discuss several possible applications of the learning curve technique.

8-16. What is an *asymptote?* Explain its relationship to the individual unit time learning curve.

PROBLEMS

8-1. Develop an equation for a 90 per cent accumulated average unit time learning curve. Graph the equation on both arithmetic and log-log graph paper.

8-2. Develop an equation for a total production time 90 per cent learning curve. Graph the equation on log-log graph paper carrying the graph through several logarithmic cycles.

8-3. Develop an equation for an individual unit time 90 per cent learning curve. Graph the equation on log-log graph paper. Develop the equation for the asymptote for the foregoing curve and graph it on the same paper.

8-4. A subcontractor has an 83 per cent learning curve operating experience on its cost components other than raw materials. It has produced unit 1 of a complicated assembly at a cost of $60,000, $10,000 of which was for materials. It has agreed to accept a 15 per cent profit based on selling price, and it is willing to contract on the basis of its 83 per cent curve. Compute the contract price for 500 units.

8-5. Just before the completion of the 500 units of Problem 8-4, the purchaser placed an order for an additional 500 units provided that the subcontractor was willing to price on the same basis. Compute the contract price for the second 500 units.

8-6. Before the parties in Problem 8-5 signed the contract at the price computed in Problem 8-5, the subcontractor learned that his material prices had been increased 20 per cent and his labor and overhead costs had gone up 15 per cent. The parties agreed to adjust the contract price for the second 500 units to allow for these changes. Compute the revised contract price for the second 500 units.

8-7. Company A had never computed its learning rate. From its records it compiled the following recent experience data for a given job: Accumulated total hours for the eighteenth unit were 755 and accumulated total hours at the fortieth unit were 1300. Compute the learning rate.

8-8. The subcontractor in Problem 8-5 found that upon completion of the first 500 units at the price agreed upon in Problem 8-4, he did not earn a 15 per cent profit but in fact merely broke even. He explained to the prime contractor, who was interested in contracting for an additional 500 units, that since his costs had not changed, the 83 per cent learning rate must not have been correct for this job. Both parties agreed to negotiate the contract for the second 500 units at a price which would permit the subcontractor to realize his 15 per cent profit on the entire 1000-unit run. Compute the new contract price, not including any payments already made for the original 500-unit order, for which the original contract price had been paid in full.

8-9. The subcontractor in Problem 8-4 explained to the prime contractor that he needed financial help in the early stages of the contract. The parties therefore arranged for progress payments to be made as follows: Each time that 50 units were completed and delivered, the prime contractor would pay the costs of that 50 units plus a proportionate share of the total profits. The prime contractor insisted that the payment schedule be computed in advance, and that the schedule be included in the contract. The profit *rate* will be constant, but the profit *amount* will be decreasing since the reimbursed costs paid to the subcontractor will also be decreasing. Prepare the schedule of payments to be included in the contract.

8-10. The Apex Company has experienced a 75 per cent learning rate. It has constructed the first unit of a 100-unit run using 8000 direct labor hours. It wishes to know the expected labor hours for each of the next 5 units. Prepare the schedule of hours required.

BIBLIOGRAPHY

Andress, Frank J., "The Learning Curve as a Production Tool," *Harvard Business Review* (January–February, 1954), 87-93.

Asher, Harold, *Cost-Quantity Relationships in the Airframe Industry*. Santa Monica, Calif.: The RAND Corporation, 1956.

Brenneck, Ronald, "Break-even Charts Reflecting Learning," *N. A. A. Bulletin* (January, 1959), 34-38.

_____, "Learning Curve Techniques for More Profitable Contracts," *N. A. A. Bulletin*, Sec. 2 (July, 1959), 59-69.

_____, "The Learning Curve for Labor Hours—for Pricing," *N. A. A. Bulletin*, Sec. 1 (June, 1959), 77-78.

Ghormley, Glen E., "The Learning Curve—for Evaluating Management Decisions," *Western Industry*, February, 1953.

———, "The Learning Curve—Fitting the Worker to the Job," *Western Industry*, December, 1952.

———, "The Learning Curve—Its Application May Call for Revision of Time Study and Time Standards," *Western Industry*, September, 1952.

———, "The Learning Curve—You Use It Whether You Know It or Not," *Western Industry*, October, 1952.

Jordan, Raymond B., "Learning How to Use the Learning Curve," *N. A. A. Bulletin*, Sec. 2 (January, 1958), 27-39.

Morgan, A. W., *Experience Curves Applicable to the Aircraft Industry*. Baltimore, Md.: The Glenn L. Martin Company, 1952.

Nagely, Rulon, "Learning Curve—Short Cut to Cost Reduction," *Purchasing*, Sept. 29, 1958, 80-83.

Raborg, W. A., Jr., "Mechanics of the Learning Curve," *Aero Digest*, March, 1952.

———, "Theory of the Learning Curve," *California CPA*, April, 1955.

Wright, T. P., "Factors Affecting the Cost of Airplanes," *Journal of Aeronautical Sciences* (February, 1956), 11-43.

Wyer, Rolfe, "Industrial Accounting with the Learning Curve," *California CPA*, 23 (Feb. 24, 1956).

———, "Learning Curve Helps Figure Profits, Control Costs," *N.A.C.A. Bulletin*, December, 1953.

———, "Learning Curve Techniques for Direct Labor Management," *N. A. A. Bulletin*, Sec. 2 (July, 1958), 19-25.

9

Probability
and Probability Distributions

SEC. 9-1. STATEMENT OF THE PROBLEM TO BE SOLVED

A department store manager is making a study of his complaint department. He watched his customers arrive to make complaints, and kept a record for 1000 minutes. In each of 610 of these minutes, no one arrived at the complaint counter; in each of 290 minutes, one person arrived; in each of 90 minutes, two people arrived; and in each of 10 minutes, three people arrived. Never during any single minute did four people arrive. He took these figures to his statistician, and asked him whether the figures could be used in analyzing the complaint department situation.

The statistician was quite interested and said that he would make some tests to see whether the arrival rate appeared to approximate a binomial, a Poisson, or a normal probability distribution. He remarked that there were many other probability distributions that could be considered, but that these were among the more useful.

SEC. 9-2. BASIC PROBABILITY CONCEPTS AND THEOREMS

The theory of probability has been rigorously developed; it is quite complex, and its complete investigation requires a knowledge of advanced mathematics. In order to understand some of the more common probability distributions, it is appropriate to discuss a very few of the more simple concepts and theorems.

Most people have some intuitive feeling for probabilities. It is commonplace to assign a probability to the toss of a coin. A person is usually willing to bet even money on either heads or tails coming up after the toss. Few, however, have made any empirical tests to ascertain the validity of this intuitive judgment. The use of probabilities has even spread to weather bureau forecasts. The forecast formerly was for one type of weather— rain, cloudy, fair, and so forth. Today, the report may be "60 per cent chance of showers in the afternoon."

Exactly what does the term *probability* mean? Unfortunately, there is no general agreement on a precise definition—in fact there are rather wide areas of disagreement. Some authorities believe that many probabilities are primarily *subjective* or judgmental. The weatherman really was unable to measure his 60 per cent probability. The 60 per cent was actually an expression of his judgment, based, to be sure, on long experience and a careful analysis of existing conditions.

Other authorities are of the opinion that probabilities must be measured, usually inferred from a sample taken from a larger body of data. The observations of the arrivals of complaining customers is an example of the kind of data used for such an inference. These are referred to as *objective* probabilities.

Whether the evaluation of the probability is based upon intuition or judgmental factors, or upon some form of more or less accurate measurement, the end uses and intermediate manipulations of probabilities are usually quite similar. Generally speaking, *probability* refers to a universe or totality of possible occurrences or events. To take an extremely simple example, consider once again the toss of a coin. If the coin lands on a hard surface, and its landing and remaining on edge is regarded as impossible, there are two possible events to the universe: (1) the coin will land head up; (2) it will land tail up. It is, of course, impossible for the coin to land both head up and tail up with one and the same toss.

The universe may be represented by a small rectangle, thus:

The area inside the rectangle has the probability of 1, representing 100 per cent of the universe, head or tail. It is certain that the coin will fall either head or tail up. Therefore, the probability of 1 represents certainty or 100 per cent. Since there are only two possible events in the universe, and it is popularly considered that these events are equally likely to happen, a line may be drawn down the center of the rectangle, the area on each side of the line representing the event head or tail:

Each of these areas occupies 1/2 of the universe. One-half of a probability of 1 is 0.5, and the probability assigned to the event "head" is 0.5. Similarly, the probability assigned to the event "tail" is also 0.5. The probability of a tail, 0.5, plus the probability of a head, 0.5, equals the probability of the universe, 1.

This illustrates the first important theorem of probability, the *addition theorem*:

> When events are mutually exclusive, their probabilities are additive, and the sum of the probabilities of all of the mutually exclusive events is equal to 1.

Suppose that the coin is tossed a second time. This toss is in no way affected by the first toss. They are, in fact, independent tosses. The second toss may be represented by a rectangle, thus:

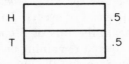

What, then, is the probability that a head on the first toss is followed by a head on the second toss? This may be represented by superimposing the second rectangle on the first one:

H   T

H | HH | HT | .5
  | .25 | .25 |
T | TH | TT | .5
  | .25 | .25 |
      .5   .5

The small rectangle in the upper left may be said to represent the event "head followed by a head." The new universe, two tosses of a coin, contains four possible events—*HH*, *HT*, *TH*, and *TT*. Since these events appear also to be equally likely to occur, it seems reasonable to assign them ¼ of the available probability, or a probability of 0.25. But notice that the probability of getting a head on the first toss, 0.5, times the probability of getting a head on the second toss, 0.5, is also equal to 0.25.

This illustrates the second important theorem of probability, the *multiplication theorem*:

If events are mutually independent, then the probability of their occurring together or in a specified order is the product of their individual probabilities.

Probability Distributions

A probability distribution pertains to the possible events usually categorized by class, of a universe of events, and the related probabilities of these events or categories of events. Since the entire distribution is the universe, the total probabilities of all events or categories of events must equal 1.

The toss of a coin represents a universe, and hence the total probabilities of its events are equal to 1. There are two possible events in this universe, head or tail. The probability distribution therefore is

Event	Probability
H	0.5
T	0.5

The probability may be graphically portrayed as in Figure 9-1. The area within the two columns is equal to 1 and represents the probability of the universe. The area of each column represents the probability of each possible event or class of events, in this case head, 0.5, and tail, 0.5. Note that the events are labeled 0 and 1, respectively.

The probability distribution of the universe of two tosses of a coin may be viewed in at least two different ways. (It is frequently possible to derive more than one probability distribution from a given set of data.) Viewed in one way, there are four separate classes of events, each with a probability of 0.25. The *HT* arrangement is considered to be different from the *TH* arrangement. This probability distribution is shown in Figure 9-2(a). A second distribution may be the combinations: (1) two heads; (2) one head, one tail; (3) two tails. The related probabilities are now (1) 0.25 for two heads; (2) 0.50 for one head and one tail, because this classifica-

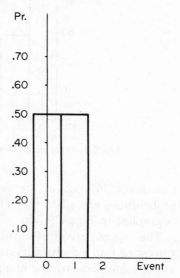

Fig. 9-1. Probability Distribution of One Toss of a Coin

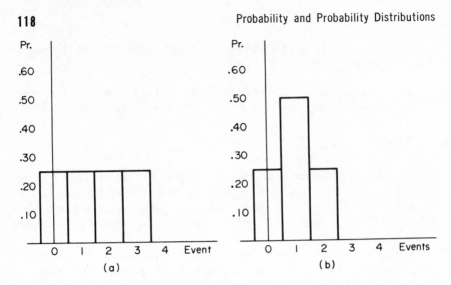

Fig. 9-2. Probability Distribution of Two Tosses of a Coin

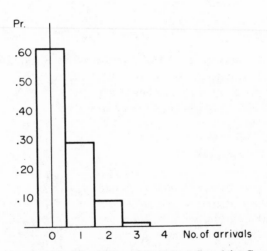

Fig. 9-3. Probability Distribution of Arrivals at Complaint Counter

tion takes in both of the arrangements *HT* and *TH*, and the related probabilities are additive, (3) 0.25 for two tails. This second distribution is graphed in Figure 9-2(b).

The rate of arrival of customers as counted by the manager may be converted into a probability distribution by listing the events as the number of customers arriving in a given minute and then assigning as probabilities the proportion of minutes in which that event occurred:

Event	Proportion of Minutes	Assigned Probability
Zero arrivals	610/1000	0.61
One arrival	290/1000	0.29
Two arrivals	90/1000	0.09
Three arrivals	10/1000	0.01

This probability distribution is graphed in Figure 9-3.

The binomial, the Poisson, and the normal distributions are probability distributions meeting the preceding description, but are considerably more complex than the simple examples given so far. The binomial distribution will be considered in Sec. 9-3, the Poisson in Sec. 10-1, and the normal in Sec. 10-4.

Random Variables

The concept of a random variable is intimately associated with the concept of a probability distribution. A random variable may be either *discrete* or *continuous*. A variable is discrete if it can take on only finite, specific values, such as integers or rational fractions. It is continuous if it can take on any value within a specified range of values. Continuous random variables are considered in Chapter 10.

A *discrete random variable* is a variable, say x, which may take on any *one* of a specified number of values, and for each of the possible values of the variable, a related probability can be assigned.

Notice that a random variable has two important characteristics: (1) it can take on only one value of a specified set of values; (2) there is an assignable related probability.

The possible values that the variable may assume is a universe, and the related probabilities form a probability distribution. Consider the toss of a coin once again. Let x, the random variable, be the number of heads that can come up. The variable x can take on one of two possible values:

Value of x	Related Probability
$x_0 =$ no heads	0.5
$x_1 =$ one head	0.5

Figure 9-1, therefore, is also a graph of the random variable x, the number of heads resulting from one toss of a coin.

A rather similar random variable, x, may result from two tosses of a coin. Once again, let x stand for the number of heads. The variable, x, can now take on one of three possible values: 0, 1, or 2. The variable and its related probabilities are:

Value of x	Related Probability
$x_0 =$ no heads	0.25
$x_1 =$ one head	0.50
$x_2 =$ two heads	0.25

Figure 9-2 (b) is a graph of this random variable.

The standardized probability distributions to be considered in this and the following chapters are described by formulas containing three types of values: (1) constants, (2) variables, (3) parameters. A *constant* is a value, such as π (3.1416) which remains the same from problem to problem. A *variable* changes within the problem, usually within a specified range of values, for example, "the variable x may take on any integer from 1 through 10." The variable of a probability distribution, therefore, is a random variable. A *parameter* remains constant within a problem but changes from problem to problem. With reference to the standard probability distributions, the parameters, if known, will completely describe the distribution.

Three of the more important parameters are the mean, μ (the lower-case Greek letter *mu*), the variance, σ^2 (the lower-case Greek letter *sigma*), and the standard deviation, σ.

The *mean* is the arithmetic average. It is a statistical measure of central tendency. The formula for the mean of a random variable is

$$\mu = \sum_{i=0}^{n} x_i \cdot \Pr(x_i)$$

The symbol $\sum$ (the Greek letter capital *sigma*) is the summation sign. It signifies that the value to the right of the $\sum$ should be summed as shown by the values of the subscripts. In this case, the subscript i stands for each value of the random variable, starting the count at 0 and ending at n.

The arrival rate of the customers at the complaint counter may be regarded as a random variable. It has the values:

Arrivals	Probability
$x_0 = 0$	0.61
$x_1 = 1$	0.29
$x_2 = 2$	0.09
$x_3 = 3$	0.01

The formula:

$$\mu = \sum_{i=0}^{n} x_i \cdot \Pr(x_i)$$

says, in effect, to multiply each item in the column *Arrivals* by the corresponding item in the column *Probability* and sum the products:

$$0 \times 0.61 = 0.00$$
$$1 \times 0.29 = 0.29$$
$$2 \times 0.09 = 0.18$$
$$3 \times 0.01 = \underline{0.03}$$
$$\mu = 0.50$$

The mean arrival, μ, is equal to 0.5 persons per minute.

The *variance* is the mean squared deviations from the mean. It is a statistical measure of the spread of the data. The formula for computing the variance is

$$\sigma^2 = \sum_{i=0}^{n} x_i^2 \cdot \Pr(x_i) - \mu^2.$$

This formula may be used to obtain the variance of the arrival rate:

x_i	x_i^2	$\Pr(x_i)$	$x_i^2 \cdot \Pr(x_i)$
0	0	0.61	0.00
1	1	0.29	0.29
2	4	0.09	0.36
3	9	0.01	0.09
		Sum =	0.74
		Less $\mu^2 = (0.5)^2 =$	0.25
		$\sigma^2 =$	0.49

The *standard deviation* is the square root of the variance:

$$\sigma = \sqrt{\sigma^2}.$$

The standard deviation for the arrival rate is

$$\sigma = \sqrt{0.49} = 0.7.$$

The concept of a random variable is frequently used in applying the theory of probability to practical situations and is repeatedly referred to in later sections of the book.

SEC. 9-3. THE BINOMIAL DISTRIBUTION

One of the basic and more important probability distributions is the binomial distribution. It applies to a wealth of practical problems, such as work sampling which is treated in Chapter 14, and other problems which involve proportions of occurrences. The binomial distribution is based upon the binomial theorem, or the expansion of the binomial to the *nth* power.

The coin-tossing problem may once again serve as a basis for illustration. Each toss of a coin has a two-event result, head or tail. A two-event result is the necessary prerequisite for application of the binomial distribution.

The result of one toss of a coin may be represented by the tree diagram:

Each leg of the tree is rated at 0.5 because the probability of tossing a head equals 0.5 and the probability of tossing a tail is also 0.5. The 0.5's alongside the *H* and the *T* represent the probabilities assigned to the event *H* or the event *T*. These probabilities sum to 1.

The diagram may be expanded to represent two tosses of a coin:

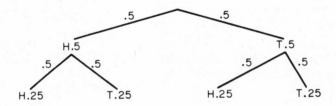

There are four possible results from two tosses, reading down each leg of the tree diagram: *HH, HT, TH*, and *TT*. Each of these has the probability 0.25, obtained by multiplying the leg values in a descending direction (the multiplication theorem). The probabilities summed across are again equal to 1 (the addition theorem).

Three tosses diagramed are

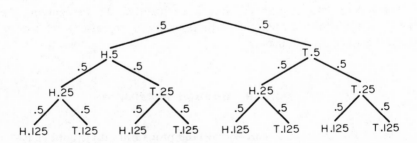

For one toss of the coin there were 2^1 possible events, namely, head or tail. For two tosses, there were 2^2 or 4 possible events, *HH, HT, TH*, and *TT*. Now for three tosses there are 2^3 or 8 possible events, again reading down each leg of the tree diagram, *HHH, HHT, HTH, HTT, THH, THT, TTH*, and *TTT*.

The tree diagram could be expanded to represent any number of tosses of the coin, but it quite soon becomes very unwieldy to handle. The same tree diagram, however, is also a representation of the binomial raised to the *nth* power. Illustrated so far have been the cases where $n = 1$, $n = 2$, and $n = 3$.

Thus the toss of one coin may be represented by the binomial:

$$(H + T)^1 = H + T.$$

Substituting the related probabilities.

$$H + T$$
$$0.5 + 0.5 = 1.$$

Two tosses of a coin are then represented by

$$(H + T)^2 = HH + HT + TH + TT$$
$$= H^2 + 2HT + T^2.$$

Again substituting the related probabilities,

$$= (0.5)^2 + 2(0.5)(0.5) + (0.5)^2$$
$$= 0.25 + 0.50 + 0.25 = 1.$$

Notice that these are the same probabilities that were obtained in the discussion of probability distributions and random variables in Sec. 9-2, and that were obtained from the tree diagram.

The variables H and T are representative when considering coin tosses. The variables most frequently used in illustrating or using the binomial distribution are p and q, where $p + q = 1$, and therefore $q = 1 - p$.

The expansion of the binomial $(p + q)^n$ for several values of *n* are

$n = 1$: $p + q$

$m = 1$ $0.$

$n = 2$: $p^2 + 2pq + q^2$

$m = 2$ 1 $0.$

$n = 3$: $p^3 + 3p^2q + 3pq^2 + q^3$

$m = 3$ 2   1   0.

$n = 4$: $p^4 + 4p^3q + 6p^2q^2 + 4pq^3 + q^4$

$m = 4$ 3   2   1   0.

$n = 5$: $p^5 + 5p^4q + 10p^3q^2 + 10p^2q^3 + 5pq^4 + q^5$

$m = 5$ 4   3   2   1   0.

$n = 6$: $p^6 + 6p^5q + 15p^4q^2 + 20p^3q^3 + 15p^2q^4 + 6pq^5 + q^6$

$m = 6$ 5   4   3   2   1   0.

$n = 7$: $p^7 + 7p^6q + 21p^5q^2 + 35p^4q^3 + 35p^3q^4 + 21p^2q^5 + 7pq^6 + q^7$

$m = 7$ 6   5   4   3   2   1   0.

Some relationships may be observed which will permit the development of the general term for the binomial. The general term will permit the derivation of any term in an expansion for any value of n.

First notice the relationship between n and the number of terms:

n	Number of Terms
1	2
2	3
3	4
4	5
5	6
6	7
7	8

Therefore the number of terms in the expanded binomial is equal to $n + 1$. The term may be designated by the letter m, and m may take on any value $0, 1, 2, \ldots, (n - 1), n$. Thus for $n = 1$, $m = 0, 1$; for $n = 2$, $m = 0, 1, 2$; and for $n = 6$, $m = 0, 1, 2, 3, 4, 5, 6$. The rightmost term of the expansion is labeled $m = 0$, the next term, $m = 1$, and so forth.

Inspection of the exponent of any p in any term will show that it is always equal to m, that is, p^m. The term on the right, where $m = 0$, may require some explanation. The rule p^m is still followed, and the p factor becomes p^0. But any value taken to the zero power is equal to 1. Therefore, $p^0 = 1$, and the p disappears from the first term on the right.

A similar inspection of the exponent of any q will show that it is equal to $(n - m)$, that is, $q^{(n-m)}$. For the term to the right (term 0), q is represented by $q^{(n-0)}$ or q^n; the next term to the left by $q^{(n-1)}$, and so forth.

Up to this point, both the p segment and the q segment of the general term of the binomial expansion have been derived, and the general term appears:

$$p^m q^{(n-m)}.$$

Further inspection of the expanded binomials reveals that each term also has a coefficient (the coefficient may be equal to 1, and therefore not explicitly written). Three methods for deriving the coefficient will be discussed: (1) Pascal's triangle, (2) the formula for combinations, (3) a simple computational relationship using the preceding term.

Probably the easiest of the three to describe and to understand is Pascal's triangle:

$$
\begin{array}{ll}
n = 1: & \quad 1 \quad 1 \\
n = 2: & \quad 1 \quad 2 \quad 1 \\
n = 3: & \quad 1 \quad 3 \quad 3 \quad 1 \\
n = 4: & \quad 1 \quad 4 \quad 6 \quad 4 \quad 1 \\
n = 5: & \quad 1 \quad 5 \quad 10 \quad 10 \quad 5 \quad 1 \\
n = 6: & \quad 1 \quad 6 \quad 15 \quad 20 \quad 15 \quad 6 \quad 1 \\
n = 7: & \quad 1 \quad 7 \quad 21 \quad 35 \quad 35 \quad 21 \quad 7 \quad 1
\end{array}
$$

To start Pascal's triangle, merely write down two 1's as on the first line. For each succeeding line write down a 1 in a column outside the 1 in the preceding line. Every other figure is obtained by summing the two figures in the preceding line. The last figure is always 1. The lines are labeled $n = 1$, $n = 2$, and so forth. Reference to the expanded binomial reveals that each line of Pascal's triangle may be used for the coefficients of the expansion of the binomial for the same n value.

Although Pascal's triangle is very simple to use, it has the disadvantage that all lines in the triangle up to and including the one desired must be derived. For large values of n, this can be a somewhat tedious process. The next method, that of using the formula for combinations, permits the user to go directly to the coefficient for any term in the expansion for any value of n. It should be mentioned, perhaps, that Pascal's triangle is also based upon the mathematics of combinations.

A combination should be differentiated from a permutation or arrangement. In a *combination*, order is not considered; whereas in a *permutation*, order is considered. This will be made clear by examining the possible results of two tosses of a coin, *HH, HT, TH, TT*. There are represented *four* permutations, but only *three* combinations. *HT* and *TH* are different permutations, but the same combination. The coefficients of the binomial expansion are combinations; the expansion representing two tosses of a coin is $H^2 + 2HT + T^2$. This says, in effect, that there is one combination of *HH*, two combinations of *HT*, and one combination of *TT*.

Several symbols are in general use to denote a combination, such as nCm, C_m^n, and $\binom{n}{m}$. All are read, "the number of combinations of n things taken m at a time." The formula for a combination is

$$nCm = \frac{n!}{(n-m)!\,m!}.$$

The symbol $n!$ is read "n factorial," and

$$n! = n \times (n-1) \times (n-2) \times \cdots \times 3 \times 2 \times 1.$$

For example:

$$6! = 6 \times 5 \times 4 \times 3 \times 2 \times 1 = 720.$$

By convention, $0! = 1$.

In using the combination formula for deriving the coefficients of the binomial expansion, the variables n and m have the same meaning as previously described; n is the exponent of the binomial, $(p+q)^n$, and m is the term of the expansion where $m = 0, 1, 2, \ldots, (n-1), n$.

The use of the formula for combinations to compute the coefficients of the expansion for $n = 3$, is

first term: $_3C_0 = \dfrac{3!}{(3-0)!\,0!} = \dfrac{3!}{3!\,0!} = 1$

second term: $_3C_1 = \dfrac{3!}{(3-1)!\,1!} = \dfrac{3!}{2!\,1!} = 3$

third term: $_3C_2 = \dfrac{3!}{(3-2)!\,2!} = \dfrac{3!}{1!\,2!} = 3$

fourth term: $_3C_3 = \dfrac{3!}{(3-3)!\,3!} = \dfrac{3!}{0!\,3!} = 1.$

These coefficients could have been derived much more easily by using Pascal's triangle. But suppose that the coefficient for the tenth term of the expansion $n = 20$ is required. To use Pascal's triangle would be quite inconvenient. Note at this point that all three segments (the coefficient, p, and q) for the general term have now been derived. The complete general term for the binomial expansion is

$$nCm\,p^m q^{(n-m)}.$$

The general term will now be used to derive the tenth term of the expansion $n = 20$. For the tenth term, $m = 9$:

$$_{20}C_9\,p^9 q^{(20-9)}$$

$$_{20}C_9 = \frac{20!}{(20-9)!\,9!} = \frac{20!}{11!\,9!} = 167{,}960.$$

Therefore the tenth term of the expansion $n = 20$ is

$$167,960 \, p^9 q^{11}.$$

The third method for developing the coefficients requires the application of three simple rules. The expansion of $n = 7$ will be used for illustration:

Rule 1. Write down the p's and q's starting at $p = n$ and $q = 0$, and ending at $p = 0$ and $q = n$.

Thus,

$$p^7 q^0 + p^6 q^1 + p^5 q^2 + p^4 q^3 + p^3 q^4 + p^2 q^5 + p^1 q^6 + p^0 q^7.$$

Of course, the q^0 and the p^0 may be left off, since they are equal to one, and the exponents of 1 need not be explicitly written.

Rule 2. The coefficient of the first term always equals 1.

Rule 3. The coefficient for all other terms is equal to the exponent of p in the preceding term times the coefficient of that same preceding term divided by the exponent of q for the term for which the coefficient is being derived.

To derive the coefficient of the second term of the expansion $n = 7$, take the exponent of p for the first term (7), multiply it by the coefficient of the first term (1), and divide the product by the exponent of q of the second term (1):

$$\frac{7 \times 1}{1} = 7$$

and the expansion so far is

$$p^7 + 7p^6 q + \cdots\cdots$$

Following the same rule for the third term,

$$\frac{6 \times 7}{2} = 21$$

and the term is $21p^5 q^2$.
Fourth term,

$$\frac{5 \times 21}{3} = 35$$

and the term is $35p^4q^3$.
Fifth term,

$$\frac{4 \times 35}{4} = 35$$

and the term is $35p^3q^4$.
Sixth term,

$$\frac{3 \times 35}{5} = 21$$

and the term is $21p^2q^5$.
Seventh term,

$$\frac{2 \times 21}{6} = 7$$

and the term is $7pq^6$.
Eighth term,

$$\frac{1 \times 7}{7} = 1$$

and the term is q^7.

The use of the binomial expansion is not limited to computing the elements of the binomial probability distribution. There is no requirement that the two terms of the binomial, p and q, should sum to 1. In the present context, however, $p + q$ must be equal to 1, which is a basic requirement of the binomial distribution. The use of the distribution will be illustrated by several simple examples:

Problem 1. Four coins are tossed. A random variable, number of heads, is thereby generated. Completely describe this random variable.

Solution. Since each coin can take on two values, head or tail, this is therefore a problem in the binomial distribution where: $n = 4$ (four coins); $m = 0, 1, 2, 3, 4$; and $p = q = \frac{1}{2}$.

Random Variable (x = no. heads)	Computation $nCm \; p^m q^{(n-m)}$	Probability
x_0 = no heads	$_4C_0 \, p^0 q^{(4-0)} = 1(\frac{1}{2})^0(\frac{1}{2})^4 = 1/16$	0.0625
x_1 = 1 head	$_4C_1 \, p^1 q^{(4-1)} = 4(\frac{1}{2})^1(\frac{1}{2})^3 = 4/16$	0.2500
x_2 = 2 heads	$_4C_2 \, p^2 q^{(4-2)} = 6(\frac{1}{2})^2(\frac{1}{2})^2 = 6/16$	0.3750
x_3 = 3 heads	$_4C_3 \, p^3 q^{(4-3)} = 4(\frac{1}{2})^3(\frac{1}{2})^1 = 4/16$	0.2500
x_4 = 4 heads	$_4C_4 \, p^4 q^{(4-4)} = 1(\frac{1}{2})^4(\frac{1}{2})^0 = 1/16$	0.0625
	$\overline{16/16}$	$\overline{1.0000}$

Problem 2. Assume that a thumb tack, if tossed in the air, will land on its side with a probability of 2/3 and on its head with a probability of 1/3. Five tacks

are tossed in the air. What is the probability that 2 *or more* will fall on their sides?

Solution. Again, this is a problem in the binomial distribution because of the two-state result of each thumb tack; $n = 5$; $m = 0, 1, 2, 3, 4$; $p = 2/3$; and $q = 1/3$. The mathematical expression of the solution formula is

$$\text{Pr (2 or more sides)} = \sum_{m=2}^{5} {}_5C_m \left(\tfrac{2}{3}\right)^m \left(\tfrac{1}{3}\right)^{(5-m)}.$$

Remember that the symbol $\sum$ (Greek capital letter *sigma*) is the summation sign and signifies that the quantity to the right is to be summed over the values shown below and above the $\sum$. In this case, four values are to be summed, ${}_5C_m (2/3)^m (1/3)^{(5-m)}$ when $m = 2, 3, 4$, and 5. Notice that the random variable involved is "thumb tacks that fall on their sides." The problem can be set up exactly as the previous problem, but the values for x_0^- and x_1 need not be computed:

Random Variable (x = no. of sides)	Computation ${}_5C_m \ (2/3)^m(1/3)^{(5-m)}$	Probability
$x_2 = 2$ on sides	${}_5C_2(\tfrac{2}{3})^2(\tfrac{1}{3})^{(5-2)} = 40/243$	0.1646_+
$x_3 = 3$ on sides	${}_5C_3(\tfrac{2}{3})^3(\tfrac{1}{3})^{(5-3)} = 80/243$	0.3292_+
$x_4 = 4$ on sides	${}_5C_4(\tfrac{2}{3})^4(\tfrac{1}{3})^{(5-4)} = 80/243$	0.3292_+
$x_5 = 5$ on sides	${}_5C_5(\tfrac{2}{3})^5(\tfrac{1}{3})^{(5-5)} = 32/243$	0.1316_+
	$232/243$	0.9547_+

Therefore, the probability of obtaining two or more thumb tacks on their sides is 0.9547_+.

This problem can be solved with considerably less computation. Consider the following relationship:

$$\sum_{m=0}^{n} {}_nC_m \, p^m q^{(n-m)} = 1.$$

This is true because the value to the right of $\sum$ represents one term of a probability distribution. The symbol $\sum_{m=0}^{n}$ says to sum the probabilities of all of the terms, and the total probability of any distribution is always equal to 1. Furthermore, the foregoing summation represents the expansion of $(p + q)^n$. But $p + q = 1$, and 1 to any power is still equal to 1.

Therefore,

$$\sum_{m=0}^{1} {}_5C_m(\tfrac{2}{3})^m(\tfrac{1}{3})^{(5-m)} + \sum_{m=2}^{5} {}_5C_m(\tfrac{2}{3})^m(\tfrac{1}{3})^{(5-m)} = 1.$$

This merely says that the sum of the probabilities of the first two terms plus the sum of the probabilities of the last four terms is equal to 1. Hence,

$$\sum_{m=2}^{5} {}_5C_m(\tfrac{2}{3})^m(\tfrac{1}{3})^{(5-m)} = 1 - \sum_{m=0}^{1} {}_5C_m(\tfrac{2}{3})^m(\tfrac{1}{3})^{(5-m)}.$$

Thus the left-hand side, which requires the computation of four terms, may be evaluated by solving the right-hand side, which requires the computation of only two terms, as follows:

x = no. of sides	Computation $_5C_m(2/3)^m(1/3)^{(5-m)}$	Probability
x_0 = none on sides	$_5C_0(\frac{2}{3})^0(\frac{1}{3})^{(5-0)} = 1/243$	0.00411_+
x_1 = 1 on side	$_5C_1(\frac{2}{3})^1(\frac{1}{3})^{(5-1)} = 10/243$	0.04115_+
	$11/243$	0.04526_+

Therefore, the probability of two or more tacks on their sides $= 1 - 0.04526_+ = 0.9547_+$.

Problem 3. A coin game is played tossing 6 coins in the air. For each head that comes up, B pays A \$2.00, and for each tail, A pays B \$1.00. Regard A's winnings as a random variable. List the possible values of the random variable and their related probabilities.

Solution. The computation of the probabilities for this problem follows the same pattern as in the preceding two problems. The evaluation of the random variable is, however, somewhat different:

Random Variable x = A's Winnings	Computation $_6C_m(1/2)^m(1/2)^{(6-m)}$	Probability
(All heads) $x_0 = \$12$	$_6C_0(\frac{1}{2})^0(\frac{1}{2})^{(6-0)} = 1/64$	0.015625
(5H, 1T) $x_1 = \$9$	$_6C_1(\frac{1}{2})^1(\frac{1}{2})^{(6-1)} = 6/64$	0.093750
(4H, 2T) $x_2 = \$6$	$_6C_2(\frac{1}{2})^2(\frac{1}{2})^{(6-2)} = 15/64$	0.234375
(3H, 3T) $x_3 = \$3$	$_6C_3(\frac{1}{2})^3(\frac{1}{2})^{(6-3)} = 20/64$	0.312500
(2H, 4T) $x_4 = \$0$	$_6C_4(\frac{1}{2})^4(\frac{1}{2})^{(6-4)} = 15/64$	0.234375
(1H, 5T) $x_5 = -\$3$	$_6C_5(\frac{1}{2})^5(\frac{1}{2})^{(6-5)} = 6/64$	0.093750
(All tails) $x_6 = -\$6$	$_6C_6(\frac{1}{2})^6(\frac{1}{2})^{(6-6)} = 1/64$	0.015625
	$64/64$	1.000000

The binomial distribution is a discrete distribution. That is m, its variable, can assume only a finite number of values, normally integers(you cannot,for example, make 1/2 a toss of a coin), namely, from 0 through n. It has two parameters, p and n (q is determined if p is known). If both parameters are known, the binomial distribution is completely described. Nevertheless, the usual parameters, μ, σ^2, and σ may be computed. The formula for μ is

$$\mu = np,$$

and for σ^2

$$\sigma^2 = npq.$$

The binomial distribution of Problem 3 may be used for illustration; $p = 1/2$, $q = 1/2$, $n = 6$.
Therefore,

$$\mu = np = 6 \times \frac{1}{2} = 3.$$

$$\sigma^2 = npq = 6 \times \frac{1}{2} \times \frac{1}{2} = \frac{3}{2} = 1.5$$

$$\sigma = \sqrt{\sigma^2} = \sqrt{1.5} \doteq 1.224.$$

The symbol $\doteq$ is read "is approximately equal to."

SEC. 9-4. TESTING THE PROBLEM DATA

The nature of the complaint counter problem and the appearance of the data suggests to the company's statistician that the arrivals of the customers at the complaint counter may be distributed binomially.

The parameters σ^2 and μ of the arrival rate were computed in Sec. 9-2 as

$$\sigma^2 = 0.49$$

$$\mu = 0.5.$$

The variance and mean of a binomial distribution are

$$\sigma^2 = npq$$

$$\mu = np.$$

Therefore, if the arrival rate is distributed binomially, then:

(a) $$npq = 0.49$$
(b) $$np = 0.5.$$

Dividing (a) by (b):

$$q = \frac{0.49}{0.5} = 0.98,$$

and

$$p = 1 - q = 1 - 0.98 = 0.02.$$

From $np = 0.5$,

$$n \times 0.02 = 0.5$$

$$n = \frac{0.5}{0.02} = 25.$$

Thus, the binomial distribution with the same parameters is $n = 25$, $p = 0.02$, $q = 0.98$. By partially expanding this binomial and computing the related probabilities, it becomes

Term no.	Term Formula	Computation	Probability
4-25	$\sum\limits_{m=4}^{25} {}_{25}C_m\, p^m q^{(25-m)}$	Residual probability	0.0014
3	$2300 p^3 q^{22}$	$2300(0.02)^3(0.98)^{22}$	0.0118
2	$300 p^2 q^{23}$	$300(0.02)^2(0.98)^{23}$	0.0754
1	$25 pq^{24}$	$25(0.02)(0.98)^{24}$	0.3079
0	q^{25}	$(0.98)^{25}$	0.6035

The comparisons between the observed and computed probabilities are

No. Arrivals	Observed Probability	Computed Probability
0	0.61	0.6035
1	0.29	0.3079
2	0.09	0.0754
3	0.01	0.0118
4 or more	-0-	0.0014

These relationships are fairly close, indicating that the rate of arrivals may in fact be distributed according to a binomial distribution with $n = 25$, $p = 0.02$ and $q = 0.98$.

SEC. 9-5. PERFORMING THE CHI SQUARE TEST

Visual inspection of the fairly close approximation of the computed probabilities to the observed probabilities gives a reasonably strong presumption that the true arrival rate is distributed binomially. By applying the χ^2 (χ is the lower case Greek letter *chi*) test, this presumption may be further strengthened, or it may be rejected.

The χ^2 test is based upon the observation that a sample taken from a population or universe will rarely have the same characteristics as the population. This fact may be illustrated by taking some samples from a standard deck of playing cards. Figure 9-4(a) shows a graph of the number of suits represented in ten 100 per cent samples. Naturally, each sample contained representatives of each of the 4 suits. Figure 9-4(b), however, shows that 10 samples of only 4 cards each show very different characteristics. In this example, the most unrepresentative sample would contain only 1 suit, and the most representative sample, 4 suits. More samples would undoubtedly contain either 2 or 3 suits than 1 or 4 suits. (In this case, there were no 1- or 4-suit samples, and only one 2-suit sample.)

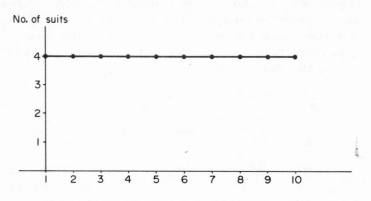

(a) Ten 100% samples from a standard deck of cards

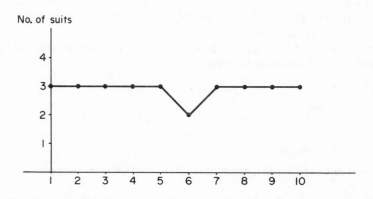

(b) Ten samples of four cards each from a standard deck of cards

Fig. 9-4. Characteristic Differences of Samples as Compared to Universes

If a very large number of sets of 10 samples were taken, a probability distribution of the difference between the samples and the population could be constructed.

In effect, the χ^2 distribution is a generalized distribution of this type. The statistic

$$\chi^2 = \Sigma \frac{(O - E)^2}{E}$$

is distributed according to the χ^2 distribution. In the statistic, E stands for the expected frequency of occurrence as computed according to some standard probability distribution. The O stands for the occurrences actually observed. (Note that these must be occurrences, not probabilities.)

The complaint counter figures were based upon 1000 observations. Multiplying the probabilities obtained from the binomial distribution by 1000 gives the number expected, E:

Arrivals	Observed (O)	Binomial Prob.	Expected (E)	(O − E)	(O − E)²	(O − E)²/E
0	610	0.6035	603.5	6.5	42.25	0.070
1	290	0.3079	307.9	−17.9	320.41	1.041
2	90	0.0754	75.4	14.6	213.16	2.827
3	10	0.0118	11.8	−3.2	10.24	0.776
4 or more	0	0.0014	1.4			

$$\chi^2 = 4.714$$

In this case, $\chi^2 = 4.714$. One of the requirements of the χ^2 test is that each cell must have an *expected value* or 5 or more. Cells with values below 5 are lumped together until their total is equal to, or greater than, 5. Thus cells 3 and "4 or more" were lumped together, since the latter cell has an expected value of only 1.4.

The χ^2 distribution is tabulated in Appendix B. To enter the table, df (degrees of freedom) must be known:

$$df = k - s - 1,$$

where

$k =$ the number of cells

$s =$ the number of parameters estimated from the sample.

In this case, $s = 2$, since two parameters, p (or q) and n were estimated from the mean and standard deviation of the sample. Hence,

$$df = 4 - 2 - 1 = 1.$$

The headings across the top of the table represent the percentage of samples from a known population or universe which would differ from the characteristics of the universe sufficiently to have a χ^2 greater than the figures in that column. The cut-off point frequently selected by statisticians is either the 10 per cent (0.10) or the 5 per cent (0.05) column. The 2.71 at the intersection of the $df = 1$ row and the 10 per cent column signifies that 10 per cent of all samples from a known population will have a χ^2 greater than 2.71. The present χ^2 of 4.714 is larger than the 2.71 at the 10 per cent level. A cut-off point of 10 per cent would infer that, although 1 in 10 samples, on the average, from a known population would have a χ^2 larger than 2.71, the concept that this sample is among that 1 in 10 is rejected. The similar cut-off point at the 5 per cent level is 3.85, or 1 in 20 samples, on the average, have a χ^2 larger than 3.85. The present χ^2 of 4.714 is still larger than this, so the hypothesis that the sample comes from a population distributed binomially with $p = 0.02$, $q = 0.98$, and $n = 25$ is rejected.

DISCUSSION QUESTIONS

9-1. What is meant by *subjective* and *objective* probabilities?

9-2. Discuss the concept of a *universe* and its relationship to probabilities.

9-3. What is an *event*, and how does it relate to a *universe*?

9-4. State the *addition theorem*, describing specifically when probabilities may be *added* and when they may not.

9-5. State the *multiplication theorem*, describing specifically when probabilities may be *multiplied* and when they may not.

9-6. What is a *probability distribution*?

9-7. Define the term *discrete random variable*.

9-8. Discuss (a) *constants*, (b) *variables*, (c) *parameters* in relation to probability distributions.

9-9. Define the term *mean*, and explain how to compute the mean of a random variable.

9-10. Explain the meaning of the symbol $\sum\limits_{i=0}^{n}$.

9-11. Define the term *variance*, and explain how to compute the variance of a random variable.

9-12. Describe the basic characteristics of the *binomial distribution*.

9-13. Explain the use of a *tree diagram* in showing probability relationships.

9-14. Give the *general term* for the binomial distribution, and explain its derivation.

9-15. Describe the variable m as it pertains to the binomial expansion.

9-16. What is *Pascal's triangle* and how is it used?

9-17. State the formula for computing combinations and explain its relation to the binomial expansion.

9-18. How does a *combination* differ from a *permutation*?

9-19. Describe the "three-rule" method for obtaining the binomial coefficients.

9-20. Describe how to derive n, p, and q, given only σ^2 and μ.

9-21. Describe the χ^2 test. What is its purpose? How is this purpose achieved?

PROBLEMS

9-1. A, B, C, D, and E are events of universe X. Their probabilities are:

Event	A	B	C	D	E
Pr.	0.1	0.05	0.15	0.3	0.4

What are the probabilities that

    a. Either *A* or *B* will occur.

    b. Either *A* or *C* or *E* will occur.

    c. Either *A* or *B* or *C* or *D* or *E* will occur.

9-2. There are two automobiles, one in Los Angeles and the other in New York. The Los Angeles car has been breaking down on the average once every 20 days. The New York car has been breaking down on the average once every 50 days. What is the probability that they will both break down on the same day?

9-3. A random variable, number of heads, is generated by the single toss of three coins. Develop the probability distribution for this variable.

9-4. Four coins are tossed. What is the probability that there will be three or more heads?

9-5. a. *A* plays a coin game with *B* by tossing three coins. If exactly two heads come up, *B* pays *A* \$2; otherwise *A* pays *B* \$1. What is the probability of *A*'s winning \$2.

    b. *A* and *B* play the preceding game five times. Consider *A*'s winnings on the entire five plays as a random variable. Tabulate the values of the random variable and their related probabilities.

9-6. Assume that the store manager in Sec. 9-1 counted 216 no arrivals, 432 single arrivals, 288 arrivals of two people at the same time, and 64 arrivals of three people at the same time.

    a. Ascertain the nearest binomial distribution to fit these facts.

    b. Compare the observed values with the expected values.

9-7. Assume that the store manager in Sec. 9-1 counted 200 no arrivals, 300 single arrivals, 300 arrivals of two people at the same time, and 200 arrivals of three people at the same time.

    a. Ascertain the nearest binomial distribution to fit these facts.

    b. Apply the χ^2 test.

BIBLIOGRAPHY

Feller, William, *An Introduction to Probability and Its Applications*. New York: John Wiley & Sons, Inc., 1950, pp. 104–10.

Fry, Thornton C., *Probability and its Engineering Uses*. New York: D. Van Nostrand Company, Inc., 1928, pp. 25–31; 91–101.

Moroney, M. J., *Facts from Figures*. Baltimore, Md.: Penguin Books, Inc., 1956, pp. 82–95.

Mosteller, Frederick, Robert E. K. Rourke, and George B. Thomas, Jr., *Probability and Statistics*. Reading, Mass.: Addison-Wesley Publishing Company, Inc., 1961, pp. 241–84.

Neyman, J., *First Course in Probability and Statistics*. New York: Henry Holt & Company, 1950, pp. 179–200.

Sprowls, R. Clay, *Elementary Statistics*. New York: McGraw-Hill Book Company, Inc., 1955, pp. 25–107.

10

The Poisson, the Gamma, and the Normal Distributions

SEC. 10-1. THE POISSON DISTRIBUTION

When time is divided into relatively short periods, and events which occur on a basically random basis are collected by time periods, the number of time periods containing an equal number of events tend to form in a distribution known as the *Poisson distribution*. The concept is similarly applicable to space equally divided. An important basic requirement for applying the Poisson distribution is that the probability of an event occurring within a given time or space division be constant.

The formula for the Poisson distribution is

$$\Pr(n) = \frac{e^{-\lambda}\lambda^n}{n!}.$$

This equation looks quite formidable at first glance, but upon analysis, it will appear to be reasonably simple to use. Two symbols may be unfamiliar, e and λ.

The letter e is the basis for the natural logarithms. It has a value of $2.718 +$, which may be calculated to any degree of precision desired by use of the formula:

$$e = \sum_{n=0}^{\infty} \frac{1}{n!} = \frac{1}{0!} + \frac{1}{1!} + \frac{1}{2!} + \frac{1}{3!} + \cdots.$$

This becomes the sum of

1.00000
1.00000
0.50000
0.16666+
0.04166+
0.00833+
0.00138+
0.00019+
0.00002+
2.7182+

In use, the final preceding figure should be rounded up to become 2.7183. The λ (the Greek lower-case letter *lambda*) is used here merely because this is the symbol found in most writings on the Poisson distribution. Actually λ stands for the mean of the distribution, and hence has the same meaning as μ. Therefore, the formula could just as well be written:

$$\Pr(n) = \frac{e^{-\mu}\mu^n}{n!},$$

remembering that μ or λ is the average or mean occurrence per time period under consideration. The $n!$ (n factorial) has the same meaning as discussed in Sec. 9-2.

The e is a constant which retains its same value, $2.718+$, wherever it is used. The n, a variable, represents the number of occurrences within the basic time period, and may range from 0 to infinity $(0, 1, 2, \ldots, \infty)$. The Poisson distribution has only one parameter, λ, since in the Poisson, the mean is equal to the variance, that is, $\lambda = \sigma^2$.

Because the Poisson is a probability distribution and the probability assigned to one term of the distribution is

$$\Pr(n) = \frac{e^{-\lambda}\lambda^n}{n!},$$

it follows that

$$\sum_{n=0}^{\infty} \frac{e^{-\lambda}\lambda^n}{n!} = 1.$$

That is, the sum of the probabilities of all of the terms is equal to 1. Note again that the Poisson is a discrete distribution, and that the variable n can assume only the values of integers, ranging from 0 to infinity.

The relationship between the Poisson and the binomial distributions is an important one. The Poisson distribution is the limit of the binomial distribution as the p of the binomial approaches zero and n approaches infinity.

This relationship can be demonstrated by the trend of μ and σ^2 as p becomes small. Let $n = 100$, and to start, $p = 0.5$ and $q = 0.5$:

n	p	q	μ (np)	σ^2 (npq)
100	0.5	0.5	50	25
100	0.1	0.9	10	9
100	0.01	0.99	1	0.99
100	0.001	0.999	0.1	0.0999

When $p = q$, μ and σ^2 are definitely unequal. As p becomes smaller, the difference between μ and σ^2 rapidly decreases. Thus as p approached zero, μ approaches σ^2, and the basic parameter relationship of the Poisson distribution is established.

The inference is that when p is small in relation to q, and n is large, the Poisson distribution may serve as a usable approximation to the binomial distribution. It is often convenient to be able to make this substitution.

SEC. 10-2. CHECKING THE TEST DATA FOR POISSON FIT

Returning once more to the complaint counter problem (see Sec. 9-1), the data observed are

Arrivals	Observed	Computed Probability
0	610	0.61
1	290	0.29
2	90	0.09
3	10	0.01

In Sec. 9-4 and Sec. 9-5, we tried to ascertain whether the rate of arrivals might be a binomially distributed variable. Although the χ^2 test for goodness of fit cannot positively establish or refute this relationship, it provided evidence to cause the hypothesis to be rejected. A similar test may be performed to ascertain whether the arrival rate may be distributed according to the Poisson distribution. There would not, however, necessarily be any inconsistency in passing both tests, since the Poisson may be regarded as a special case (or limit) of the binomial.

Using the formula,

$$\mu = \sum_{i=0}^{n} x_i \cdot \text{Pr}(x_i),$$

the mean, μ, of the arrival rate has been computed as 0.5 (see Sec. 9-2).

This value is substituted in the Poisson formula:

$$\Pr(n) = \frac{e^{-0.5}(0.5)^n}{n!}.$$

Notice that the right-hand portion may be broken down into two factors: $e^{-0.5}$ and $(0.5)^n/n!$. The $e^{-0.5}$ is a constant and need be computed only once. Logarithms must be used to evaluate this factor. The $e^{-0.5}$ may be rewritten $1/e^{0.5}$ and may be set up for solving thus:

$$\log 1 = \qquad\qquad 0.0000$$
$$-(0.5 \times \log e) = -(0.5 \times 0.4343) = -0.2172$$
$$\log e^{-0.5} = \qquad\qquad -0.2172$$

Converting the negative logarithm to a positive mantissa:

$$10.0000 - 10$$
$$-0.2172$$
$$\overline{9.7828 - 10}$$

The antilog of $9.7828 - 10 = 0.6065$. Therefore $e^{-0.5} = 0.6065$.

Then the probability for several values of n, starting with $n = 0$, are computed:

$$e^{-0.5} \qquad (0.5)^n/n!$$

$$\Pr(0) = 0.6065 \times (0.5)^0/0! = 0.6065 \times 1.00000 = 0.6065$$
$$\Pr(1) = 0.6065 \times (0.5)^1/1! = 0.6065 \times 0.50000 = 0.3033$$
$$\Pr(2) = 0.6065 \times (0.5)^2/2! = 0.6065 \times 0.12500 = 0.0758$$
$$\Pr(3) = 0.6065 \times (0.5)^3/3! = 0.6065 \times 0.02083 = 0.0126$$

$$\Pr(4 \text{ or more}) = 1 - \sum_{n=0}^{3} \Pr(n) = 1 - 0.9982 = \underline{0.0018}$$
$$1.0000$$

The expected arrivals are obtained by multiplying the foregoing probabilities by 1000 (the number of observations), and the comparison between the observed and the expected is

Arrivals	Observed	Expected
0	610	606.5
1	290	303.3
2	90	75.8
3	10⎫	12.6⎫
4 or more	0⎭	1.8⎭

This comparison may be tested for goodness of fit by the χ^2 method (see Sec. 9-5). To perform the χ^2 test, the number of cells will be reduced to three by making the last cell refer to 3 or more arrivals. This is necessary because, it will be recalled, the χ^2 test requires frequencies of at least 5 in each of the expected categories:

Arrivals	Observed	Expected	$(O-E)$	$(O-E)^2$	$(O-E)^2/E$
0	610	606.5	−3.5	12.25	0.020
1	290	303.3	−13.3	176.89	0.583
2	90	75.8	14.2	201.64	2.660
3 or more	10	14.4	−4.4	19.36	1.344
					$\chi^2 = \overline{4.607}$

In order to enter the χ^2 table, degrees of freedom (df) must be found:

$$df = k - s - 1,$$

where

$$k = 4 \text{ cells}$$
$$s = 1 \text{ parameter inferred, } \lambda$$
$$df = 4 - 1 - 1 = 2.$$

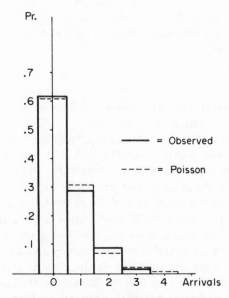

Fig. 10-1. The Poisson Distribution Fitted to the Test Data

The table of χ^2 values (Appendix B) at the 5 per cent level gives a χ^2 of 5.991. That is, 5 per cent of all samples from a known population would have a χ^2 exceeding 5.991. The present χ^2 of 4.607 is well within this value. Therefore, there is no reason to reject the hypothesis that the arrival rate is distributed according to the Poisson distribution. (The two distributions are graphed in Figure 10-1.)

SEC. 10-3. THE GAMMA AND EXPONENTIAL DISTRIBUTIONS

The gamma and exponential distributions are closely related to the Poisson. The Poisson distribution answers the question: What is the probability of the occurrence of a specified number of events within a given division of time or space? The *gamma distribution* refers to a Poisson-distributed random variable. It answers the question: What is the waiting time to the first event? to the second event? to the third event? to the rth event? Its formula is

(a) $$Y = \frac{\mu}{(r-1)!}(\mu t)^{(r-1)} e^{-\mu t}; \qquad t \geq 0$$

where μ = the average number of events per unit of time, t = the length of time (and must be ≥ 0), and r = the event = $1, 2, 3, \ldots$.
In the context of this book, however, the waiting time to the first event ($r = 1$) is of primary interest. Substituting $r = 1$ into Eq. (a), the gamma formula reduces to

(b) $$Y = \mu e^{-\mu t}; \qquad t \geq 0.$$

This is the formula for the *exponential* distribution, which is a special case of the gamma distribution for $r = 1$.
Both the gamma and exponential distributions are continuous distributions, since time is a continuum. The use of a continuous distribution differs somewhat from the discrete distributions (for example, the binomial and the Poisson) discussed so far. These differencess are considered in greater detail in the discussion of the normal distribution in Sec. 10-4. Several uses of the exponential distribution are treated in Chapters 11 and 12. It should be clear, however, that the gamma and exponential distributions have potential uses in such problems as the complaint counter problem, since the expected waiting time to the first, second, and so forth, arrival could be very useful. The exponential distribution for the time to next arrival for the complaint counter problem is graphed in Figure 10-2.In drawing the graph, μ is set equal to 0.5 (the mean of the test

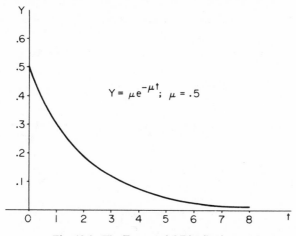

Fig. 10-2. The Exponential Distribution

data of the complaint counter problem), and the equation then becomes

$$Y = 0.5e^{-0.5t}; \qquad t \geq 0.$$

Y is the ordinate (vertical value) and t is time, the variable under consideration. Note that Y does not indicate probability, since probability is indicated by area, and Y is merely a line indicating height. A mathematical line, of course, has no width, and hence no area. More will be said of this concept in Sec. 10-4. The computations to obtain Y are

t	Constant	$e^{-0.5t}$	Y
0	0.5	$e^{0}\ \ = 1.000$	0.500
1	0.5	$e^{-0.5} = 0.607$	0.304
2	0.5	$e^{-1}\ \ = 0.368$	0.184
3	0.5	$e^{-1.5} = 0.223$	0.112
4	0.5	$e^{-2}\ \ = 0.135$	0.068
5	0.5	$e^{-2.5} = 0.082$	0.041
6	0.5	$e^{-3}\ \ = 0.050$	0.025
7	0.5	$e^{-3.5} = 0.030$	0.015
8	0.5	$e^{-4}\ \ = 0.018$	0.009

SEC. 10-4. THE NORMAL DISTRIBUTION

Many authorities are of the opinion that the occurrences of a large number of phenomena are distributed according to a probability distribution generally referred to as the *normal distribution*. Because of this opinion and other facts, the normal distribution is of great interest in and of itself. But like the Poisson, the normal distribution is also a limit of the binomial (when $p = q$ and n approaches infinity) and can, under certain circumstances, act as a practical substitute for the latter distribution. This substitution is usually acceptable when $p \doteq q$ and $n \geq 30$. As n increases in size, the relationship between p and q becomes less significant.

The equation for the normal distribution is

(c) $$Y = \frac{1}{\sigma\sqrt{2\pi}} e^{-(x-\mu)^2/2\sigma^2}; \qquad -\infty \leq x \leq \infty.$$

The constants 2 and π have their usual meanings, π being $3.1415+$. The constant $e = 2.718+$ was explained in Sec. 10-1. The parameters σ, σ^2, and μ have the meanings described in Sec. 9-2. Except for the gamma and exponential, the previous distributions discussed have been discrete distributions; that is, the main variable could assume only finite values, usually integers. The normal distribution, however is a continuous distribution; that is, its variable, x, can range from $-\infty$ to ∞, with the x taking on any possible value within these limits.

Because the normal distribution is continuous, the Y in Eq. (c) cannot represent the probability of x, the variable. The reasoning for this conclusion is that the ordinate (the vertical value at any point on the graph) is a mathematical line, which has no width. But the area of the graph of a probability distribution must be equal to 1; therefore, probability on the graph is represented by area. This area was represented when graphing the binomial, the Poisson, and other discrete distributions by using a bar chart technique as shown in Figure 10-3(a). At times, nevertheless, it is convenient to use a polygon to represent a discrete distribution. The *polygon* is formed by connecting the center points of each bar, Figure 10-3(a). Although some accuracy is lost by the use of the polygon, such a presentation tends to assume the characteristics of a continuous curve. Notice, however, that the bar chart reflects the probability of one occurrence by extending the base of the bar from 0.5 to 1.5, or a width of 1 unit.

A normal probability curve with the same μ and σ as a binomial distribution with parameters $n = 10$ and $p = q = \frac{1}{2}$ is shown in Figure 10-3(b). The probability of an occurrence of one may also be represented by the area extending from 0.5 to 1.5. This probability is represented mathematically as:

(d) $$\Pr(1) = \int_{0.5}^{1.5} \frac{1}{\sigma\sqrt{2\pi}} e^{-(x-\mu)^2/2\sigma^2} \, dx.$$

The right-hand value says, in effect, that the area under the curve extend-

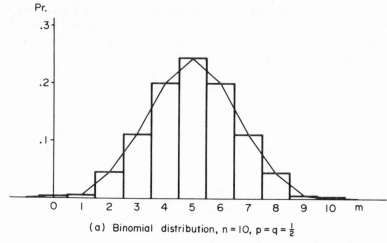

(a) Binomial distribution, $n = 10$, $p = q = \frac{1}{2}$

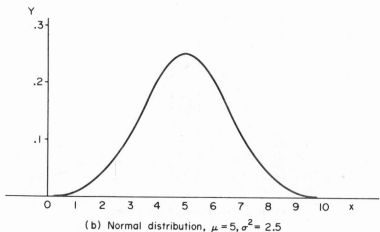

(b) Normal distribution, $\mu = 5$, $\sigma^2 = 2.5$

Fig. 10-3. Graphing Discrete and Continuous Distributions

ing from 0.5 to 1.5 is summed. The $\int$ is an integral sign, and has the same meaning for continuous variables (summation), as does $\sum$ for discrete variables. The dx represents very small widths of x values; that is, a large number of very narrow areas are summed to find the total area. The continuous variable, x, in the normal distribution may take on any value from $-\infty$ to ∞. Therefore,

(e)
$$\int_{-\infty}^{\infty} \frac{1}{\sigma\sqrt{2\pi}}\, e^{-(x-\mu)^2/2\sigma^2}\, dx = 1,$$

since this represents the summation of the total probability area.

The solution of Eq. (d) cannot be obtained directly. To avoid the need for the individual solution of such integrations, tables have been developed for the determination of areas under the standard normal curve. The *standard normal curve* has a mean $= 0$ and a standard deviation $= 1$. (A table of areas is presented in Appendix C.)

When $\sigma = 1$ and $\mu = 0$, then Eq. (c) becomes:

(f)
$$Y = \frac{1}{\sqrt{2\pi}} e^{-Z^2/2}.$$

A graph of Eq. (f) is shown in Figure 10-4. The table in Appendix C represents

$$\int_{-\infty}^{Z} \frac{1}{\sqrt{2\pi}} e^{-Z^2/2} \, dz.$$

This area is shaded in Figure 10-4.

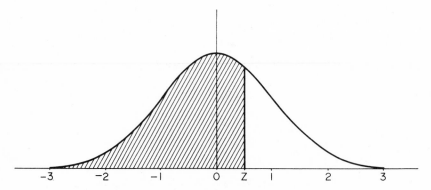

Fig. 10-4. The Standard Normal Curve

Using the Table of Areas under the Normal Curve

To use the table of areas under the standard normal curve, the parameter μ must be converted to zero, and the distance of $x - \mu$ must be stated in terms of sigmas (σ's). If $x = 3$ and $\mu = 2$, these relationships graphed are

$$
\begin{array}{cccc}
 & & \mu & x \\
\cdot & \cdot & \cdot & \cdot \\
\hline
0 & 1 & 2 & 3
\end{array} \; .
$$

Then,

$$x - \mu = 3 - 2 = 1.$$

The result of this subtraction is the same as moving the origin, 0, to μ; or,

$$
\begin{array}{cc}
\mu & x \\
\bullet & \bullet \\
\hline
0 & 1
\end{array}
\ .
$$

Therefore, μ is effectively converted to zero by subtracting it from x. Further, if the value $x - \mu$ is divided by σ,

$$\frac{x - \mu}{\sigma},$$

then the new value of x is expressed in sigmas. Reference to Figure 10-4 will show that the x axis is scaled in sigmas, since $\sigma = 1$ in the standard normal distribution. This relationship is frequently referred to as the Z statistic, where

$$Z = \frac{x - \mu}{\sigma},$$

and the Z statistic is the conversion used for entry into the standard normal table.

Example. The probability of $x = 1$ in Figure 10-3(b) may be represented by

$$
\mathrm{Pr}\,(x = 1) = \int_{x=-\infty}^{x=1\,5} \frac{1}{\sigma\sqrt{2\pi}}\, e^{-(x-\mu)^2/2\sigma^2}\, dx
$$
$$
- \int_{x=-\infty}^{x=0.5} \frac{1}{\sigma\sqrt{2\pi}}\, e^{-(x-\mu)^2/2\sigma^2}\, dx.
$$

The $x = 1.5$ and $x = 0.5$ are first converted by means of the Z statistic:

$$Z(x = 1.5) = \frac{1.5 - 5}{2.5} = -1.4$$

$$Z(x = 0.5) = \frac{0.5 - 5}{2.5} = -1.8$$

or

$$
\mathrm{Pr}\,(x = 1) = \int_{Z=-\infty}^{Z=-1.4} \frac{1}{\sqrt{2\pi}}\, e^{-Z^2/2}\, dZ - \int_{Z=-\infty}^{Z=-1.8} \frac{1}{\sqrt{2\pi}}\, e^{-Z^2/2}\, dZ.
$$

This relationship is shown in Figure 10-5(a). The table, however, gives only positive values for Z. Since the normal curve is symmetrical, the probabilities

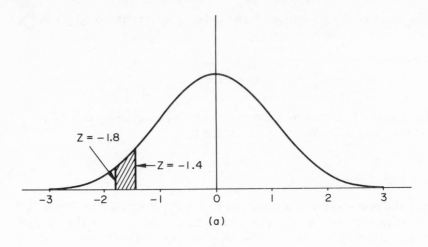

(a)

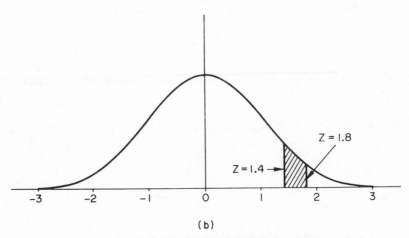

(b)

Fig. 10-5. Use of the Z-Statistic

shown in Figure 10-5(b) are the same as for Figure 10-5(a). From the table,

$$\Pr(-\infty \le Z \le 1.8) = 0.96407$$
$$\Pr(-\infty \le Z \le 1.4) = 0.91924.$$

Therefore, the probability that $x = 1$ in the original distribution is

$$\Pr(x = 1) = 0.96407 - 0.91924 = 0.04483.$$

Of great practical interest is the concentration of occurrences distributed normally in relation to the standard deviation, σ. This relationship is shown in Figure 10-6.

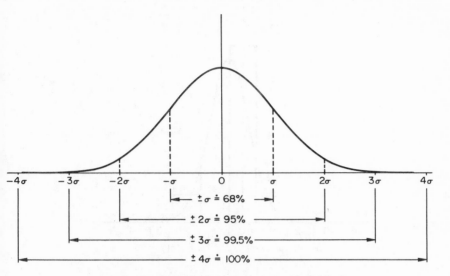

Fig. 10-6. Distribution of Occurrences in Relation to σ

SEC. 10-5. CHECKING THE TEST DATA FOR NORMAL FIT

The computed probabilities of the test data are

Arrivals	Probability
0	0.61
1	0.29
2	0.09
3	0.01

This distribution is shown graphed in Figure 10-7 with the curve of the normal distribution superimposed on it. The points on the normal curve were computed by using the equation,

(g) $$Y = \frac{1}{\sigma\sqrt{2\pi}} e^{-(x-\mu)^2/2\sigma^2}$$

In Sec. 9-2, the mean, μ, of the test data was computed to be 0.5; the variance, σ^2, 0.49; and the standard deviation, σ, 0.7.

Substituting these values into Eq. (g), the equation becomes

$$Y = \frac{1}{0.7\sqrt{2\pi}} e^{-(x-0.5)^2/2(0.49)},$$

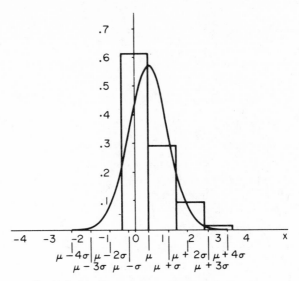

Fig. 10-7. The Normal Curve Fitted to the Test Data

or

$$Y = 0.5699\, e^{-(x-0.5)^2/0.98}.$$

The ordinates (vertical values) are computed for $x = \mu \pm$ various multiples of σ in the accompanying table:

x	$\dfrac{1}{0.7\sqrt{2\pi}}$	$e^{-(x-0.5)^2/0.98}$	Y
$\mu = 0.5$	0.5699	$e^{0} = 1.0000$	0.5699
$\mu + \sigma = 1.2$	0.5699	$e^{-0.5} = 0.6065$	0.3459
$\mu + 2\sigma = 1.9$	0.5699	$e^{-2.0} = 0.1353$	0.0769
$\mu + 3\sigma = 2.6$	0.5699	$e^{-4.5} = 0.0111$	0.0063
$\mu + 4\sigma = 3.3$	0.5699	$e^{-8.0} = 0.0003$	0.0002

That the normal curve is symmetrical is shown by the following continuation of the table:

$\mu - \sigma = -0.2$	0.5699	$e^{-0.5} = 0.6065$	0.3459
$\mu - 2\sigma = -0.9$	0.5699	$e^{-2.0} = 0.1353$	0.0769
$\mu - 3\sigma = -1.6$	0.5699	$e^{-4.5} = 0.0111$	0.0063
$\mu - 4\sigma = -2.3$	0.5699	$e^{-8.0} = 0.0003$	0.0002

A glance at Figure 10-7 is almost enough to be convincing that the arrival rate is not distributed as a normal variable. The data can, nevertheless, be subjected to the χ^2 goodness-of-fit test. The approach is, however, somewhat different from that used for the binomial and Poisson tests because of the continuous nature of the normal distribution. Referring once again to Figure 10-7, the probability for the normal distribution to be compared with 0 arrivals for the test data is that area under the normal curve extending from $-\infty$ to 0.5. But, since $\mu = 0.5$, this area includes half the area under the normal curve. The total area under the curve is, of course, 1 (representing a total probability of 1), and, therefore, the area from $-\infty$ to 0.5 = 0.5.

The area corresponding to 1 arrival is that extending from 0.5 to 1.5. To obtain the probability relating to this area, the table of areas under the normal curve (Appendix C) must be used. To enter the table, the Z transformation is required.

$$Z = \frac{x - \mu}{\sigma}$$

$$Z(x = 0.5) = \frac{0.5 - 0.5}{0.7} = 0; \qquad \Pr(-\infty \leq Z \leq 0) = 0.5$$

$$Z(x = 1.5) = \frac{1.5 - 0.5}{0.7} = 1.43; \qquad \Pr(-\infty \leq Z \leq 1.43) = 0.9236.$$

Therefore the probability associated with the area 0.5 to 1.5 = 0.9236 − 0.5 = 0.4236.

The area corresponding to 2 arrivals ranges from 1.5 to 2.5:

$$Z(x = 1.5) = 1.43; \qquad \Pr(-\infty \leq Z \leq 1.43) = 0.9236$$

$$Z(x = 2.5) = \frac{2.5 - 0.5}{0.7} = 2.86; \qquad \Pr(-\infty \leq Z \leq 2.86) = 0.9978$$

$$\Pr(1.5 \leq x \leq 2.5) = 0.9978 - 0.9236 = 0.0742.$$

The area corresponding to 3 or more arrivals ranges from 2.5 to ∞:

$$Z(x = 2.5) = 2.86; \qquad \Pr(-\infty \leq Z \leq 2.86) = 0.9978$$
$$\Pr(-\infty \leq Z \leq \infty) = 1.0000$$
$$\Pr(2.5 \leq x \leq \infty) = 1.0000 - 0.9978 = 0.0022.$$

Arrivals	Observed	Computed Normal Probabilities	Expected	$(O - E)$	$(O - E)^2$	$(O - E)^2/E$
0	610	0.5	500.0	110.0	12,100.00	24.20
1	290	0.4236	423.6	133.6	17,848.96	42.14
2	90⎱	0.0742	74.2⎱	23.6	556.96	7.29
3 or more	10⎰	0.0022	2.2⎰			
					$\chi^2 =$	$\overline{73.63}$

For entrance into the χ^2 table (Appendix B):

$$df = k - s - 1$$

$$k = 3 \text{ cells}$$

$$s = 2 \text{ parameters inferred, } \mu \text{ and } \sigma$$

$$df = 3 - 2 - 1 = 0.$$

Reference to Appendix B reveals that there is no χ^2 listing for $df = 0$, and therefore the table cannot be entered for this problem. However, the table shows that the 5 per cent (0.05) cut-off point for $df = 1$ is 5.991. For a lower df, if this were possible, the χ^2 value would be even smaller. The present χ^2 of 73.63 would unquestionably exceed this value, and the hypothesis that the sample comes from a normal distribution with $\mu = 0.5$ and $\sigma = 0.7$ is rejected.

DISCUSSION QUESTIONS

10-1. Under what circumstances is the Poisson distribution applicable?

10-2. What is the constant e? How can it be evaluated to any degree of precision desired, that is, to any number of decimal places desired?

10-3. What is the meaning of λ in the Poisson formula? Why was it chosen here rather than some other perhaps more desirable symbol?

10-4. In the Poisson distribution, what is the relationship between the mean and the variance?

10-5. What relationship exists, if any, between the Poisson and binomial distributions?

10-6. In evaluating the χ^2 goodness-of-fit test, what interpretations may be given to very large values of χ^2?

10-7. Under what circumstances is the *gamma distribution* applicable?

10-8. What is the relationship, if any, between the gamma and Poisson distributions?

10-9. Under what circumstances is the *exponential distribution* applicable?

10-10. What is the relationship, if any, between the gamma and the exponential distributions?

10-11. Under what circumstances is the *normal distribution* applicable?

10-12. What is the relationship, if any, between the binomial and the normal distributions?

10-13. How do *continuous* distributions differ from *discrete* distributions.

10-14. How is probability represented on a graph of a discrete distribution? of a continuous distribution?

10-15. Explain how to compute probabilities pertaining to the normal distribution.

10-16. Describe the concentration of occurrences in the normal distribution.

10-17. Describe the technique of fitting the normal curve to experimental data.

10-18. Explain how to perform the χ^2 test for goodness of fit of the normal curve.

10-19. Give and explain the rule for computing degrees of freedom.

PROBLEMS

10-1. Given the following 1000 observations of the variable x:

Value of x	Occurrences
0	729
1	243
2	27
3	1

   a. Compute μ, σ^2, and σ.

   b. Draw graphs showing the foregoing data and the fit of
     1. the binomial distribution with the same μ and σ^2.
     2. the Poisson distribution with the same μ.
     3. the normal distribution with the same μ and σ.

   c. Perform the χ^2 test for each of the preceding distributions, where possible.

   d. State which distributions, if any, you would be willing to substitute for the test data.

10-2. Given the following 1000 observations of the variable y:

Value of y	Occurrences
0	540
1	340
2	100
3	20

Answer a.–d. as in Problem 10-1.

10-3. Given the following 1000 observations of the variable z:

Value of z	Occurrences
0	63
1	244
2	388
3	242
4	61
5	2

Answer a.–d. as in Problem 10-1.

10-4. Evaluate the constant e to eight decimal places using the formula $e = \sum_{n=0}^{\infty} 1/n!$.

10-5. Graph the exponential distribution with μ equal to
a. Mean of the data in Problem 10-1
b. Mean of the data in Problem 10-2
c. Mean of the data in Problem 10-3.

BIBLIOGRAPHY

Bierman, Harold, Jr., Lawrence E. Fouraker, and Robert K. Jaedicke, *Quantitative Analysis for Business Decisions*. Homewood, Ill.: Richard D. Irwin, Inc., 1961, pp. 39–47, 185–88.

Feller, William, *An Introduction to Probability and Its Applications*. New York: John Wiley & Sons, Inc., 1950, pp. 110–45.

Freund, John E., *Mathematical Statistics*. Englewood Cliffs, N.J.: Prentice-Hall, Inc., 1962, pp. 72–75; 125–31.

Fry, Thornton C., *Probability and its Engineering Uses*. New York: D. Van Nostrand Company, Inc., 1928, pp. 205–51.

Neymann, J., *First Course in Probability and Statistics*. New York: Henry Holt and Company, 1950, pp. 212–34.

Parzen, Emanuel, *Modern Probability Theory and Its Applications*. New York: John Wiley & Sons, Inc., 1960, pp. 237–67.

Wadsworth, George P., and Joseph G. Bryan, *Introduction to Probability and Random Variables*. New York: McGraw-Hill Book Company, Inc., 1960, pp. 67–112.

11

The Monte Carlo Method

A complaint-counter study was described in Sec. 9-1. Assume the same distribution of the rate of arrivals, that is,

Arrivals	Probability
0	0.61
1	0.29
2	0.09
3	0.01

In analyzing the complaint-counter problem, two initial simplifying assumptions will be made in order to keep all distributions discrete rather than continuous. These simplifying assumptions will be relaxed later. The assumptions cited are (1) that the arrivals occur only on the whole minute; (2) that service times are constant at exactly one minute (that is, it takes precisely the same time to handle each complaint).

Because it is possible for people to arrive faster than service can be rendered, a waiting line is likely to be formed. It has been noted that the number of arrivals in any given minute may be regarded as a random variable. Similarly, the number of people in line may be regarded as another random variable. Since the line can theoretically range in length from zero persons to an infinitely large number of persons, the random variable may appear

Length of Line	Probability
0	?
1	?
2	?
.	.
.	.
.	.
∞	?

The results of the analysis should provide the missing probabilities, at least to a point where the probability associated with a given length of line is too small to be significant. Notice, however, that the random variable is the *length of the line*, and that therefore the probabilities of 0, $1, 2, \ldots, \infty$ in line must sum to 1.

The *Monte Carlo method* is a means of simulating, for the sake of analysis, business and other problems wherein events occur in accordance with assigned or computed probabilities. The method may be used, for example, to simulate the functioning of the complaint counter.

SEC. 11-2. PROBABILITY-GENERATING DEVICES

The early development of the mathematics of probability was based upon attempts to analyze various games of chance. The concepts of probability and chance are intimately related. Probabilities, as usually conceived, relate to events which have not yet occurred. Events which have occurred have a probability of 1. Furthermore, probabilities have a "long-run" connotation. A fair coin when tossed may have probabilities of falling heads, 0.5 and tails, 0.5. Nevertheless, this concept would not be outraged by the coin landing heads-up on 10 consecutive tosses. In fact, the probability of this occurring is $(0.5)^{10}$ or approximately 0.000986. That is, if 10 coins were tossed a million times, 10 heads would be expected to occur approximately 986 times.

A coin, then, appears to be an excellent probability-generating device. Should the probability assigned to an event be 0.5, a toss of a coin may be used to determine whether or not the event occurred. For example, assume that the probability of a customer arriving at the complaint counter in any given minute is 0.5. Then a coin may be tossed for each minute being simulated. A *head* may represent an arrival, and a *tail*, no arrival.

Since the coin toss has a two-state result, the tossing of n coins may be used to simulate a binomially distributed variable when $p = q = \frac{1}{2}$. Assume that the arrivals at the complaint counter had the probabilities: $0 = 0.25$; $1 = 0.50$; $2 = 0.25$. These are the probabilities of the binomial $n = 2, p = q = 0.5$. Thus the toss of two coins could be used to simulate each minute's arrivals:

No. Heads	No. Arrivals
0	0
1	1
2	2

Almost any device used in games of chance may be used as a probability-generating device. The roll of a die (one-half of a pair of dice) may be used for probabilities of multiples of 1/6, and so forth. Since our numbering system has a base of ten, a 10-state device would be desirable. Such a device could be used to simulate any probability stated as a decimal fraction. A 10-sided die is available for this purpose and is quite effective. Simulation requiring one or more rolls of the 10-sided die to determine the occurrence or nonoccurrence of an event could be very time-consuming and tedious. A highly acceptable substitute is a table of random digits. A *table of random digits* is, in effect, a tabulation of a large number of rolls of a 10-sided die. (Such a table is, of course, generated by other methods.) At least one of the available tables contains a million random digits—the equivalent of a million rolls of the 10-sided die. (Appendix D contains a short table of random digits.)

It is important to note that a table of random digits has certain characteristics *not* found in such listings as telephone books, and so forth, which are, therefore, not acceptable substitutes. Each digit in the table is *independent* of every other digit. Hence, in a truly random table of large size there would be approximately an equal number of each digit—the million-digit table would contain *about* 100,000 zeros, 100,000 ones, and so forth. Similarly, various combinations would be expected to occur in approximately their probability ratios. The probability of the occurrence of the series of digits 0, 1, 2, and 3 in that sequence is, according to the multiplication theorem, $1/10 \times 1/10 \times 1/10 \times 1/10 = 1/10,000$. This series would be expected to appear *about* 100 times in a table of one million random digits.

Other types of randomized tables are also available, and are very useful aids in problem simulation. The numbers in a table of normal random deviates, for example, are distributed according to the probabilities of the normal distribution. There are similar tables with digits or numbers distributed according to the exponential (see Appendix E) and other probability distributions.

SEC. 11-3. FLOW CHARTING THE MONTE CARLO SIMULATION

The Monte Carlo simulation of a business or other problem requires a preparation similar to that required for electronic computation (Sec. 2-4). In fact, most complex Monte Carlo simulations are run on computers. The first step is to prepare a flow chart showing all the logical and computational relationships. A flow chart for the complaint-counter problem is presented in Figure 11-1.

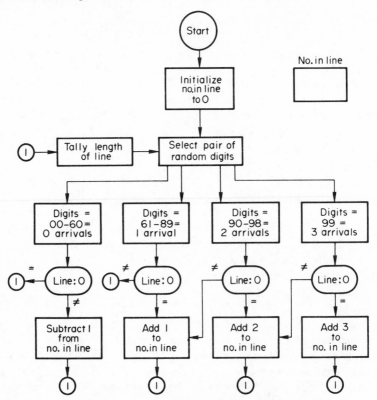

Fig. 11-1. Flow Chart of Complaint Counter Simulation

In order to interpret the flow chart (or to prepare it, for that matter) certain background relationships must be clearly understood. First the length of the line can assume any integral value, $0, 1, 2, \ldots$. Therefore, given any time, t, the possible conditions at time $t + 1$ are shown by the following:

These relationships show, for example, that, given 0 people in line at time t, there may be either 0, 1, 2, or 3 people in line at time $t + 1$, depending upon the number of arrivals at the end of time t. Similar facts are shown for 1, 2, 3, and n at time t.

The paths in the flow chart may now be traced. The chart is entered at the start box at the top of the diagram. The next operation places a 0 in the box indicating the length of the line. Thus the line commences with zero length. The next step is to select a pair of random digits from the table of random digits. These digits may range from 00 through 99. If they are 00 through 60 (indicating 0 arrivals), the flow goes to the far left; if 61 through 89 (indicating 1 arrival), the center left; if 90 through 98 (indicating 2 arrivals), the center right, and if 99 (indicating 3 arrivals), the far right path.

Taking the far left path (0 arrivals), first, the number in line is tested. If the line $= 0$, then a 0 length is tallied, and the next pair of random digits are selected; if, however, the line $\neq 0$, then the length of the line is reduced by 1. These relationships can be verified by inspecting the t, $t + 1$ chart. The left leg of each tree diagram represents a 0 arrival. If 0 were in line at time t, the line remains the same length, 0, at $t + 1$, otherwise, the length of the line decreases by 1. After the length of the line has been adjusted, its length is tallied, and another pair of random digits selected.

Consider next the center left path (1 arrival). Again the length of the line is tested. If not equal to 0, there is no change; just tally the length, and select another pair of digits. If equal to 0, however, the length of the line is increased by 1, the length tallied, and a new pair of digits selected. These relationships are shown by the center left leg of the tree diagrams.

Next consider the center right path (2 arrivals). This time the line is again tested for 0 length. If the line $= 0$, its length is increased by 2; if the line $\neq 0$, its length is increased by 1.

The remaining path, the far right (3 arrivals) requires a similar test. If the length of the line $\neq 0$, its length is increased by 2; if the line $= 0$, its length is increased by 3.

SEC. 11-4. PERFORMING THE SIMULATION RUN

In order to perform the simulation run, the table of random digits (Appendix D) is used. Figure 11-2 shows the results of the run for 50 minutes. Since, however, the probabilities desired are long-run averages, a longer simulation is required to obtain the necessary accuracy. The length of the simulation to obtain various degrees of accuracy is considered in Sec. 11-5.

The Monte Carlo Method

RD (1)	Line (2)	RD (3)	Line (4)	RD (5)	Line (6)	RD (7)	Line (8)	RD (9)	Line (10)
	0								
55	0	97	2	06	0	90	2	24	0
13	0	72	2	48	0	80	2	23	0
78	1	50	1	48	0	40	1	43	0
21	0	61	1	69	1	95	2	90	2
86	1	55	0	19	0	56	1	83	2
02	0	86	1	84	1	14	0	39	1
02	0	44	0	65	1	35	0	69	1
21	0	49	0	48	0	37	0	47	0
98	2	70	1	87	1	37	0	16	0
19	1	01	0	75	1	73	1	43	0

Line Length	Tally
0	∧
1	∧
2	∧
3	∧

Fig. 11-2. Results of the Simulation Run

The first 50 pairs of digits were selected from Appendix D so that the reader might more easily trace their source. In actual practice, some means of randomly entering the table is to be preferred. One method is to open the book of say 1,000,000 digits at random, then, with the eyes closed, to select a digit with the point of a pin. This digit and the following ones are then used to select the page, column, and row at which to start.

The digits selected are listed in columns (1), (3), (5), (7), and (9) of Figure 11-2. Entering the flow chart (Figure 11-1) at the start box, the first instruction is to place a 0 in the length of line indicator. The 0 at the top of column (2) is that 0. The next box says to select a pair of random digits. The first two digits selected are 5, 5. The number 55 (any number from 00 through 60) represents 0 arrivals, so the flow goes to the far left. The length of the line is compared to 0. It is equal to 0, so a 0 is tallied and also listed in column (2), which represents the length-of-line indicator, and the next iteration is started. The second pair of digits is 1, 3, or 13, again representing 0 arrivals. As a result another 0 is tallied. The third pair of digits is 7, 8, or 78. This represents 1 arrival, and the flow path goes to the center left. The line is tested for 0, is 0, and therefore 1 is added to the line length, and a 1 is tallied. The remaining iterations may be traced by the reader.

The probabilities for the random variable, the length of the line, are estimated by the formula:

$$Pr = \frac{\text{no. minutes of line length}}{\text{total no. minutes simulated}}.$$

For the possible length of the line, this becomes

0	1	2	3 or more
$25/50 = 0.5$	$17/50 = 0.34$	$8/50 = 0.16$	$0/50 = 0$

SEC. 11-5. THE SIZE OF THE SIMULATION SAMPLE

The question immediately arises: How reliable are these estimates? First, it must be emphasized that the estimates are supposed to represent long-run averages. If a photograph of the line were taken every minute over a long period, the photographs well shuffled, and one picked at random, the probabilities are 0.5 that there would be no people in the line, 0.34 that there would be one person, 0.16 that there would be two people, and there would be no chance of picking a photograph with three or more people in the line.

But the simulation certainly did not represent long-run conditions. It did, in fact, represent only 50 minutes of real time. Furthermore, the values obtained are indeed estimates derived from a sample from what is necessarily an unknown population or universe. The use of statistical techniques does not ordinarily permit perfect, error-free inferences to be made. Instead, the techniques permit the user to estimate the probability of error in his inference, or to set up a range of values that he may assume, with a given degree of confidence, to include the actual value sought. For example, the probability of 0.5 for zero people in line cannot be regarded as a firm figure. Rather the user may be, say, 95 per cent confident that the actual value lies within the range of, perhaps, 0.46 to 0.54.

The important figure basic to the attainment of desired confidence levels and confidence intervals is N, the size of the sample. The condition, for instance, of zero people in line is a two-state condition—either zero or not-zero— hence the applicable theory is that of the binomial distribution. For a given level of confidence (95 per cent is a commonly used level), the width of the confidence interval is a function of N. As N increases, the width of the confidence interval decreases. If an accuracy of 0.46–0.54 is acceptable, a given sample size may suffice. But if the accuracy needs to be increased to, say, 0.49–0.51, then the sample size must be much larger than for the 0.46–0.54 interval.

Probability	Confidence Interval (%)		
	± 1	± 5	± 10
0.01	3,960,000	158,400	39,600
0.05	760,000	30,400	7,600
0.10	360,000	14,400	3,600
0.20	160,000	6,400	1,600
0.30	93,333	3,733	933
0.40	60,000	2,400	600
0.50	40,000	1,600	400
0.60	26,667	1,067	267
0.70	17,143	686	171
0.80	10,000	400	100
0.90	4,444	178	44
0.95	2,105	84	21
0.99	404	16	4

(Confidence level = 95%)

Fig. 11-3. Chart of Sample Sizes

Figure 11-3 shows the sample sizes required to estimate various probabilities within ± 1 per cent, ± 5 per cent, and ± 10 per cent confidence intervals with a confidence level of 95 per cent. Thus, to estimate a probability of approximately 0.5 with a confidence interval of ± 10 per cent or from 0.45 to 0.55, would require a sample size of approximately 400. If the confidence interval were to be decreased to ± 5 per cent, or 0.475–0.525, the sample size would be increased to about 1600. If the confidence interval were further decreased to ± 1 per cent, or 0.495–0.505, the required sample size would be around 40,000. It can be readily appreciated that, with a sample size of 50, little faith can be placed in the estimate of 0.5.

It is also important to note that the sample size is a function of the actual probability or proportion of occurrences rather than of any preconceived estimate—although such a preliminary estimate is necessary to obtain a tentative sample size.

Assume, for example, that the preliminary estimate is a probability of 0.6. For a ± 5 per cent confidence interval, a sample of 1067 would be required. Assume further, however, that after the 1067 sample, a probability of 0.5 appeared to be more realistic. Now to achieve the same limits of ± 5 per cent the sample size would have to be increased to 1600.

The techniques of computing actual sample sizes are considered in Sec. 14-3.

Figure 11-4 presents a comparison of the results of the 50-minute simulation shown in Figure 11-2 with the results of a computer simulation of 50,000 minutes and with the theoretical results computed by mathematical analysis. (For an explanation of the latter approach see Sec. 12-2.) In spite of the small sample ($N = 50$), the probabilities compare

	0	1	2	3	4	5 or More
50-minute simulation	0.5	0.34	0.16	— 0 —	— 0 —	— 0 —
50,000-minute simulation	0.5004	0.3225	0.1336	0.0333	0.0073	0.0028
Theoretical probabilities	0.5000	0.3197	0.1344	0.0355	0.0080	0.0024

Fig. 11-4. Comparison of Probabilities from Simulation Runs with Theoretical
Probabilities—I

quite favorably with the $N = 50,000$ computer simulation and with the
computed probabilities.

SEC. 11-6. SIMULATION WITH POISSON ARRIVALS AND CONSTANT SERVICE TIMES

In Sec. 10–2, the observed distribution of arrivals coming to the complaint counter was tested for Poisson fit. The test results revealed no reason
to reject the hypothesis that the observations were taken from the universe
of a Poisson random variable. This, of course, left the strong inference
(but no absolute proof) that the rate of arrival is, in fact, distributed
according to the Poisson distribution. The Poisson would therefore appear
to be a valid basis upon which to conduct the simulation.

To simulate Poisson arrivals, the relationship between the Poisson and
exponential distributions (see Sec. 10–3) is going to be used. Remember,
if the rate of arrivals is distributed according to the Poisson, then the time
to the first arrival is distributed according to the exponential distribution.

First a cumulative probability curve of the exponential distribution is
constructed. Figure 10–2 showed the exponential curve with $\mu = 0.5$.
Computation of the ordinates (Y values) used to graph that curve was
explained in Sec. 10–3. The cumulative probability curve for the exponential distribution is shown in Figure 11–5. Here, however, $\mu = 1$.

The transition from the exponential curve of Figure 10–2 to the cumulative curve of Figure 11–5 is not merely an additive process involving
the Y values of Figure 10–2. The exponential distribution is a continuous
function (see Sec. 10–4 for a discussion of continuous functions). Therefore
the cumulative curve will be based upon the continuous summation:

$$Y = \int_0^t \mu\, e^{-\mu t}\, dt,$$

which says that the ordinate of the cumulative curve at point t is equal

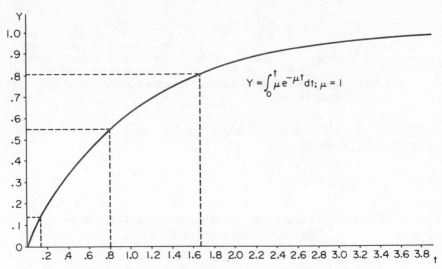

Fig. 11-5. Cumulative Probability Curve of the Exponential Distribution

to the area under the exponential curve from 0 to t. This equation may be simplified somewhat by setting $\mu = 1$:

$$Y = \int_0^t e^{-t}\, dt.$$

By applying the calculus to the equation, it becomes:

$$Y = 1 - e^{-t}.$$

The latter equation is easily graphed, as is shown in Figure 11–5.

Figure 11–5 in conjunction with a table of random digits (Appendix D) may be used to ascertain the time to the next arrival. The first two digits from the table in Appendix D are 55. At $Y = 0.55$, a horizontal line is drawn to the cumulative curve, and at the point of intersection, a vertical line is drawn to the t axis. The t value, or time to the next arrival, is 0.8 minute. The curve of Figure 11–5 is based upon a mean of 1; whereas the mean arrival rate is 0.5. To put this somewhat differently, the graph is based upon an average of 1 arrival each minute, whereas the data show an average of 1 arrival every 2 minutes. To compensate for this difference (a ratio of 2 to 1), the 0.8 minute is multiplied by 2 to get 1.6 minutes to the first arrival. The next 2 digits from the table of random digits are 13. Again setting $Y = 0.13$, Figure 11–5 is used to obtain the time to the second arrival as 0.14×2 or 0.28 minute.

A problem arises when the random number selected equals 99. Since 99 is the largest possible 2-digit number, it would appear that the graph should end at 0.99. It does not. In fact, the cumulative curve is *asymptotic* to the 1.00 line, that is, the curve continues to approach the 1.00 line but never reaches it (except at infinity). When a 99 random number is selected, the next digit is also used. This may be 990–999. If 999 comes up, 4 digits are used, 9990–9999, and so forth. These latter situations will, of course, rarely occur.

The flow chart for simulating the complaint-counter problem with Poisson arrivals and constant service times is shown in Figure 11–6. Figure 11–7 shows the computations resulting from the use of the flow chart for the simulation. Figure 11–7 can be understood only in conjunction with the flow chart.

The flow chart is entered at the *start box*. The second box requires that the *Line Change Time* (LCT, the time at which the line changes in length), the *Arrival Time* (AT) the *Departure Time* (DT), the *Line Length* (LL), and the *Cumulative Line Length Times* be set to 0. This is done in the first line of Figure 11–7. Next a random number (2 digits) is selected from Appendix D. Number 55 was selected. Using Figure 11–5, the 0.55 is

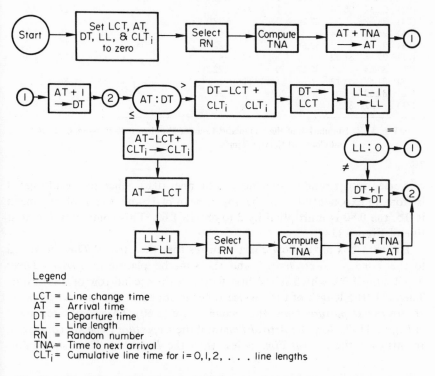

Legend

LCT = Line change time
AT = Arrival time
DT = Departure time
LL = Line length
RN = Random number
TNA = Time to next arrival
CLT_i = Cumulative line time for $i = 0, 1, 2, \ldots$ line lengths

Fig. 11-6. Flow Chart of Simulation with Poisson Arrivals and Constant Service Times

The Monte Carlo Method

| | LCT | AT | DT | LL$_i$ | Cumulative Line Time | | | | | RN | Exp. No. | 2X Exp. No. |
					0	1	2	3	4			
(1)	0.00	0.00	0.00	0	0.00	0.00	0.00	0.00	0.00	55	0.80	1.60
(2)		1.60	2.60									
(3)	1.60	1.88		1	1.60					13	0.14	0.28
(4)	1.88	4.90		2		0.28				78	1.51	3.02
(5)	2.60		3.60	1			0.72					
(6)	3.60		5.90	0		1.28						
(7)	4.90	5.38		1	2.90					21	0.24	0.48
(8)	5.38	9.32		2		1.76				86	1.97	3.94
(9)	5.90		6.90	1			1.24					
(10)	6.90		10.32	0		2.76						
(11)	9.32	9.36		1	5.32					02	0.02	0.04
(12)	9.36	9.40		2		2.80				02	0.02	0.04
(13)	9.40	9.88		3			1.28			21	0.24	0.48
(14)	9.88	17.70		4				0.48		98	3.91	7.82
(15)	10.32		11.32	3					0.44			
(16)	11.32		12.32	2				1.48				
(17)	12.32		13.32	1			2.28					
(18)	13.32		18.70	0		3.80						
(19)	17.70	18.12		1	9.70					19	0.21	0.42
(20)	18.12	25.72		2		4.22				97	3.51	7.02
(21)	18.70		19.70	1			2.86					
(22)	19.70		26.72	0		5.22						
(23)	25.72	28.26		1	15.72					72	1.27	2.54
(24)	26.72		29.26	0		6.22						
(25)	28.26	29.64		1	17.26					50	0.69	1.38
(26)	29.26		30.64	0		7.22						
(27)	29.64	31.52		1	17.64					61	0.94	1.88
(28)	30.64		32.52	0		8.22						
(29)	31.52	33.12		1	18.52					55	0.80	1.60
(30)	32.52		34.12	0		9.22						
(31)	33.12	37.06		1	19.12					86	1.97	3.94

Fig. 11-7. Simulation of the Complaint-Counter Problem with Poisson Arrivals and Constant Service Times

converted into a random exponential number (0.8). Since the resulting 0.8 is from an exponential chart having a mean of 1, and the problem mean is 0.5, the 0.80 is multiplied by 2 to obtain 1.60. This completes the first line of Figure 11–7.

The next box of the flow chart requires that the *Arrival Time* be added to the *Time to Next Arrival*, and the sum be placed in *Arrival Time*: 0 + 1.60 = 1.60, which is the first figure in the second row of the table. Then a 1 (the length of the service time) is added to the *Arrival Time* to obtain the *Departure Time*, the second figure (2.60). This completes row 2 of Figure 11–7. Now the *Arrival Time* and the *Departure Time* are compared. In this case, the *Arrival Time* is less than the *Departure Time*, so the flow goes downward. The next box computes the time that the *Line Length* has remained unchanged. The *Line Change Time* (0) is subtracted from the *Arrival Time* (1.60), the difference (1.60) is added to the *Cumulative Line Time* sub (0) (in this case sub *i*, the *Line Length*, is set to length 0), and the total (1.60) is placed in the *Cumulative Time* for a line length of 0. The line has changed length from 0 to 1, so the *Arrival Time* (1.60) is placed in the *Line Change Time* column, a 1 is added to the *Line Length*, a new *Time to Next Arrival* is computed, added to the previous *Arrival Time*, and the sum (1.88) recorded in the *Arrival Time* column. Notice that each line of Figure 11–7 pertains to a new comparison of *Arrival Time* and *Departure Time*. Since *Arrival Time* is still less than *Departure Time*, the computations for row 4 follow the downward path of the flow chart.

For row 5, however, the new *Arrival Time* is compared to the *Departure Time* and the *Arrival Time* is greater, so the flow goes to the right. Once again the time since the last line change is computed and added to the accumulated line time, but this time for *Line Length 1*. The *Line Change Time* is recorded, the *Line Length* decreased by 1 (one customer has departed after having been serviced), and a new *Departure Time* is computed. Since the *Line Length* is not equal to 0, the flow goes to the downward path, and the new *Departure Time* is equal to the old *Departure Time* plus 1 (3.60). If the *Line Length* had been equal to 0, the new *Departure Time* would have been equal to the *Arrival Time* plus 1.

The foregoing description should be sufficient to permit the reader to trace each of the remaining lines in Figure 11–7.

Figure 11–7 represents only 33.12 minutes of simulation. In this period, the line contained 4 people once, and never 5 people. After 50,000 minutes of computer simulation, the line achieved a maximum length of over 6 people. Figure 11–8 shows the probabilities computed after 33.12 minutes of hand simulation and 50,000 minutes of computer simulation. Also shown are the theoretical probabilities computed in Sec. 12–4.

The technique described for simulation where the Poisson or exponential distribution is involved may be applied to any other type of distribution

Length of Line	0	1	2	3	4	5	6 or More
33.12-minute simulation	0.577	0.279	0.086	0.045	0.013	–0–	–0–
50,000-minute simulation	0.498	0.326	0.124	0.038	0.010	0.003	0.001
Theoretical probabilities	0.500	0.324	0.123	0.038	0.011	0.003	0.001

Fig. 11-8. Comparison of Probabilities from Simulation Runs with Theoretical Probabilities—II

whether that distribution is one of the standard distributions or one empirically obtained. In each case a cumulative probability curve is prepared, and the random numbers obtained from a table of random digits are converted to random numbers distributed according to the desired distribution.

If the need for random numbers from a given distribution arises frequently, tables of such numbers may be prepared. One such table, a short table of random exponential numbers is presented in Appendix E.

SEC. 11-7. SIMULATION WITH POISSON ARRIVALS AND EXPONENTIAL SERVICE TIMES

Although situations do exist where service times remain constant, it is more usual to find that service times fluctuate about some norm or mean. In fact the probability distribution of departures frequently closely approximates the Poisson *if the time when departures cannot take place is ignored.* Naturally, no departure can occur at those times when there is nobody in line. For those occasions when the departure rate closely approximates the Poisson, the length of service time closely approximates the exponential distribution. That is to say, given a Poisson departure distribution, the time to the next departure (the service time) is distributed according to the exponential distribution. For the following simulation, assume that the complaint-counter department problem has a mean departure rate of 1.

The simulation of Poisson arrivals and exponential service times is only slightly more complex than is the simulation with constant service times. The flow chart for the simulation is shown in Figure 11-9 and the results of the simulation in Figure 11-10.

The simulation with exponential service times is quite similar to that with constant service times. The first box (Figure 11-9) sets to 0 the *Line Change Time, Arrival Time, Departure Time, Line Length,* and *Cumulative Line Length Times.* This is shown in line 1 of Figure 11-10. The next operation requires that a random exponential number be selected from the Table of Random Exponential Numbers (Appendix E). The table is used here in lieu of the conversion method employed in the preceding simulation. Since the mean arrival rate is 0.5 and the corresponding value for the Table of Random Exponential Numbers is 1, the random exponential number selected (the first being 0.20, in this case) is multiplied by 2 to obtain the *Time to Next Arrival* (0.40 in this case). The first line of Figure 11-10 is now completed.

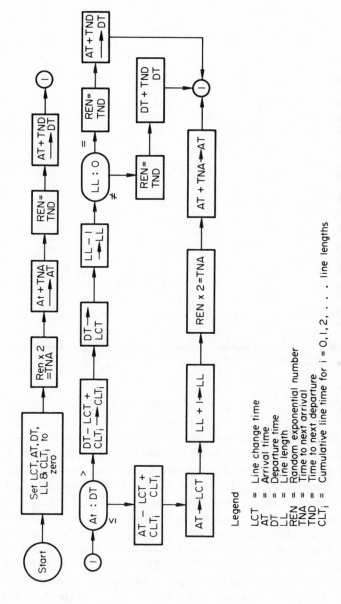

Legend

LCT = Line change time
AT = Arrival time
DT = Departure time
LL = Line length
REN = Random exponential number
TNA = Time to next arrival
TND = Time to next departure
CLT$_i$ = Cumulative line time for $i = 0, 1, 2, \ldots$ line lengths

Fig. 11-9. Flow Chart of Simulation with Poisson Arrivals and Exponential Service Times

169

	LCT	AT	DT	LL$_i$	Cumulative Line Time 0	1	2	3	REN	Twice REN
(1)	0.00	0.00	0.00	0	0.00	0.00	0.00	0.00	0.20	0.40
(2)		0.40	2.44						2.04	
(3)	0.40	3.62		1	0.40				1.61	3.22
(4)	2.44		3.95	0		2.04			0.33	
(5)	3.62	11.44		1	1.58				3.91	7.82
(6)	3.95		11.59	0		2.37			0.15	
(7)	11.44	12.86		1	9.07				0.71	1.42
(8)	11.59		14.90	0		2.52			2.04	
(9)	12.86	20.68		1	10.34				3.91	7.82
(10)	14.90		21.07	0		4.56			0.39	
(11)	20.68	20.88		1	16.12				0.10	0.20
(12)	20.88	24.54		2		4.76			1.83	3.66
(13)	21.07		23.11	1			0.19		2.04	
(14)	23.11		25.16	0		6.80			0.62	
(15)	24.54	26.22		1	17.55				0.84	1.68
(16)	25.16		26.41	0		7.42			0.19	
(17)	26.22	28.44		1	18.61				1.11	2.22
(18)	26.41		29.41	0		7.61			0.97	
(19)	28.44	31.86		1	20.64				1.71	3.42
(20)	29.41		32.91	0		8.58			1.05	
(21)	31.86	32.24		1	23.19				0.19	0.38
(22)	32.24	32.78		2		8.96			0.27	0.54
(23)	32.78	36.10		3			0.73		1.66	3.32
(24)	32.91		33.06	2				0.13	0.15	
(25)	33.06		35.10	1			0.88		2.04	
(26)	35.10		36.13	0		11.00			0.03	
(27)	36.10	36.30		1	24.09				0.10	0.20
(28)	36.13		36.59	0		11.03			0.46	

Fig. 11-10. Simulation of Complaint-Counter Problem with Poisson Arrivals and Exponential Service Times

The next operation is to add the *Time to Next Arrival* (0.40) to the *Arrival Time* (0) to get the new *Arrival Time* (0.40). Another random exponential number is selected (2.04) to ascertain the length of service or the *Time to Next Departure*. Since the mean rate of departure is 1, no adjustment need be made to the random exponential number selected. The *Arrival Time* (0.40) is added to the *Time to Next Departure* (2.04) to obtain the *Departure Time* (2.44). This completes line 2 of Figure 11–10.

The *Arrival Time* is now compared to the *Departure Time*. The *Arrival Time* (0.40) is less than the *Departure Time* (2.44) so the flow path leads downward. The *Cumulative Line Time* sub *i* (*i* at this point equals 0) is computed by subtracting the *Line Change Time* (0) from the *Arrival Time* (0.40). Since the line has changed length as the result of an arrival, the *Line Change Time* is made equal to the *Arrival Time*, and the *Line Length* is increased by 1. A new *Arrival Time* is then computed and the flow returns to the *Arrival Time–Departure Time* comparison. The reader should now be able to trace the remaining lines in Figure 11–10.

Figure 11–10 represents only 36.13 minutes of simulation. In this period the line never exceeded a length of three people. Figure 11–11 shows the probabilities computed after 36.13 minutes of hand simulation, after 50,000 minutes of computer simulation, and according to the theoretical probabilities as computed in Sec. 12–3.

Length of Line	0	1	2	3	4	5	6	7	8 or More
36.13-minute simulation	0.6667	0.3053	0.0244	0.0036	–0–	–0–	–0–	–0–	–0–
50,000-minute simulation	0.4987	0.2485	0.1245	0.0638	0.0326	0.0170	0.0075	0.0040	0.0034
Theoretical probabilities	0.5000	0.2500	0.1250	0.0625	0.0313	0.0156	0.0078	0.0039	0.0039

Fig. 11-11. Comparison of Probabilities from Simulation Runs to Theoretical Probabilities—III

DISCUSSION QUESTIONS

11-1. Describe why the length of the line in the complaint-counter problem may be regarded as a random variable.

11-2. The *Monte Carlo method* gets its name from the use of devices from games of chance. Describe how these devices are used and what relationship this use has to business problems.

11-3. What is a *table of random digits?* Describe some of its characteristics and its uses.

11-4. Name two types of random number tables other than the table of random digits.

11-5. Discuss the relationship or similarity of preparation for Monte Carlo simulation with preparation for electronic computation.

11-6. Describe a method of entering a table of random numbers designed to eliminate possible bias in selecting the point of entry.

11-7. In what way does the size of the simulation sample affect the accuracy of the results?

11-8. What effect if any does the value of the probability of occurrence have upon accuracy and/or sample size?

11-9. Describe the method of converting ordinary (or rectangular) random numbers into random exponential numbers. Explain how this method may be applied to a distribution other than the exponential distribution.

11-1. A waiting-line situation has the following characteristics:

Observed Arrivals per Minute		Observed Service Time	
Arrivals	Number	Minutes	Number
0	800	1	400
1	100	2	300
2	80	3	200
3	20	4	100
	1000		1000

All events occur on the whole minute. Simulate 100 minutes to obtain the estimated probabilities of the length of the line, that is, 0 length, 1 length, 2 lengths, and so forth.

11-2. A system cycles in 1 minute, after which it may break down. If it does not break down at the end of one cycle, it will continue through the next cycle. The system has two subsystems, A and B. If either A or B breaks down, the system is down. After each cycle, subsystem A breaks down 3 out of 10 times and subsystem B breaks down 2 out of 10 times (on the average). Both A and B can, of course, break down at the same time. If A breaks down it will be repaired in the following times with the associated probabilities:

Time of repair (minutes)	1	2	3
Probability	0.3	0.5	0.2

Similarly, if B breaks down:

Time of repair (minutes)	1	2	3	4
Probability	0.2	0.4	0.3	0.1

If both A and B break down simultaneously:

Time of repair (minutes)	2	3	4	5	6
Probability	0.1	0.3	0.3	0.2	0.1

All events occur on the whole minute. Simulate 100 minutes in order to estimate the percentage of down time of the system.

11-3. A waiting-line situation has arrivals distributed according to a Poisson variable with $\lambda = 0.2$. Service times are constant at 2 minutes. Simulate 50 minutes to obtain the estimated probabilities of the various line lengths, that is, 0 length, 1 length, 2 length, and so forth.

11-4. A waiting-line situation is similar to that in Problem 11-3, except that service times are distributed exponentially with $\mu = 0.5$. Simulate 50 minutes as in Problem 11-3.

11-5. A waiting-line situation has constant service times of 1 minute and the following observed arrival data:

Time between Arrivals (Minutes)	Number of Observation
0–0.99	200
1–1.99	350
2–2.99	250
3–3.99	100
4–4.99	50
5–5.99	30
6–6.99	15
7 or more	5
	1000

Required
a. Construct a smooth cumulative probability curve from the above data.
b. Simulate 50 minutes to estimate the long-run line length probabilities.

11-6. Rework Problem 11-3 by adding a second service facility.

11-7. Rework Problem 11-4 by adding a second service facility.

11-8. Rework Problem 11-4 by adding a third service facility.

BIBLIOGRAPHY

Bierman, Harold, Jr., Lawrence E. Fouraker, and Robert K. Jaedicke, *Quantitative Analysis for Business Decisions.* Homewood, Ill.: Richard D. Irwin, Inc., 1961, pp. 189-96.

Churchman, C. West, Russell L. Ackoff, E. Leonard Arnoff, *Introduction to Operations Research.* New York: John Wiley & Sons, Inc., 1957, pp. 174-83; 407-11.

Flagle, Charles D., William H. Huggins, and Robert H. Roy, *Operations Research and Systems Engineering.* Baltimore, Md: The Johns Hopkins Press, 1960, pp. 425-46; 711-62.

Green, Paul, S., Reed Calhoun, and I. Landis Haines, "Solving Your Plant Problems by Simulation," *Factory,* 117 (February, 1959), 80-85.

Harling, J., "Simulation Techniques in Operations Research—A Review," *Operations Research,* 6 (May-June, 1958), 307-319.

McCloskey, Joseph F., and John M. Coppinger (eds.), *Operations Research for Management.* Baltimore, Md.: The Johns Hopkins Press, 1956, pp. 376-400.

RAND Corporation, *A Million Random Digits.* Glencoe, Ill.: The Free Press, 1955.

Sasieni, Maurice, Arthur Yaspan, and Lawrence Friedman, *Operations Research—Methods and Problems.* New York: John Wiley & Sons, Inc., 1959, pp. 58-67; 146-51.

12

Waiting Lines

The problems considered in Chapter 11 and which were solved by simulation were waiting-line problems. Many waiting-line problems are too complex for easy mathematical analysis; hence the Monte Carlo approach may be the preferred method of solution. The problems of Chapter 11 were, however, quite simple in nature, and thus may be solved by means of fairly easy mathematical techniques. Three waiting-line problems were described in Chapter 11: (1) a problem with observed frequencies of arrival and constant service times, with the additional requirement that events occurred evenly spaced; (2) a problem with Poisson arrivals and constant service times; (3) a problem with Poisson arrivals and exponential service times. Each of these problems will now be subjected to mathematical analysis. In addition, the case of multiple service facilities will also be treated.

SEC. 12-2. THE USE OF RECURSION EQUATIONS

The first problem to be considered is that described in Sec. 9-1. It has a distribution of the rate of arrivals as follows:

Arrivals	Probability
0	.61
1	.29
2	.09
3	.01

Service times are considered to be constant at exactly 1 minute, and it is assumed that all events occur only on the whole minute.

In analyzing the possible conditions at any time t, a tree diagram may be used. Starting at t_0, with no one in the waiting line, the possible conditions at t_1 are

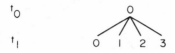

That is, given 0 in line at t_0, there may be either 0, 1, 2, or 3 in line at t_1. There would be 0 in line if there were 0 arrivals, 1 if there were 1 arrival, 2 if there were 2 arrivals, and 3 if there were 3 arrivals. Since the probability of there being 0 arrivals equals 0.61, the probability of there being 0 in line at t_1 is 0.61. Similarly, the probability of 1 in line at t_1 equals 0.29, 2 in line equals 0.09, and 3 in line equals 0.01.

The tree diagram may be extended to t_2 as shown in Figure 12–1. Thus by t_2 there are 16 possible paths that the flow through the tree diagram may take. A 0–length line may occur via two paths, namely, a 0 arrival in t_1 followed by a 0 arrival in t_2, and by a 1 arrival in t_1 followed by a 0 arrival in t_2. The probability of there being a 0–length line from the first sequence is the product of the probability of a 0 arrival in t_1 (0.61) and the probability of a 0 arrival in t_2 (0.61) which is 0.3721. Similarly, the probability of there being a 0-length line via the second path is the product of the probability of a 1 arrival in time t_1 (0.29) and the probability of a 0 arrival in t_2 (0.61) which is 0.1769. Therefore, the probability that there will be a 0-length line in t_2 is equal to $0.3721 + 0.1769 = 0.5490$.

Thus the probabilities of the various lengths of the line at t_2 are

0	1	2	3	4	5
0.3721	0.1769	0.0549	0.0061	0.0009	0.0001
0.1769	0.0841	0.0261	0.0029	0.0009	
	0.0549	0.0261	0.0081		
		0.0061	0.0029		
0.5490	0.3159	0.1132	0.0200	0.0018	0.0001

A check shows that $0.5490 + 0.3159 + 0.1132 + 0.0200 + 0.0018 + 0.0001 = 1.0000$, which represents the universe of the random variable, the length of the line.

A tree diagram showing the possible flows t_0 through t_3 could also be constructed, but the potential complexity of the number of flow paths is already apparent. At t_0 there was $4^0 = 1$ flow path; at t_1, $4^1 = 4$ flow paths; at t_2, $4^2 = 16$; and at t_3 there would be $4^3 = 64$. It is clear that at

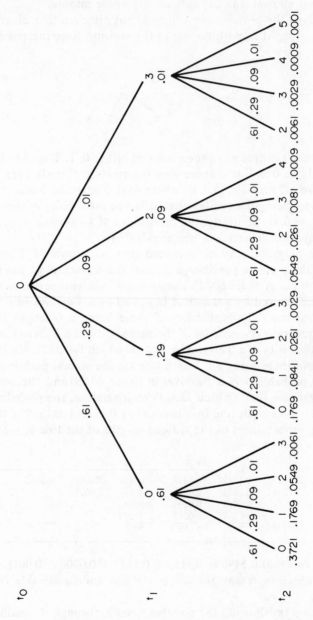

Fig. 12-1. Tree Diagram of a Waiting Line

any t_i there will be 4^i flow paths, and that the tree diagram method of analysis soon becomes too unwieldy to be practical. Nevertheless, some very useful relationships have already been revealed. For a 0–length line at any t_i, the line-length possibilities in t_{i+1} are:

For all other line lengths at t_i, the line lengths at t_{i+1} may be expressed by

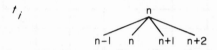

Thus for any line length n at t_i, the only possible line lengths at t_{i+1} are $n,- 1, n, n + 1$, or $n + 2$. These relationships may be used to construct a system of recursion equations. A *recursion equation* is an equation expressing subsequent-state conditions in terms of preceding-state conditions. In the problem under consideration, the objective would be, given certain conditions at t_i, to express the conditions that would exist at t_{i+1}.

Figure 12-2 shows the approach used in developing the recursion equations. Frequencies of 0's are followed 0.61 of the time by frequencies of 0's, 0.29 of the time by frequencies of 1's, 0.09 of the time by frequencies of 2's, and 0.01 of the time by frequencies of 3's (line 1 of Figure 12-2). Frequencies of 1's are also followed by f_0 0.61 of the time, by f_1 0.29 of the time, by f_2 0.09 of the time, and by f_3 0.01 of the time (line 2, Figure 12-2). Frequencies of 2's, however, are followed 0.61 of the time by f_1, 0.29 of the time by f_2, 0.09 of the time by f_3, and 0.01 of the time by f_4 (line 3, Figure 12-2). The reader can trace the relationships for f_3, f_4, and so forth. The pattern will continue as the i of the f_i grows larger.

Figure. 12-2 also shows that conditions at t_{i+1} can be expressed in terms of t_i. Frequencies of 0's at time t_{i+1} come from 0.61 of the frequencies of the 0's in t_i plus 0.61 of the frequencies of the 1's in t_i. This may be expressed:

$$f_0 = 0.61f_0 + 0.61f_1.$$

The f_0 on each side of the equation is generically identical, and hence can be manipulated algebraically. This concept is not always self-evident, but may be explained as follows:

Consider a table of one million random digits. It would be reasonable to expect the table to contain approximately one-tenth or 100,000 0's.

$$t_{i+1}$$

	f_0	f_1	f_2	f_3	f_4	f_5	f_6	f_7	f_8	f_9	f_{10}
f_0	.61	.29	.09	.01							
f_1	.61	.29	.09	.01							
f_2		.61	.29	.09	.01						
f_3			.61	.29	.09	.01					
f_4				.61	.29	.09	.01				
f_5					.61	.29	.09	.01			
f_6						.61	.29	.09	.01		
f_7							.61	.29	.09	.01	
f_8								.61	.29	.09	.01
f_9									.61	.29	.09

t_i

Fig. 12-2. The Recursion Relationships—I

These 0's would be followed by approximately 10,000 0's, 10,000 1's, 10,000 2's and so forth. But the 10,000 0's which follow the 100,000 0's are not different 0's. They are in fact part of that same 100,000 0's. Similarly the t_i represents all t's, and the t_{i+1} merely represents the following period.

Thus reading down in Figure 12-2, the recursion equations are

(a) $f_0 = 0.61 f_0 + 0.61 f_1$

(b) $f_1 = 0.29 f_0 + 0.29 f_1 + 0.61 f_2$

(c) $f_2 = 0.09 f_0 + 0.09 f_1 + 0.29 f_2 + 0.61 f_3$

(d) $f_3 = 0.01 f_0 + 0.01 f_1 + 0.09 f_2 + 0.29 f_3 + 0.61 f_4$

(e) $f_4 = 0.01 f_2 + 0.09 f_3 + 0.29 f_4 + 0.61 f_5$

(f) $f_5 = 0.01 f_3 + 0.09 f_4 + 0.29 f_5 + 0.61 f_6$

(g) $f_6 = 0.01 f_4 + 0.09 f_5 + 0.29 f_6 + 0.61 f_7$

(h) $f_7 = 0.01 f_5 + 0.09 f_6 + 0.29 f_7 + 0.61 f_8$.

An infinite number of such equations could be constructed.

Equation (a) may be solved for f_1 in terms of f_0, thus,

(a) $$f_0 = 0.61 f_0 + 0.61 f_1$$

$$0.61 f_1 = f_0 - 0.61 f_0$$

(a1) $$f_1 = 0.6393 f_0.$$

By substituting $f_1 = 0.6393 f_0$ into Eq. (b), f_2 may be obtained in terms of f_0:

(b) $$f_1 = 0.29\,f_0 + 0.29\,f_1 + 0.61\,f_2.$$

Substituting (a1),

$$0.6393\,f_0 = 0.29\,f_0 + (0.29)(0.69393)\,f_0 + 0.61\,f_2$$

$$0.61\,f_2 = 0.6393\,f_0 - 0.29\,f_0 - 0.1854\,f_0$$

(b1) $$f_2 = 0.2687\,f_0.$$

By similarly substituting $f_1 = 0.6393\,f_0$ and $f_2 = 0.2687\,f_0$ into Eq. (c), f_3 may be obtained in terms of f_0:

(c) $$f_2 = 0.09\,f_0 + 0.09\,f_1 + 0.29\,f_2 + 0.61\,f_3.$$

Substituting (a1) and (b1),

$$0.2687\,f_0 = 0.09\,f_0 + (0.09)(0.6393)\,f_0 + (0.29)(0.2687)\,f_0 + 0.61\,f_3$$

$$0.61\,f_3 = 0.2687\,f_0 - 0.09\,f_0 - 0.0575\,f_0 - 0.0779\,f_0$$

$$f_3 = 0.0709\,f_0.$$

Similar calculations for succeeding f_i result in

$$f_0 = 1.0000\,f_0$$
$$f_1 = 0.6393\,f_0$$
$$f_2 = 0.2687\,f_0$$
$$f_3 = 0.0709\,f_0$$
$$f_4 = 0.0160\,f_0$$
$$f_5 = 0.0038\,f_0$$
$$f_6 = 0.0009\,f_0$$
$$f_7 = 0.0002\,f_0$$

$$\sum_{i=0}^{7} f_i = 1.9998\,f_0$$

Thus it is quite evident that the evaluation of each succeeding f_i in terms of f_0 will add slightly to the above sum until

(i) $$\sum_{i=0}^{\infty} f_i = 2.00\,f_0.$$

Moreover, since the probability of the total frequencies encountered must sum to 1, then:

(j) $$\mathrm{Pr}\left(\sum_{i=0}^{\infty} f_i\right) = 1.$$

Substituting Eq. (i) into Eq. (j):

$$Pr(2 f_0) = 1.$$

Hence,

$$Pr(f_0) = 0.5.$$

Now, since the other frequencies (f_1, f_2, and so forth) have been evaluated in terms of f_0, then

$$Pr(f_0) = \qquad\qquad\qquad\qquad\qquad 0.50000$$
$$Pr(f_1) = 0.6393 \, Pr(f_0) = 0.6393 \times 0.5 = 0.31965$$
$$Pr(f_2) = 0.2687 \, Pr(f_0) = 0.2687 \times 0.5 = 0.13435$$
$$Pr(f_3) = 0.0709 \, Pr(f_0) = 0.0709 \times 0.5 = 0.03545$$
$$Pr(f_4) = 0.0160 \, Pr(f_0) = 0.0160 \times 0.5 = 0.00800$$
$$Pr(f_5) = 0.0037 \, Pr(f_0) = 0.0037 \times 0.5 = 0.00185$$
$$Pr(f_6) = 0.0009 \, Pr(f_0) = 0.0009 \times 0.5 = 0.00045$$
$$Pr(f_7) = 0.0002 \, Pr(f_0) = 0.0002 \times 0.5 = 0.00010$$
$$Pr(f_8 \text{ or more}) = \qquad\qquad\qquad\qquad \underline{0.00015}$$
$$\qquad\qquad\qquad\qquad\qquad\qquad\qquad 1.00000$$

These probabilities are, of course, the long-run probabilities of the various line lengths. (For a comparison of the probabilities obtained from a Monte Carlo simulation of this problem see Figure 11-4.)

SEC. 12-3. POISSON ARRIVALS AND EXPONENTIAL SERVICE TIMES

The concept of the arrival rate of persons entering a waiting line assuming the characteristics of a Poisson random variable was discussed in Sec. 11–6, and the concept of the service times assuming the characteristics of an exponential random variable was discussed in Sec. 11–7. The assumptions of the examples presented there were that the mean arrival rate was 0.5 and the mean departure rate was 1. These values were used as a basis for obtaining the various line-length probabilities by means of Monte Carlo simulation techniques. These same values will now be used as a basis for analysis by mathematical methods.

In order to distinguish the mean arrival rate from the mean departure rate, λ will be used for arrivals and μ for departures. Therefore, in this case, $\lambda = 0.5$ in the Poisson equation,

$$\Pr(n) = \frac{e^{-\lambda}\lambda^n}{n!},$$

and $\mu = 1$ in the exponential equation,

$$f(t) = Y = \mu e^{-\mu t}.$$

The Poisson probability distribution is discussed in Sec. 10–1, and the exponential distribution in Sec. 10–3.

Once again recursion relationships will be used to develop formulas for the probabilities of the various line-length possibilities. Time t will be considered one point in the recursion relationship and time $t + \Delta t$ the next succeeding time. In this context, Δt is conceived as a very short period of time. Since the average arrival rate is equal to λ, the probability of an arrival during the period Δt is $\lambda \Delta t$. Similarly, since the average departure rate is equal to μ, the probability of a departure during the period Δt is $\mu \, \Delta t$. The probability of two arrivals occurring during Δt is therefore equal to $(\lambda \, \Delta t)(\lambda \, \Delta t) = \lambda^2 (\Delta t)^2$. Because Δt is a very small quantity, Δt^2 is a very much smaller quantity—so small, in fact, as to be regarded as negligible, hence for all practical purposes, equal to zero. Similarly, the probability of two departures occurring during Δt is equal to $\mu^2 (\Delta t)^2$, and therefore also equal to zero, as is the probability of an arrival and a departure both occurring during Δt, since the probability is equal to $\lambda \mu (\Delta t)^2$.

Given, then, that two arrivals, two departures, or a simultaneous arrival and departure during Δt are impossible, the following tree diagrams show the possible conditions which can exist at $t + \Delta t$, given that there is 0, 1, or n in line at t:

That is, given 0 in line at time t, there will be 0 in line at $t + \Delta t$ if there are no arrivals or departures during Δt, and there will be 1 in line at $t + \Delta t$ if there is 1 arrival during Δt. There can, of course be no departures during Δt if there is no one in line at t. Similarly, given 1 in line at t, there will be 0 in line at $t + \Delta t$ if there is a departure during Δt, 1 in line if there is neither an arrival nor a departure, and 2 in line if there is an arrival. And for any n in line at t ($n \neq 0$), there can be $n - 1$, n, or $n + 1$ at $t + \Delta t$.

$$t + \Delta t$$

	Pr(0)	Pr(1)	Pr(2)	Pr(3)	Pr(4)	Pr(5)	Pr(6)
Pr(0)	$1 - \lambda \Delta t$	$\lambda \Delta t$					
Pr(1)	$\mu \Delta t$	$1 - \mu \Delta t - \lambda \Delta t$					
Pr(2)		$\mu \Delta t$	$1 - \mu \Delta t - \lambda \Delta t$	$\lambda \Delta t$			
Pr(3)			$\mu \Delta t$	$1 - \mu \Delta t - \lambda \Delta t$	$\lambda \Delta t$		
Pr(4)				$\mu \Delta t$	$1 - \mu \Delta t - \lambda \Delta t$	$\lambda \Delta t$	
Pr(5)					$\mu \Delta t$	$1 - \mu \Delta t - \lambda \Delta t$	$\lambda \Delta t$
Pr(6)						$\mu \Delta t$	$1 - \mu \Delta t - \lambda \Delta t$

(left label: t)

Fig. 12-3. The Recursion Relationships—II

Figure 12-3 shows the relationships which can be used to develop the recursion equations. The values in the squares represent probabilities. Given 0 in line in time t, the probability of there being 1 in line in time $t + \Delta t$ is equal to $\lambda \Delta t$, which is, of course, the probability of an arrival occurring during the period Δt. Since there can only be either 0 or 1 in line at $t + \Delta t$, given 0 in line at t, the probability of there being 0 in line at $t + \Delta t$ is equal to $1 - \lambda \Delta t$.

Given 1 in line at t, the probability of there being 0 in line at $t + \Delta t$ is equal to $\mu \Delta t$, that is, the probability of a departure occurring during Δt. Similarly, the probability of there being 2 in line at $t + \Delta t$ is equal to $\lambda \Delta t$, the probability of an arrival occurring during Δt. There are only three possibilities at $t + \Delta t$ given 1 in line at t—0, 1, or 2. Therefore the probability of there being 1 in line at $t + \Delta t = 1 - (\mu \Delta t + \lambda \Delta t)$. This same reasoning applies to obtain the probabilities in each of the other rows in Figure 12-3.

The recursion equations may now be obtained by reading down the columns of Figure 12-3:

(k) $\quad \Pr(0) = (1 - \lambda \Delta t)\, \Pr(0) + (\mu \Delta t)\, \Pr(1)$

(l) $\quad \Pr(1) = (\lambda \Delta t)\, \Pr(0) + (1 - \mu \Delta t - \lambda \Delta t)\, \Pr(1) + (\mu \Delta t)\, \Pr(2)$

(m) $\quad \Pr(n) = (\lambda \Delta t)\, \Pr(n - 1) + (1 - \mu \Delta t - \lambda \Delta t)\, \Pr(n)$
$\qquad\qquad + (\mu \Delta t)\, \Pr(n + 1).$

Equation (k) may be solved for $\Pr(1)$ in terms of $\Pr(0)$:

(k)
$$Pr(0) = (1 - \lambda \, \Delta t) \, Pr(0) + (\mu \, \Delta t) \, Pr(1)$$

$$(\mu \, \Delta t) \, Pr(1) = Pr(0) - (1 - \lambda \, \Delta t) \, Pr(0)$$

$$Pr(1) = \frac{Pr(0) - Pr(0) + (\lambda \, \Delta t) \, Pr(0)}{\mu \, \Delta t}$$

(k1)
$$Pr(1) = \frac{\lambda}{\mu} \, Pr(0).$$

Equation (m) may similarly be solved for $Pr(n + 1)$ in terms of $Pr(n)$ and $Pr(n - 1)$. Equation (l) need not be separately solved since it follows the pattern of Equation (m).

(m)
$$Pr(n) = (\lambda \, \Delta t) \, Pr(n - 1) + (1 - \mu \, \Delta t - \lambda \, \Delta t) \, Pr(n)$$
$$+ (\mu \, \Delta t) \, Pr(n + 1)$$

$$(\mu \, \Delta t) \, Pr(n + 1) = Pr(n) - (\lambda \, \Delta t) \, Pr(n - 1) - (1 - \mu \, \Delta t$$
$$- \lambda \, \Delta t) \, Pr(n)$$

$$Pr(n + 1)$$
$$= \frac{Pr(n) - (\lambda \, \Delta t) \, Pr(n - 1) - Pr(n) + (\mu \, \Delta t) \, Pr(n) + (\lambda \, \Delta t) \, Pr(n)}{\mu \, \Delta t}$$

$$Pr(n + 1) = \frac{\mu Pr(n) + \lambda Pr(n) - \lambda Pr(n - 1)}{\mu}$$

(m1)
$$Pr(n + 1) = \frac{\mu + \lambda}{\mu} \, Pr(n) - \frac{\lambda}{\mu} \, Pr(n - 1).$$

By substituting $n = 1$ and $Pr(1) = \lambda/\mu \, Pr(0)$ into Eq. (m1), the $Pr(2)$ may be obtained:

$$Pr(2) = \frac{\mu + \lambda}{\mu} \, Pr(1) - \frac{\lambda}{\mu} \, Pr(0)$$

$$= \frac{\mu + \lambda}{\mu} \left[\frac{\lambda}{\mu} \, Pr(0) \right] - \frac{\lambda}{\mu} \, Pr(0)$$

$$= \frac{\lambda}{\mu} \, Pr(0) \left[\frac{\mu + \lambda}{\mu} - 1 \right]$$

$$= \frac{\lambda}{\mu} \, Pr(0) \left[\frac{\mu + \lambda - \mu}{\mu} \right]$$

$$= \left(\frac{\lambda}{\mu} \right)^2 Pr(0).$$

The $Pr(3)$, $Pr(4)$, $Pr(5)$, and so forth, may be obtained by similar substitutions:

$$Pr(0) = \left(\frac{\lambda}{\mu}\right)^0 Pr(0)$$

$$Pr(1) = \left(\frac{\lambda}{\mu}\right)^1 Pr(0)$$

$$Pr(2) = \left(\frac{\lambda}{\mu}\right)^2 Pr(0)$$

$$Pr(3) = \left(\frac{\lambda}{\mu}\right)^3 Pr(0)$$

$$Pr(4) = \left(\frac{\lambda}{\mu}\right)^4 Pr(0)$$

$$Pr(5) = \left(\frac{\lambda}{\mu}\right)^5 Pr(0)$$

and hence,

(n) $$\qquad Pr(n) = \left(\frac{\lambda}{\mu}\right)^n Pr(0).$$

But, since the probabilities of the individual line lengths must sum to 1,

$$\sum_{n=0}^{\infty} Pr(n) = 1.$$

Therefore, substituting Eq. (n),

$$\sum_{n=0}^{\infty} \left(\frac{\lambda}{\mu}\right)^n Pr(0) = 1.$$

Because $Pr(0)$ is a constant, it may be moved outside the summation sign, $\sum$,

$$Pr(0) \sum_{n=0}^{\infty} \left(\frac{\lambda}{\mu}\right)^n = 1$$

(o) $$\qquad Pr(0) = \frac{1}{\sum\limits_{n=0}^{\infty} (\lambda/\mu)^n}.$$

The denominator on the right side is merely an infinite geometric progression which has the form:

$$1 + \left(\frac{\lambda}{\mu}\right)^1 + \left(\frac{\lambda}{\mu}\right)^2 + \left(\frac{\lambda}{\mu}\right)^3 + \left(\frac{\lambda}{\mu}\right)^4 \cdots.$$

The formula for evaluating the sum of an infinite geometric series is

$$\text{sum} = \frac{a}{1-r},$$

where a stands for the first term and r for the ratio between terms. In this case $a = 1$, and $r = \lambda/\mu$. Thus,

$$\text{sum} = \frac{1}{1 - \lambda/\mu}.$$

Equation (0) then becomes

$$\Pr(0) = \frac{1}{1/[1 - \lambda/\mu]}$$

(o1) $$\Pr(0) = 1 - \frac{\lambda}{\mu}.$$

By substituting Eq. (o1) into Eq. (n), one has the formula for obtaining the probability of n

(n) $$\Pr(n) = \left(\frac{\lambda}{\mu}\right)^n \Pr(0),$$

(p) $$\Pr(n) = \left(\frac{\lambda}{\mu}\right)^n \left(1 - \frac{\lambda}{\mu}\right), \qquad \text{for all } n.$$

The ideal service situation might seem to be one where the mean arrival rate λ is equal to the mean service rate μ. Such, however, is not the case. As λ approaches μ, the length of the line tends to increase explosively; it would tend to approach an infinite length if λ were equal to, or greater than, μ. Therefore, Eq. (p) is valid only for those conditions where λ is less than μ.

The groundwork is now set to solve the problem where the arrival rate λ is equal to 0.5 and the departure rate μ is equal to 1. These values may be substituted into Equation (p), setting $n = 0, 1, 2$, and so forth, until the probability of n is sufficiently small to be negligible.

(p) $$\Pr(n) = \left(\frac{\lambda}{\mu}\right)^n \left(1 - \frac{\lambda}{\mu}\right)$$

$$= \left(\frac{0.5}{1}\right)^n \left(1 - \frac{0.5}{1}\right)$$

$$= (0.5)^n (0.5)$$

$$= (0.5)^{n+1}$$

$$\Pr(0) = (0.5)^{0+1} = 0.50000000$$

$$\Pr(1) = (0.5)^{1+1} = 0.25000000$$

$$\Pr(2) = (0.5)^{2+1} = 0.12500000$$

$$\Pr(3) = (0.5)^{3+1} = 0.06250000$$

$$Pr(4) = (0.5)^{4+1} = 0.03125000$$
$$Pr(5) = (0.5)^{5+1} = 0.01562500$$
$$Pr(6) = (0.5)^{6+1} = 0.00781250$$
$$Pr(7) = (0.5)^{7+1} = 0.00390625$$
$$Pr(8 \text{ or more}) = \underline{0.00390625}$$
$$1.00000000$$

These computed or theoretical probabilities are compared, in Figure 11–11, to those obtained by means of a Monte Carlo simulation.

SEC. 12-4. POISSON ARRIVALS AND CONSTANT SERVICE TIMES

The constant-service-time case appears, at first glance, to be more simple than the exponential-service-times case. That is true if the problem is approached as a Monte Carlo simulation problem rather than as a problem to be subjected to mathematical analysis; hence, the constant-service-time case was presented before the exponential-service-time case in Chapter 11.

From an analytical viewpoint, however, these positions are reversed. In the case of the exponential service time, the occurrence of a departure during time Δt, is dependent upon arrivals only insofar as the requirement that the system must be occupied in order that a departure may take place. Given, however, that there is an occupant in the system, the time of the departure is completely independent of the time or times of arrival.

In the case of the constant service times, on the other hand, no such independence exists. The time of the departure is in fact determined by the time of an arrival, but not necessarily by the time of the arrival of the unit departing. As a result, the development of the line-length probability formulas is more complex than was the development for the case of the exponential service times. The resulting formulas also happen to be much more complex.

No attempt will be made to derive the formulas for the constant-service-times case. Instead the formulas are merely presented here. One objective in doing so is to permit computation of the theoretical probabilities of the constant-service-times case considered in Sec. 11-6, where the probabilities were estimated by means of a Monte Carlo simulation.

The formulas for the case of Poisson arrivals and constant service times are

$$Pr(0) = 1 - \frac{\lambda}{\mu}$$

$$\Pr(1) = \left(1 - \frac{\lambda}{\mu}\right)(e^{\lambda/\mu} - 1)$$

$$\Pr(n) = \left(1 - \frac{\lambda}{\mu}\right) \sum_{k=1}^{n} (-1)^{n-k} e^{k(\lambda/\mu)} \left[\frac{(k\lambda/\mu)^{n-k}}{(n-k)!} + \frac{(k\lambda/\mu)^{n-k-1}}{(n-k-1)!}\right]; n \geq 2.$$

The denominator of the last term to the right $(n - k - 1)!$ may give the reader some difficulty when $k = n$ in the summation from $k = 1$ to $k = n$. This term then becomes $(n - n - 1)! = (-1)!$ Minus one factorial is equal to infinity, and as a result, when $k = n$, that last term disappears.

In the simulation in Sec. 11-6, the values used were the rate of arrivals, $\lambda = 0.5$, and the service time was constant at 1. Thus the average departure rate, given that the system is occupied, is equal to 1, that is, $\mu = 1$. By substituting these values into the preceding formulas, the following line-length probabilities, rounded to three decimal places, may be obtained:

Line Length	Probability
0	0.500
1	0.324
2	0.123
3	0.038
4	0.011
5	0.003
6	0.001
7	0.000
	1.000

These probabilities are compared to those obtained from the Monte Carlo simulation in Figure 11-8.

SEC. 12-5. POISSON ARRIVALS, EXPONENTIAL SERVICE TIMES, AND TWO-SERVICE FACILITIES

So far we have dealt with waiting-line problems involving single-service facilities or channels. One method of relieving service congestion is to increase the number of service facilities. The case of two-service facilities will be considered first.

The same symbols will be used, that is, $\lambda =$ the mean arrival rate, and μ the mean departure rate. Since a departure can occur from either of the two service facilities at those times when both facilities are occupied, μ pertains to the departure from each facility. Therefore, the probability of an arrival occurring during time Δt is $\lambda \Delta t$, the probability of a departure occurring (1) when the system is unoccupied is equal to 0, (2) when there is only 1 occupant, $\mu \, \Delta t$, (3) when there are 2 or more occupants, $2\mu \, \Delta t$. The last is true because, when there are at least 2 in the system, a departure can occur from either of the two service facilities. The probability that a departure will occur from service facility I is $\mu \, \Delta t$. Similarly, the probability that a departure will occur from service facility II is $\mu \, \Delta t$. Hence the probability that a departure will occur from *either* facility I *or* facility II is equal to $2\mu \, \Delta t$. The probability that a departure will occur from *both* facilities in the same Δt period is equal to $(\mu \, \Delta t)(\mu \, \Delta t) = \mu^2 (\Delta t)^2$. Since Δt is conceived of as being very small, the quantity $(\Delta t)^2$ approaches insignificance and is regarded as being zero (see Sec. 12–3 for a discussion of other coincidental events).

Figure 12-4 shows the relationships needed to develop the recursion equations. These relationships were derived from the following tree diagrams:

The relationships for the first row are from the tree diagram at the left. Given 0 in line at time t, there may be either 0 or 1 in line at $t + \Delta t$. There will be 1 in line only if there is an arrival during Δt, and the probability of there being an arrival is $\lambda \, \Delta t$. Hence, the probability of there

$t + \Delta t$

	Pr(0)	Pr(1)	Pr(2)	Pr(3)	Pr(4)	Pr(5)	Pr(6)
Pr(0)	$1 - \lambda \Delta t$	$\lambda \Delta t$					
Pr(1)	$\mu \Delta t$	$1 - \mu \Delta t - \lambda \Delta t$	$\lambda \Delta t$				
Pr(2)		$2\mu \Delta t$	$1 - 2\mu \Delta t - \lambda \Delta t$	$\lambda \Delta t$			
Pr(3)			$2\mu \Delta t$	$1 - 2\mu \Delta t - \lambda \Delta t$	$\lambda \Delta t$		
Pr(4)				$2\mu \Delta t$	$1 - 2\mu \Delta t - \lambda \Delta t$	$\lambda \Delta t$	
Pr(5)					$2\mu \Delta t$	$1 - 2\mu \Delta t - \lambda \Delta t$	$\lambda \Delta t$
Pr(6)						$2\mu \Delta t$	$1 - 2\mu \Delta t - \lambda \Delta t$

Fig. 12-4. The Recursion Relationships—III

being no arrival is $1 - \lambda\,\Delta t$. So far the pattern follows that of a one-service facility system, as do the probabilities in the second row. In the third row, however, the probability of a departure is equal to $2\mu\,\Delta t$, since the use of two service facilities comes into play. The probability of an arrival occurring remains at $\lambda\,\Delta t$, and the probability of there being neither an arrival nor a departure is equal to $1 - (2\mu\,\Delta t + \lambda\,\Delta t)$. The remaining rows are derived in a similar manner. The recursion equations are now derived by reading downward in each column:

(q) $\Pr(0) = (1 - \lambda\,\Delta t)\,\Pr(0) + (\mu\,\Delta t)\,\Pr(1)$

(r) $\Pr(1) = (\lambda\,\Delta t)\,\Pr(0) + (1 - \mu\,\Delta t - \lambda\,\Delta t) + (2\mu\,\Delta t)\,\Pr(2)$

(s) $\Pr(n) = (\lambda\,\Delta t)\,\Pr(n-1) + (1 - 2\mu\,\Delta t - \lambda\,\Delta t)\,\Pr(n)$
        $+ (2\mu\,\Delta t)\,\Pr(n+1).$

Equation (q) may be solved for $\Pr(1)$ in terms of $\Pr(0)$:

(q) $$\Pr(0) = (1 - \lambda\,\Delta t)\,\Pr(0) + (\mu\,\Delta t)\,\Pr(1)$$

$$\Pr(1) = \frac{\Pr(0) - \Pr(0) + (\lambda\,\Delta t)\,\Pr(0)}{\mu\,\Delta t}$$

(q1) $$\Pr(1) = \frac{\lambda}{\mu}\,\Pr(0).$$

Equation (r) may be solved for $\Pr(2)$ in terms of $\Pr(1)$ and $\Pr(0)$:

(r) $$\Pr(1) = (\lambda\,\Delta t)\,\Pr(0) + (1 - \mu\,\Delta t - \lambda\,\Delta t)\,\Pr(1) + (2\mu\,\Delta t)\,\Pr(2)$$

$$\Pr(2) = \frac{\Pr(1) - \Pr(1) + (\mu\,\Delta t)\,\Pr(1) + (\lambda\,\Delta t)\,\Pr(1) - (\lambda\,\Delta t)\,\Pr(0)}{2\mu\,\Delta t}$$

(r1) $$\Pr(2) = \frac{\mu + \lambda}{2\mu}\,\Pr(1) - \frac{\lambda}{2\mu}\,\Pr(0).$$

Equation (s) may be solved for $\Pr(n+1)$ in terms of $\Pr(n)$ and $\Pr(n-1)$:

(s) $$\Pr(n) = (\lambda\,\Delta t)\,\Pr(n-1) + (1 - 2\mu\,\Delta t - \lambda\,\Delta t)\,\Pr(n)$$
        $$+ (2\mu\,\Delta t)\,\Pr(n+1)$$

$$\Pr(n+1)$$
$$= \frac{\Pr(n) - \Pr(n) + (2\mu\,\Delta t)\,\Pr(n) + (\lambda\,\Delta t)\,\Pr(n) - (\lambda\,\Delta t)\,\Pr(n-1)}{2\mu\,\Delta t}$$

(s1) $$\Pr(n+1) = \frac{2\mu + \lambda}{2\mu}\,\Pr(n) - \frac{\lambda}{2\mu}\,\Pr(n-1).$$

Equation (s1) is valid only for $n \geq 2$. Substituting $n = 2$ into Eq. (s1), it becomes:

(s2) $$\Pr(3) = \frac{2\mu + \lambda}{2\mu} \Pr(2) - \frac{\lambda}{2\mu} \Pr(2).$$

Now let $n = 3$, and substitute in Eq. (s2), which becomes

(t) $$\Pr(n) = \frac{2\mu + \lambda}{2\mu} \Pr(n - 1) - \frac{\lambda}{2\mu} \Pr(n - 2).$$

Equation (t) is valid only for $n \geq 3$.

In summary, the three equations for the waiting line with two service facilities are

(q1) $$\Pr(1) = \frac{\lambda}{\mu} \Pr(0)$$

(r1) $$\Pr(2) = \frac{\mu + \lambda}{2\mu} \Pr(1) - \frac{\lambda}{2\mu} \Pr(0)$$

(t) $$\Pr(n) = \frac{2\mu + \lambda}{2\mu} \Pr(n - 1) - \frac{\lambda}{2\mu} \Pr(n - 2); \qquad n \geq 3.$$

In order to apply these equations, a fourth must also be used.

(u) $$\sum_{n=0}^{\infty} \Pr(n) = 1.$$

Equation (u) merely states that the sum of all the line-length probabilities is equal to 1.

Returning once again to an arrival rate $\lambda = 0.5$, and a departure rate $\mu = 1$, the case involving two service facilities may be solved by successive substitutions into Eq. (q1), (r1), and (t), and then utilizing Eq. (u):

From (q1), $$\Pr(1) = \frac{0.5}{1} \Pr(0)$$

$$= 0.5 \Pr(0).$$

From (r1), $$\Pr(2) = \frac{1 + 0.5}{2 \times 1} \Pr(1) - \frac{0.5}{2 \times 1} \Pr(0)$$

$$= 0.75 \, [0.5 \Pr(0)] - 0.25 \Pr(0)$$

$$= 0.125 \Pr(0).$$

From (t), $$\Pr(3) = \frac{2(1) + 0.5}{2(1)} \Pr(2) - \frac{0.5}{2(1)} \Pr(1)$$

$$= 1.25 \, [0.125 \Pr(0)] - 0.25 \, [0.5 \Pr(0)]$$

$$= 0.03125 \Pr(0).$$

From (t), $\Pr(4) = \dfrac{2(1) + 0.5}{2(1)} \Pr(3) - \dfrac{0.5}{2(1)} \Pr(2)$

$$= 1.25 \,[0.03125\,\Pr(0)] - 0.25\,[0.125\,\Pr(0)]$$

$$= 0.0078125\,\Pr(0).$$

The probabilities obtained so far may be summarized as follows:

$$(v) \begin{cases} \Pr(0) = 1.0000000\,\Pr(0) = 1 \; \Pr(0) \\[2mm] \Pr(1) = 0.5000000\,\Pr(0) = \dfrac{1}{2} \; \Pr(0) \\[2mm] \Pr(2) = 0.1250000\,\Pr(0) = \dfrac{1}{8} \; \Pr(0) \\[2mm] \Pr(3) = 0.0312500\,\Pr(0) = \dfrac{1}{32} \; \Pr(0) \\[2mm] \Pr(4) = 0.0078125\,\Pr(0) = \dfrac{1}{128}\,\Pr(0) \end{cases}$$

The objective is, of course, to find $\sum\limits_{n=0}^{\infty} \Pr(n)$, or in words, the sum of all the line-length probabilities. The foregoing series reveals, with the exception of the first term, a pattern that constitutes an infinite geometric series, the first term of which is $a = 1/2$ and the ratio is $r = 1/4$. The formula for finding the sum of an infinite series is

$$s = \frac{a}{1 - r}.$$

Substituting $a = 1/2$, $r = 1/4$,

$$s = \frac{1/2}{1 - 1/4} = \frac{2}{3}.$$

Hence,

$$\sum_{n=1}^{\infty} \Pr(n) = \frac{2}{3}\,\Pr(0)$$

and

$$\sum_{n=0}^{\infty} \Pr(n) = 1\frac{2}{3}\,\Pr(0).$$

Now utilizing Eq. (u), $\sum\limits_{n=0}^{\infty} \Pr(n) = 1$,

$$1\frac{2}{3}\,\Pr(0) = 1$$

$$\Pr(0) = \frac{3}{5} = 0.6.$$

The line-length probabilities are easily computed by using the relationships discovered in series (v), that is, Pr(1) is 1/2 Pr(0), and each succeeding probability is 1/4 that of the preceding one. In order to see clearly the effects of increasing the service facilities from one to two, the probabilities obtained for one facility are also presented:

Line Length	Probabilities	
	1 Service Facility	2 Service Facilities
0	0.5000	0.6000
1	0.2500	0.3000
2	0.1250	0.0750
3	0.0625	0.0187
4	0.0313	0.0047
5	0.0156	0.0012
6	0.0078	0.0003
7	0.0039	0.0001
8 or more	0.0039	0.0000
	1.0000	1.0000

Note that with one service facility, customers would be required to wait before being served (not including service time) 25 per cent of the time. By adding a second service facility, customers would be required to wait for service only 2.5 per cent of the time.

SEC. 12-6. MORE THAN TWO SERVICE FACILITIES

The extension of the case of two service facilities to any number k service facilities is relatively simple. The recursion relationships are shown in Figure. 12–5. The probability of a departure is increased by $\mu \Delta t$ for each service facility added, but when fewer service facilities are in use, the probability of a departure is the number of facilities in use times $\mu \Delta t$.

Figure 12–6 shows the case for $k = 3$, that is, three service facilities. The first column results in the same equation as (q), the case where $k = 2$, namely,

(w) $$\Pr(1) = \frac{\lambda}{\mu} \Pr(0).$$

Columns (2) and (3) will reduce to an equation similar to that derived from column (2) of Figure 12-3:

(x) $$\Pr(n) = \frac{(n-1)\mu + \lambda}{n\mu} \Pr(n-1) - \frac{\lambda}{n\mu} \Pr(n-2).$$

$t+\Delta t$

	Pr(0)	Pr(1)	Pr(2)	Pr(3)	Pr(4)	Pr(5)	Pr(6)
Pr(0)	$1-\lambda\Delta t$	$\lambda\Delta t$					
Pr(1)	$\mu\Delta t$	$1-\mu\Delta t$ $-\lambda\Delta t$	$\lambda\Delta t$				
Pr(2)		$2\mu\Delta t$	$1-2\mu\Delta t$ $-\lambda\Delta t$	$\lambda\Delta t$			
Pr(3)			$3\mu\Delta t$	$1-3\mu\Delta t$ $-\lambda\Delta t$	$\lambda\Delta t$		
Pr(4)				$4\mu\Delta t$	$1-4\mu\Delta t$ $-\lambda\Delta t$	$\lambda\Delta t$	
Pr(5)					$5\mu\Delta t$	$1-5\mu\Delta t$ $-\lambda\Delta t$	$\lambda\Delta t$
Pr(6)						$6\mu\Delta t$	$1-6\mu\Delta t$ $-\lambda\Delta t$

(left margin: t opposite Pr(3))

Fig. 12-5. The Recursion Relationships—IV

$t+\Delta t$

	Pr(0)	Pr(1)	Pr(2)	Pr(3)	Pr(4)	Pr(5)	Pr(6)
Pr(0)	$1-\lambda\Delta t$	$\lambda\Delta t$					
Pr(1)	$\mu\Delta t$	$1-\mu\Delta t$ $-\lambda\Delta t$	$\lambda\Delta t$				
Pr(2)		$2\mu\Delta t$	$1-2\mu\Delta t$ $-\lambda\Delta t$	$\lambda\Delta t$			
Pr(3)			$3\mu\Delta t$	$1-3\mu\Delta t$ $-\lambda\Delta t$	$\lambda\Delta t$		
Pr(4)				$3\mu\Delta t$	$1-3\mu\Delta t$ $-\lambda\Delta t$	$\lambda\Delta t$	
Pr(5)					$3\mu\Delta t$	$1-3\mu\Delta t$ $-\lambda\Delta t$	$\lambda\Delta t$
Pr(6)						$3\mu\Delta t$	$1-3\mu\Delta t$ $-\lambda\Delta t$

(left margin: t opposite Pr(3))

Fig. 12-6. The Recursion Relationships—$k=3$

For the case where $n = 2$, Eq. (x) becomes

(y) $$\mathrm{Pr}(2) = \frac{\mu+\lambda}{2\mu}\,\mathrm{Pr}(1) - \frac{\lambda}{2\mu}\,\mathrm{Pr}(0).$$

Equation (y) is, of course, the same as Eq. (r1). Equation (x) may be applied to $n = 2$ or $n = 3$. For $n \geq 4$, the equation is (from columns 4 and up),

(z) $$\Pr(n) = \frac{3\mu + \lambda}{3\mu}\Pr(n - 1) - \frac{\lambda}{3\mu}\Pr(n - 2).$$

If k is substituted for 3, Eq. (z) becomes

(aa) $$\Pr(n) = \frac{k\mu + \lambda}{k\mu}\Pr(n - 1) - \frac{\lambda}{k\mu}\Pr(n - 2).$$

Notice that Eq. (aa) holds for the case of $k = 2$:

(bb) $$\Pr(n) = \frac{2\mu + \lambda}{2\mu}\Pr(n - 1) - \frac{\lambda}{2\mu}\Pr(n - 2).$$

Equation (bb) is the same as Eq. (t).

The recursion relationships for $k = 4$ are shown in Figure 12-7. It will be seen that column (1) fits Eq. (w). Columns (2), (3), and (4) fit Eq. (x), and columns (5) and up fit Eq. (aa). Recursion relationships for $k = 5$, $k = 6$, and so forth, would soon convince the reader that Eq. (w), (x), and (aa) are completely general, and fit all k.

In summary, the equations for k service facilities are

(w) $$\Pr(1) = \frac{\lambda}{\mu}\Pr(0)$$

$t + \Delta t$

	Pr(0)	Pr(1)	Pr(2)	Pr(3)	Pr(4)	Pr(5)	Pr(6)
Pr(0)	$1 - \lambda\Delta t$	$\lambda\Delta t$					
Pr(1)	$\mu\lambda t$	$1 - \mu\Delta t$ $-\lambda\Delta t$	$\lambda\Delta t$				
Pr(2)		$2\mu\Delta t$	$1 - 2\mu\Delta t$ $-\lambda\Delta t$	$\lambda\Delta t$			
Pr(3)			$3\mu\Delta t$	$1 - 3\mu\Delta t$ $-\lambda\Delta t$	$\lambda\Delta t$		
Pr(4)				$4\mu\Delta t$	$1 - 4\mu\Delta t$ $-\lambda\Delta t$	$\lambda\Delta t$	
Pr(5)					$4\mu\Delta t$	$1 - 4\mu\Delta t$ $-\lambda\Delta t$	$\lambda\Delta t$
Pr(6)						$4\mu\Delta t$	$1 - 4\mu\Delta t$ $-\lambda\Delta t$

t is marked at the left of the Pr(3) row.

Fig. 12-7. The Recursion Relationships—$k = 4$

(x) $$\text{Pr}(n) = \frac{(n-1)\mu + \lambda}{n\mu} \text{Pr}(n-1) - \frac{\lambda}{n\mu} \text{Pr}(n-2);$$

for $n = 2, 3, \ldots, k$.

(aa) $$\text{Pr}(n) = \frac{k\mu + \lambda}{k\mu} \text{Pr}(n-1) - \frac{\lambda}{k\mu} \text{Pr}(n-2);$$

for $n \geq k + 1$.

An example will illustrate the use of these equations. Once again assume that $\lambda = 0.5$ and $\mu = 1$. The case for $k = 5$ is
From (w),

$$\text{Pr}(1) = \frac{0.5}{1} \text{Pr}(0)$$

$$= 0.5 \, \text{Pr}(0).$$

From (x), for Pr(2),

$$\text{Pr}(n) = \frac{(n-1)\mu + \lambda}{n\mu} \text{Pr}(n-1) - \frac{\lambda}{n\mu} \text{Pr}(n-2)$$

$$\text{Pr}(2) = \frac{(1)(1) + 0.5}{(2)(1)} \text{Pr}(1) - \frac{0.5}{(2)(1)} \text{Pr}(0)$$

$$= 0.75 \, [0.5 \, \text{Pr}(0)] - 0.25 \, \text{Pr}(0)$$

$$= 0.125 \, \text{Pr}(0).$$

From (x), for Pr(3),

$$\text{Pr}(3) = \frac{(2)(1) + 0.5}{(3)(1)} \text{Pr}(2) - \frac{0.5}{(3)(1)} \text{Pr}(1)$$

$$= 0.8333 \, [0.125 \, \text{Pr}(0)] - 0.16666 \, [0.5 \, \text{Pr}(0)]$$

$$= 0.0208333 \, \text{Pr}(0).$$

From (x), for Pr(4),

$$\text{Pr}(4) = \frac{(3)(1) + 0.5}{(4)(1)} \text{Pr}(3) - \frac{0.5}{(4)(1)} \text{Pr}(2)$$

$$= 0.875 \, [0.0208333 \, \text{Pr}(0)] - 0.125 \, [0.125 \, \text{Pr}(0)]$$

$$= 0.002604166 \, \text{Pr}(0).$$

From (x), for Pr(5),

$$Pr(5) = \frac{(4)(1) + 0.5}{(5)(1)} Pr(4) - \frac{0.5}{(5)(1)} Pr(3)$$

$$= 0.9 [0.002604166 \, Pr(0)] - 0.1 [0.0208333 \, Pr(0)]$$

$$= 0.0002604166 \, Pr(0).$$

From (aa), for Pr(6),

$$Pr(n) = \frac{k\mu + \lambda}{k\mu} Pr(n - 1) - \frac{\lambda}{k\mu} Pr(n - 2)$$

$$Pr(6) = \frac{(5)(1) + 0.5}{(5)(1)} Pr(5) - \frac{0.5}{(5)(1)} Pr(4)$$

$$= 1.1 [0.0002604166 \, Pr(0)] - 0.1 [0.002604166 \, Pr(0)]$$

$$= 0.00002604166 \, Pr(0).$$

From (aa), for Pr(7),

$$Pr(7) = \frac{(5)(1) + 0.5}{(5)(1)} Pr(6) - \frac{0.5}{(5)(1)} Pr(5)$$

$$= 1.1 [0.00002604166 \, Pr(0)] - 0.1 [0.0002604166 \, Pr(0)]$$

$$= 0.000002604166 \, Pr(0).$$

To summarize,

(cc)
$$\begin{cases} Pr(0) = 1.00000 \, Pr(0) \\ Pr(1) = 0.50000 \, Pr(0) \\ Pr(2) = 0.12500 \, Pr(0) \\ Pr(3) = 0.02083 \, Pr(0) \\ Pr(4) = 0.00260 \, Pr(0) \\ Pr(5) = 0.00026 \, Pr(0) \\ Pr(6) = 0.00003 \, Pr(0) \\ \underline{Pr(7) = 0.00000 \, Pr(0)} \end{cases}$$

$$\sum_{n=0}^{7} Pr(n) = 1.64872 \, Pr(0)$$

and

$$1.64872 \, Pr(0) = 1$$

$$Pr(0) = 0.6065.$$

The remaining probabilities are obtained by using the relationships of (cc). The following is a comparison for one-, two-, and five-service facilities respectively:

Line Length	Probabilities		
	Service Facilities		
	1	2	5
0	0.5000	0.6000	0.6065
1	0.2500	0.3000	0.3033
2	0.1250	0.0750	0.0758
3	0.0625	0.0187	0.0126
4	0.0313	0.0047	0.0016
5	0.0156	0.0012	0.0002
6	0.0078	0.0003	0.0000
7	0.0039	0.0001	0.0000
8 or more	0.0039	0.0000	0.0000
	1.0000	1.0000	1.0000

An analysis of the foregoing figures should differentiate between people actually being served and people waiting to be served. In the case of one service facility, there are people waiting to be served 25 per cent of the time. By adding another service facility this percentage is reduced to 2.5 per cent of the time. By increasing the number of service facilities to five, no person would have to wait before being served. All the preceding figures are based upon computations rounded to four decimal places.

SEC. 12-7. OTHER WAITING-LINE CONSIDERATIONS

The foregoing sections of this chapter must be regarded as being only an introduction to waiting-line or queuing theory. The theory itself will not be further developed here. (The interested reader should consult the bibliography at the end of the chapter.) There are, nevertheless, a few waiting-line considerations which should be discussed. The remainder of the chapter is devoted to these concepts.

Arrival Patterns

The discussion so far has been limited to one pattern of arrival—that following a Poisson process. Arrival patterns can, of course, be quite varied, for example, (1) complete regularity of arrivals, for instance, every minute on the minute; (2) approximate regularity of arrivals, for example, arrivals according to a predetermined schedule, but some arriving earlier than scheduled and some arriving later; (3) arrival patterns varying with time, for example, customers arriving at a restaurant tend to bunch at meal hours; (4) arrivals in a continuous flow, for example, oil arriving through a pipeline; and so forth.

Service Patterns

Service patterns also may be quite varied. Those discussed were (1) exponentially distributed service times, (2) constant-service times. Some other possibilities are (3) service times affected by queue length, for example, the server works faster when the queue is long; (4) customers of different types being assigned to specialized servers; (5) service availability affected by servers leaving the service facilities for personal or other reasons, and so forth.

Queue Discipline

Queue discipline refers to the order in which the customer is served. In the preceding sections of this chapter, the queue discipline supplied was that of first-come-first-served. Many other disciplines are possible: (1) last-come-first-served; (2) nonpreemptive priority, that is, the customer with priority is the next to be served; (3) preemptive priority, that is, the customer being served is replaced by the customer with priority; (4) formation of separate queues at each server, and first-come-first-served within each queue; and so forth.

Not all the foregoing waiting-line problems are currently amenable to mathematical analysis. Mathematical models have so far been developed only for the relatively simple problems. The more complex waiting-line problems must, at the moment, be analyzed by some other method, for example, by Monte Carlo simulation.

DISCUSSION QUESTIONS

12-1. Describe the *tree diagram* as a means of describing and analyzing a waiting-line problem.

12-2. What are *recursion equations*?

12-3. Describe the technique of using recursion equations in the analysis of waiting-line problems.

12-4. Explain the derivation of the probabilities used in Figure 12-1.

12-5. Why is the derivation of the line-length probability formulas for the constant-service-time case more difficult than for the exponential-service-time case?

12-6. Is it desirable conceptually to separate waiting time from service time?

What effect did adding a second service facility have upon waiting time? Upon service time? Having five service facilities had what effect upon waiting and service times?

12-7. Describe a number of possible arrival patterns.

12-8. Describe a number of service patterns.

12-9. What is meant by *queue discipline*? Describe a number of queue disciplines.

12-10. Can all waiting-line or queuing problems be analyzed mathematically? Discuss.

PROBLEMS

12-1. A waiting-line situation has an arrival distribution as follows:

Arrivals	Probability
0	0.4
1	0.5
2	0.1

Service times are constant at 1 minute. All events occur only on the whole minute. There is only 1 service facility. Compute the long-run line-length probabilities by using recursion equations.

12-2. A waiting-line situation has Poisson arrivals with $\lambda = 1$ and exponential service times with $\mu = 4$, and 1 service facility. Compute the long-run line-length probabilities.

12-3. Change Problem 12-2 to constant service times of $1/4$ minute (μ still equals 4). Compute the long-run line-length probabilities.

12-4. Add one more service facility (a total of two facilities) to the situation of Problem 12-2. Compute the long-run line-length probabilities. Compare the waiting time of Problems 12-2 and 12-4.

12-5. Add two service facilities (a total of three facilities) to the situation in Problem 12-2. Compute the long-run line-length probabilities. Compare the waiting time of Problems 12-2, 12-4, and 12-5.

12-6. A service counter serves an average of 48 customers in an 8-hour day. Service takes 6 minutes on the average. Customers arrive at random (Poisson) and service times are distributed exponentially. The manager wishes to assign enough clerks to the counter so that there are customers waiting to be served (not actually being served) not more than 25 per cent of the time. How many clerks should be assigned to the service counter?

BIBLIOGRAPHY

Churchman, C. West, Russell L. Ackoff, and E. Leonard Arnoff, *Introduction to Operations Research*. New York: John Wiley & Sons, Inc., 1957, pp. 389-415.

Cox, D. R., and Walter L. Smith, *Queues*. New York: John Wiley & Sons, Inc., 1961.

Flagle, Charles D., William H. Huggins, and Robert H. Roy (eds.), *Operations Research and Systems Engineering*. Baltimore, Md.: The Johns Hopkins Press, 1960, pp. 400–424.

Fry, Thornton C., *Probability and its Engineering Uses*. New York: D. Van Nostrand Company, Inc., 1928, pp. 321–88.

Morse, Philip M., *Queues, Inventories, and Maintenance*. New York: John Wiley & Sons, Inc., 1958.

Saaty, Thomas L., *Elements of Queuing Theory*. New York: McGraw-Hill Book Company, Inc., 1961.

_____, "Résumé of Useful Formulas in Queuing Theory," *Operations Research*, 5 (April, 1957), 161–200.

Sasieni, Maurice, Arthur Yaspan, and Lawrence Friedman, *Operations Research— Methods and Problems*. New York: John Wiley & Sons, Inc., 1959, pp. 125–46.

13

Quality Control Charts

The West Coast Aircraft Corporation is endeavoring to improve the control over the quality of its outgoing products. At present it relies on either 100 per cent inspection or on several systems of sampling. The 100 per cent inspection has occasionally proved ineffective in two ways: (1) the costs tend to be very high, often exceeding the costs estimated by the engineers; (2) the inspection is made at the end of the manufacturing cycle, and hence provides few controls over the manufacturing process. On the other hand, the systems of inspection by sampling have sometimes failed effectively to maintain satisfactory quality in the outgoing product.

The quality control department has suggested that quality control charts be adopted on a trial basis. The control charts would, it was asserted,

1. Be relatively inexpensive.
2. Introduce control at the point of manufacture, thus greatly reducing the production of spoiled work or pieces which must be reworked.
3. Inform management whether the manufacturing processes used would produce work within specified tolerances.
4. Aid in the isolation and correction of sources of trouble.
5. Tell management when not to look for trouble.
6. Help in ascertaining the most economical tool settings, and so forth.

Three phases of the manufacturing process were chosen for the trial tests. These phases would permit the use of d charts, p charts, c charts, and $\bar{X}$ and R charts, the latter two (or sometimes $\bar{X}$ and σ charts) ordinarily being used in conjunction to control one measurement in the production process.

Some products require testing as a separate operation away from the point of manufacture. The West Coast Aircraft Corporation produces a small tank which must withstand a pressure of 2000 lb per square inch without leaking. Thus the result of the inspection is a pass-or-fail situation. Either the d chart, which is designed to control the *number* of items defective, or the p chart, which is designed to control the *percentage* of items defective, is, therefore, the logical choice.

One of the final products of the West Coast Aircraft Corporation is the T-7000 Trainer. Before turning the planes over to the Air Force, a final inspection is made, and the number of defects discovered are recorded and corrected. The c chart is designed to control the number of defects per unit, and hence is applicable here.

Among the components of the T-7000 is a small shaft the diameter of which must be kept within specified limits. Such situations as this permit the use of perhaps the most effective of the control charts—the $\bar{X}$ and R charts. These are called *control charts of variables,* $\bar{X}$ standing for the average value of the dimension being controlled, and R for the range within which this dimension is being held. For sample sizes larger than than 12, the $\bar{X}$ and σ charts are generally substituted for the $\bar{X}$ and R charts.

SEC. 13-2. BASIC CONTROL CHART CONCEPTS

The charts under consideration in this chapter are frequently referred to as *Shewhart control charts*. The basic theory and mechanics were developed by Dr. W. A. Shewhart of the Bell Telephone Laboratories in the 1920's. Since then there have been many refinements to the basic Shewhart techniques.

Underlying control chart theory is statistical sampling theory. In its most elementary form, this theory states that a sample taken from a population or universe tends to resemble that universe, and that the larger the sample, the closer that resemblance is likely to be. Many of the phenomena in industry are distributed in a manner which will more or less closely approximate the normal distribution. Thus, if a machinist attempts to turn 1000 pieces, each with a diameter of 1 in., few, if any, would be exactly 1 in. in diameter. Assume that Figure 13-1 shows the diameter of each piece recorded as it is produced. The dimensions would tend to scatter around 1 in., most of them quite close, some a distance away.

Now assume that Figure 13-1 is turned on end so that all the recorded points pile up at the bottom. The pile of points would tend to form a

Fig. 13-1. Graph of Dimensions of Pieces

symmetrical curve as is shown in Figure 13-2. Under the assumption that this distribution is normal,[1] 99.73 per cent of the dimensions will be within plus or minus three standard deviations. If the standard deviation (σ) is 0.001 in., then about 997 of the diameters will be within the range of 0.997–1.003 in. With an engineering requirement of the piece of 1 in. $\pm$ 0.003 in., approximately three of the 1000 units would be outside acceptable requirements.

Under the circumstances previously stated, it is quite likely that the distribution of diameters would closely approximate the normal distribution. Under other circumstances the distribution may be *skewed* (one tail longer than the other), *leptokurtic* (more peaked than is a normal curve), or *platykurtic* (less peaked than is a normal curve). In practical control chart work, this difficulty is to a large extent avoided by using a statistic other than the individual unit. Examples are the *sample proportion*, which

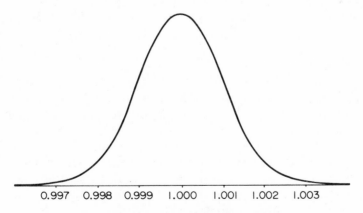

Fig. 13-2. Distribution of Dimensions of Pieces

[1]This assumption is, of course, not strictly valid, since a normal distribution requires an infinite number of cases, and here there are only 1000 cases.

tends to be distributed according to the binomial distribution; the *number of defects per unit*, which tends to be distributed according to the Poisson distribution; and the *sample mean*, which tends to be distributed according to the normal distribution.

SEC. 13-3. THE *d* CHART

The *d* chart is used in those cases where it is desired to control the number of defective items and when the test applied results in a pass-or-fail situation. The pressure tank inspection (see Sec. 13-2) is such a case. The *d* stands for the number of defectives per sample. The sample, in many instances, is the result of a 100 per cent inspection for a given period, such as an hour, day, and so forth. The universe would then be the entire production run. Control chart techniques are valid only so long as a constant-cause system exists. A *constant-cause system* implies that variations in the product are the result of chance rather than being caused by some controllable element in the process. Therefore, even during a given production run, one constant-cause system can be replaced by another if production processes are changed or any other changes are introduced into the system.

Figure 13-3 shows the results of the first 25 days' inspections of the pressure tanks. Note that each day's production was the same, 100 units. Uniform sample size is highly desirable when using the *d* chart. Where sample size varies, particularly if the variation is large, the *d* chart becomes difficult to read, and the *p* chart (Sec. 13-4) is the better choice.

Data from 25 inspections were collected before setting up the control chart. This is generally considered to be the minimum desirable number of samples for the first computations. When, however, it is urgent that the control chart be set up, or when each sample requires a long period to collect, the number may be reduced to as low as ten. New control chart limits should then be computed when more data are gathered.

If the production and inspection processes for the pressure tank are operating under a constant-cause system, the number of defectives per inspection sample should follow closely the binomial distribution where $n = 100$ and $\bar{p} = \bar{d}/n$ (that is, $\bar{p}$ is expressed as a decimal fraction). From Figure 13-3, $\bar{d}$ (the mean number of defectives per sample) is equal to 5, and $\bar{p}$ is therefore equal to $5/100 = 0.05$.

Hence, the pertinent binomial is

$$(0.05 + 0.95)^{100}.$$

Sample	Size	No. Defective (d)
1	100	4
2	100	2
3	100	3
4	100	6
5	100	1
6	100	6
7	100	9
8	100	5
9	100	6
10	100	5
11	100	4
12	100	14
13	100	3
14	100	6
15	100	4
16	100	1
17	100	6
18	100	6
19	100	4
20	100	5
21	100	4
22	100	8
23	100	6
24	100	0
25	100	7

$$\sum d = 125; \qquad \bar{d} = 5$$

Fig. 13-3. Results of First 25 Daily Inspections of Pressure Tanks

The expansion of this binomial is shown in Figure 13-4. (See Sec. 9-3 for the expansion of the binomial.) The d chart is based upon this relationship.

In setting up the d chart, a horizontal line is drawn at $\bar{d}$ (see Figure 13-5), since $\bar{d}$ is the expected value of d' (the mean number of defectives for the entire production run). Given a constant-cause system, the daily values of d will fluctuate around $\bar{d}$ (or, more precisely, d'), ranging from $d = 0$ to $d = 13$ or more.

Notice, however, that 13 or more defectives will occur, on the average, only once in 1000 samples (see Figure 13-4). Similarly, samples with no defectives would occur, on the average, six times in 1000 samples. Therefore, the occurrence of samples with either no defectives or with 13 or more defectives would be very rare. In fact, such samples would be so unusual that the analyst would be justified in assuming that they did not "just happen," but were caused by an extraneous factor introduced into the basic cause system. Such extraneous causes are referred to as *assignable causes*, of which more will be said later. In order to isolate these unusual samples, *upper* and *lower control limits* are drawn on the d chart. Because 13 or more are to be isolated, the upper control limit (UCL) is

No. Defective (d)	Probability
0	0.006
1	0.031
2	0.081
3	0.140
4	0.178
5	0.180
6	0.150
7	0.106
8	0.065
9	0.035
10	0.017
11	0.007
12	0.003
13 or more	0.001
	1.000

Fig. 13-4. The Probabilities Related to d when $n = 100$ and $\bar{d} = 5$

drawn at 12.5. Similarly, the lower control limit (LCL) is drawn at 0.5 (Figure 13-5). The d values from the samples are then plotted on the chart.

Two samples were sufficiently unusual to draw the analyst's attention. Sample 12 exceeded the upper control limit, and sample 24 the lower. The objective is to examine the conditions existing on those days in order to ascertain, if possible, the assignable causes of these unusual variations.

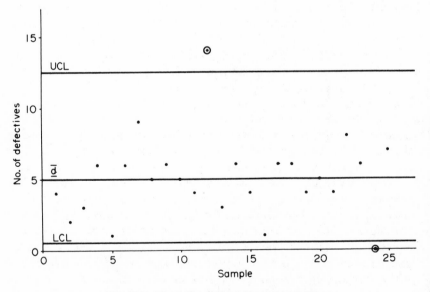

Fig. 13-5. The d Chart Based Upon Probabilities

In the case of sample 12, it is quite apparent that the cause, if discovered, should be eliminated where possible. The reason for investigating the low variation is not so readily seen. At least two types of causes may be present (1) the inspection process had failed, and there actually were defectives. The objective would be, of course, to eliminate such failures. (2) A temporary improvement in the production process had occurred. The objective here would be to adopt this improvement and thereby reduce d', the mean number of defectives.

The foregoing procedures for setting up the d chart are somewhat unwieldy because one requirement is the expansion of the pertinent binomial. A simpler, but less accurate, technique is to use the standard deviation of the binomial ($\sqrt{np'q'}$). It will be recalled that, given a normal distribution, $\pm 3\sigma$ will take in 97.73 per cent of the observations. The binomial distribution is approximated by the normal when n is large, even though p is quite small as compared to q. Therefore, in practice $3\sqrt{n\bar{p}\bar{q}}$ is used to set the control limits. Notice that $\bar{p}$ and $\bar{q}$ are substituted for p' and q', respectively.

$$\text{Upper control limit} = \bar{d} + 3\sqrt{n\bar{p}\bar{q}}$$
$$= 5 + 3\sqrt{(100)(0.05)(0.95)}$$
$$= 5 + 6.54$$
$$= 11.54.$$
$$\text{Lower control limit} = \bar{d} + 3\sqrt{n\bar{p}\bar{q}}$$
$$= 5 - 6.54$$
$$= -1.54.$$

Since d cannot be less than zero, the lower control limit is set at zero when the computed LCL is a negative value. The control chart using these limits is presented in Figure 13-6. Referring once again to the probabilities listed in Figure 13-4, the d chart of Figure 13-6 would show approximately three out of 1000 legitimate samples as being out of control. Thus, out of the average 1000 samples, the analyst would search three times for nonexistent assignable causes.

The d chart of Figure 13-6 should be regarded as merely the result of preliminary computations that are to be refined as (1) more data are collected, and (2) the process is retained under control and improved upon as a result of the elimination of assignable causes. An immediate refinement should be made by eliminating the one out-of-control sample (sample 12'), and then computing a new $\bar{d}$, UCL, and LCL:

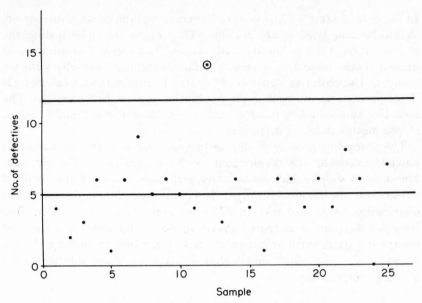

Fig. 13-6. The d Chart Based Upon Standard Deviations

$$\bar{d} = \frac{125 - 14}{25 - 1} = 4.625$$

$$\text{UCL} = 4.625 + 3\sqrt{(100)(0.04625)(0.95375)}$$

$$= 4.625 + 6.301$$

$$= 10.926$$

$$\text{LCL} = 4.625 - 6.301$$

$$= -1.676 \quad \text{or} \quad \text{LCL} = 0.$$

These values would be used to chart the succeeding samples.

The d Chart with Varying Sample Sizes

It was mentioned earlier that the d chart becomes quite unwieldy when the samples vary in size. The chart is difficult to interpret because the $\bar{d}$ line is not a straight horizontal line, but varies with the sample size. For this reason, the p chart is recommended under such circumstances. Nevertheless, for completeness, the techniques of constructing such a chart are presented at this point.

Column (2) of Figure 13-7 shows the 25 samples (n) of unequal size with the number of defectives (d) in column (3). It is necessary to compute $\bar{p}$, the weighted average proportion of defectives:

$$\bar{p} = \frac{\sum d}{\sum n} = \frac{1204}{12040} = 0.10.$$

The expected number of defectives for each sample size will then be

$$E(d) = \bar{p}n.$$

These values are shown in column (4).

The control limits are to be set at 3σ from $E(d)$. The formula for 3σ is

$$3\sigma = 3\sqrt{n\bar{p}\bar{q}}.$$

Sample No.	Sample Size (n)	Number Defective (d)	E(d) = $\bar{p}$n	$\sqrt{n}$	$3\sqrt{n(0.1)(0.9)}$	UCL	LCL
(1)	(2)	(3)	(4)	(5)	(6)	(7)	(8)
1	158	16	15.8	12.6	11.3	27.1	4.5
2	92	7	9.2	9.6	8.6	17.8	0.6
3	411	66	41.1	20.3	18.2	59.3	22.9
4	745	52	74.5	27.3	24.6	99.1	49.9
5	99	14	9.9	10.0	9.0	18.9	0.9
6	724	58	72.4	26.9	24.2	96.6	48.2
7	674	87	67.4	26.0	23.4	90.8	44.0
8	550	33	55.0	23.4	21.1	76.1	33.9
9	716	85	71.6	26.8	24.1	95.7	47.5
10	359	29	35.9	18.9	17.1	53.0	18.8
11	419	44	41.9	20.5	18.4	60.3	23.5
12	968	84	96.8	31.1	28.0	124.8	68.8
13	200	14	20.0	14.1	12.7	32.7	7.3
14	458	64	45.8	21.4	19.3	65.1	26.5
15	384	29	38.4	19.6	17.6	56.0	20.8
16	190	17	19.0	13.8	12.4	31.4	6.6
17	676	54	67.6	26.0	23.4	91.0	44.2
18	631	76	63.1	25.1	22.6	85.7	40.5
19	390	47	39.0	19.7	17.8	56.8	21.2
20	557	46	55.7	23.6	21.2	76.8	34.5
21	299	42	29.9	17.3	15.6	45.5	14.3
22	786	79	78.6	28.0	25.2	103.8	53.4
23	706	53	70.6	26.6	23.9	94.5	46.7
24	65	9	6.5	8.1	7.3	13.8	0.0
25	783	99	78.3	28.0	25.2	103.5	53.1
	12040	1204					

$$\bar{p} = \frac{1204}{12,040} = 0.10$$

Fig. 13-7. Data for the d Chart with Unequal Sample Sizes

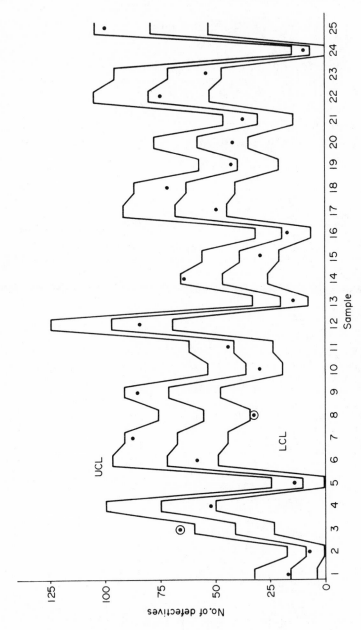

Fig. 13-8. The *d* Chart with Unequal Sample Sizes

This can be written

$$3\sigma = (3)(\sqrt{\bar{p}\bar{q}})(\sqrt{n})$$
$$= 3\sqrt{(0.1)(0.9)}\sqrt{n}$$
$$= 0.9\sqrt{n}.$$

Column (5) (Figure 13-7) shows the $\sqrt{n}$, and column (6) is 3σ or $0.9\sqrt{n}$. The control limits are then computed:

$$\text{UCL} = \bar{p}n + 3\sigma$$
$$\text{LCL} = \bar{p}n - 3\sigma.$$

These are presented in columns (7) and (8).

The data contained in Figure 13-7, columns (4), (7), and (8), are plotted in Figure 13-8. Samples 3 and 8 are out of control. These samples should be investigated for assignable causes. The data from samples 3 and 8 should then be deleted and a new $\bar{p}$ computed. The reader should at this point refer to Figure 13-11 to compare the presentation of the p chart with unequal sample sizes. One glance reveals the greater ease with which the latter chart can be read.

SEC. 13-4. THE p CHART

The p chart is designed to control the *percentage* or *proportion* of defectives per sample. Since the *number* of defectives (d) can be converted into a percentage expressed as a decimal fraction merely by dividing d by the sample size, the p chart may be used in lieu of the d chart. The p chart has at least two advantages over the d chart: (1) Expressing the defectives as a percentage or fraction of production is more meaningful and more generally understood than would be the statement of the number of defectives. The latter concept must be related in some way to the total number produced. (2) Where the size of the sample varies from sample to sample, the p chart permits a more straightforward and less cluttered presentation. The p chart requires, however, that the division d/n be made. This additional computation may be regarded as a slight disadvantage.

The same basic data are used for either chart. When the sample size remains constant from sample to sample, the primary difference lies in the computation of the control limits. The d chart control limits are set at $\bar{d}$ plus or minus three standard deviations. The p chart control limits are set at $\bar{p}$ plus or minus three standard errors of the proportion.

The formula for the standard error is

$$\sigma_p = \frac{\sigma_x}{n},$$

where

$$\sigma_x = \sqrt{np'q'}.$$

Therefore,

$$\sigma_p = \frac{\sqrt{np'q'}}{n}$$

$$= \sqrt{\frac{p'q'}{n}}.$$

Once again $\bar{p}$ and $\bar{q}$ are used for p' and q', and the computation for the control limits, using the data from Figure 13-3, is

$$\text{UCL} = \bar{p} + 3\sqrt{\frac{\bar{p}\bar{q}}{n}}$$

$$= 0.05 + 3\sqrt{(0.05)(0.95)/100}$$

$$= 0.05 + 0.0654$$

$$= 0.1154.$$

$$\text{LCL} = 0.05 - 0.0654$$

$$= -0.0154 \quad \text{or} \quad \text{LCL} = 0.$$

The control chart is shown in Figure 13-9. Its appearance is quite similar to that of the d chart of Figure 13-6.

Sample 12 again shows out of control. New values for $\bar{p}$, UCL, and LCL should be computed with sample 12 eliminated. The new values are

$$\bar{p} = \frac{125 - 14}{2500 - 100} = 0.04625$$

$$\text{UCL} = 0.04625 + 3\sqrt{(0.04625)(0.95375)/100}$$

$$= 0.04625 + 0.06301$$

$$= 0.10926.$$

$$\text{LCL} = 0.04625 - 0.06301$$

$$= -0.01676 \quad \text{or} \quad \text{LCL} = 0.$$

These values would be used to chart succeeding samples.

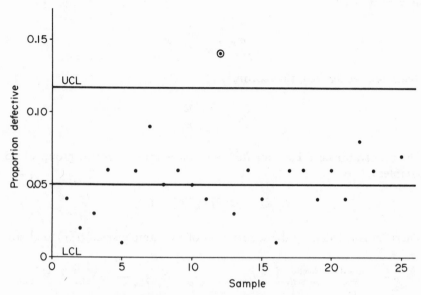

Fig. 13-9. The *p* Chart with Uniform Sample Sizes

The p Chart with Varying Sample Sizes

Frequently, daily or hourly production runs are not equal in numbers produced, and as a result the sample size varies from sample to sample. The *p* chart may still be used under these circumstances, but for best results, it is necessary to compute separate control limits for each sample size. This usually means that new control limits must be computed each day.

Assume 25 samples with sizes shown in column (2) of Figure 13-10. The number of defectives for each sample is presented in column (3). The average proportion ($\bar{p}$) is the weighted average and is obtained by the division:

$$\frac{\sum d}{\sum n} = \frac{1204}{12,040} = 0.10.$$

It is necessary next to compute the proportion defective per sample, d/n [column (4)].

The formula for the standard error of the proportion,

$$\sigma_p = \sqrt{\frac{\bar{p}\bar{q}}{n}},$$

may be written

$$\sigma_p = \frac{\sqrt{\bar{p}\bar{q}}}{\sqrt{n}}.$$

Since $3\sigma_p$ are desired, this becomes

$$3\sigma_p = \frac{3\sqrt{\bar{p}\bar{q}}}{\sqrt{n}}.$$

The numerator need be computed only once for the entire group of 25 samples:

$$3\sqrt{\bar{p}\bar{q}} = 3\sqrt{(0.1)(0.9)} = 0.9.$$

Then 0.9 is divided by the square root of the sample size ($\sqrt{n}$) to obtain

Sample No. (1)	Sample Size (n) (2)	Number of Defectives (d) (3)	d/n (4)	$\sqrt{n}$ (5)	$0.9/\sqrt{n}$ (6)	UCL (7)	LCL (8)
1	158	16	0.101	12.570	0.072	0.172	0.028
2	92	7	0.076	9.592	0.094	0.194	0.006
3	411	66	0.161	20.273	0.044	0.144	0.056
4	745	52	0.070	27.295	0.033	0.133	0.067
5	99	14	0.141	9.950	0.091	0.191	0.009
6	724	58	0.080	26.907	0.034	0.134	0.066
7	674	87	0.129	25.962	0.035	0.135	0.065
8	550	33	0.060	23.452	0.038	0.138	0.062
9	716	85	0.119	26.758	0.034	0.134	0.066
10	359	29	0.081	18.947	0.048	0.148	0.052
11	419	44	0.105	20.469	0.044	0.144	0.056
12	968	84	0.087	31.113	0.029	0.129	0.071
13	200	14	0.070	14.142	0.064	0.164	0.036
14	458	64	0.140	21.401	0.042	0.142	0.058
15	384	29	0.076	19.596	0.046	0.146	0.054
16	190	17	0.089	13.784	0.065	0.165	0.035
17	676	54	0.080	26.000	0.035	0.135	0.065
18	631	76	0.120	25.120	0.036	0.136	0.064
19	390	47	0.121	19.748	0.046	0.146	0.054
20	557	46	0.083	23.601	0.038	0.138	0.062
21	299	42	0.111	17.292	0.052	0.152	0.048
22	786	79	0.101	28.036	0.032	0.132	0.068
23	706	53	0.075	26.571	0.034	0.134	0.066
24	65	9	0.139	8.062	0.112	0.212	0.000
25	783	99	0.126	27.982	0.032	0.132	0.068
	12,040	1204					

$$\bar{p} = \frac{1204}{12,040} = 0.10$$

Fig. 13-10. Data for the p Chart with Unequal Sample Sizes

$3\sigma_p$. The $\sqrt{n}$ is given in column (5) and $3\sigma_p$ in column (6). The UCL [Column (7)] is then computed by

$$UCL = \bar{p} + 3\sigma_p$$
$$= 0.1 + 3\sigma_p.$$

The LCL [column (8)] is similarly computed:

$$LCL = \bar{p} - 3\sigma_p$$
$$= 0.1 - 3\sigma_p.$$

The resulting p chart is shown in Figure 13-11. A horizontal line is drawn at $\bar{p} = 0.10$. The UCL and LCL are not straight, as is the case with constant sample sizes, but vary in distance from the $\bar{p}$ line in proportion to the square root of the sample size. Samples 3 and 8 are out of control and should be investigated for assignable causes. The data from these samples should then be eliminated and a new $\bar{p}$ computed.

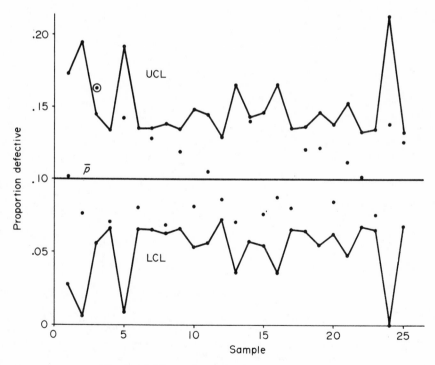

Fig. 13-11. The p Chart with Unequal Sample Sizes

SEC. 13-5. THE c CHART

The c chart is designed to control the number of defects per unit. The unit under consideration is any series of production where the units remain constant as to size and basic characteristics, and where each unit may have defects ranging from zero on up. Examples of such units are subassemblies, sheets of metal, lengths of wire, and so forth. Assuming the presence of a constant-cause system, these defects will tend to occur at random, and therefore the number of defects will tend to conform to the Poisson distribution. (See Sec. 10-1 for a discussion of the Poisson distribution.)

The assembled aircraft, T-7000, was selected for the trial application of the c chart. Figure 13-12 shows the number of defects found on the final inspection of the first 25 planes. The average number of defects is

$$\bar{c} = \frac{\sum c}{n} = \frac{375}{25} = 15.$$

Plane No.	No. of Defects (c)
1	12
2	17
3	11
4	15
5	13
6	12
7	15
8	17
9	18
10	8
11	10
12	16
13	22
14	12
15	20
16	15
17	15
18	20
19	14
20	21
21	7
22	19
23	16
24	15
25	15

$$\sum c = 375; \quad \bar{c} = \frac{375}{25} = 15$$

Fig. 13-12. Results of Inspection of First 25 Planes

Therefore, in the Poisson formula,

$$Pr(c) = \frac{e^{-\bar{c}}\bar{c}^c}{c!},$$

$\bar{c}$, the mean number of defects, is equal to 15. The probability of obtaining various values of c is shown in Figure 13-13.

No. of Defects (c)	Probability	No. of Defects (c)	Probability
1–3	0.000	17	0.085
4	0.001	18	0.071
5	0.002	19	0.056
6	0.005	20	0.042
7	0.010	21	0.030
8	0.020	22	0.020
9	0.032	23	0.013
10	0.049	24	0.008
11	0.066	25	0.005
12	0.083	26	0.003
13	0.096	27	0.002
14	0.102	28	0.001
15	0.102	29 or more	0.000
16	0.096		

Fig. 13-13. Probabilities of Number of Defects when λ (or $\bar{c}$) = 15

The control chart may now be constructed. A horizontal line at $\bar{c} = 15$ is drawn (see Figure 13-14). Figure 13-13 could be used to set the upper and lower control limits. For example, if the LCL were set at 4.5 and the UCL at 27.5, then 99.9 per cent of the results of the constant-cause system would fall between the control lines. Any count outside of these limits would be regarded as resulting from some extraneous cause to be investigated and corrected. This method would require, of course, a table of probabilities similar to that of Figure 13-13.

The more usual method is to use $\bar{c} \pm 3\sigma$ for the control limits. It will be recalled that in the Poisson distribution, $\bar{c} = \sigma^2$, and hence $\sigma = \sqrt{\bar{c}}$. The control limits may then be computed:

$$UCL = \bar{c} + 3\sqrt{\bar{c}}$$
$$= 15 + 3\sqrt{15}$$
$$= 15 + 11.62$$
$$= 26.62.$$
$$LCL = 15 - 11.62$$
$$= 3.38.$$

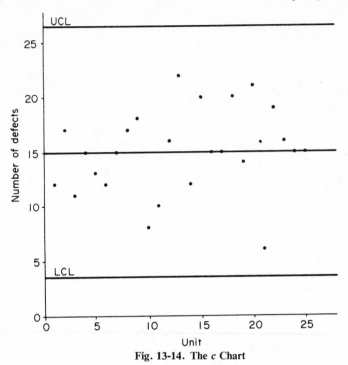

Fig. 13-14. The *c* **Chart**

These control limits are drawn on Figure 13-14, and the defects per unit plotted. The assembling of the T-7000 appears to be well under control with an average of 15 defects per plane. That the assembling process is under control does not imply that the average number of defects per plane cannot be reduced. To achieve such a reduction, however, would probably require changes in the assembling techniques.

SEC. 13-6. THE $\bar{X}$ AND σ CHARTS

The $\bar{X}$ and σ charts are frequently called *control charts of variables* and are designed to control anything measurable, such as lengths, diameters, weights, and so forth. The selection of the diameter of a shaft as the trial application is thus quite appropriate.

The $\bar{X}$ Chart Based Upon σ

The shaft under consideration has a specified diameter of 3 in. with a tolerance of $\pm$ 0.003 in. Samples of five shafts are measured. The samples are taken every two hours, and are of the last shafts produced before the inspection time. Figure 13-15, column (2), shows, in thousandths of an inch, the variations of the shaft diameters from 3.000 in. for the first 25 samples. That is, the first measurement of item 1 of sample 1 (0.5) stands for a shaft diameter of 3.0005. Column (3) is the arithmetic mean of the five samples. For sample 1, this is

$$\bar{X} = \frac{\Sigma X}{n} = \frac{0.5 + (-0.7) + 1.0 + (-0.1) + 0.9}{5} = 0.32.$$

The center line of the $\bar{X}$ chart is the grand mean or the mean of the $\bar{X}$'s, called $\bar{\bar{X}}$. In this case,

$$\bar{\bar{X}} = \frac{\Sigma \bar{X}}{k} = \frac{0.32 + 0.30 + (-0.54) \cdots + 0.48}{25} = -0.0096.$$

(1)	(2) Piece					(3)	(4)	(5)
Sample	1	2	3	4	5	$\bar{X}$	σ	R
1	0.5	−0.7	1.0	−0.1	0.9	0.32	0.640	1.7
2	0.6	2.1	−0.6	−0.7	0.1	0.30	1.018	2.8
3	−0.4	−1.7	0.6	0.2	−1.4	−0.54	0.889	2.3
4	2.1	−0.1	−1.4	1.3	−1.5	0.08	1.434	3.6
5	0.3	−1.0	−0.3	−2.0	−0.1	−0.62	0.808	2.3
6	1.9	1.1	0.1	−0.6	−0.2	0.46	0.913	2.5
7	0.1	0.3	0.3	−0.2	0.2	0.14	0.185	0.5
8	0.4	−0.6	0.8	0.2	0.9	0.34	0.535	1.5
9	−0.3	0.8	−0.3	1.3	0.8	0.46	0.647	1.6
10	1.0	−1.0	1.4	−2.0	1.3	0.14	1.382	3.4
11	0.9	−1.7	0.5	−1.8	0.5	−0.32	1.177	2.7
12	−1.0	−0.2	0.3	−0.1	0.1	−0.18	0.445	1.3
13	0.0	1.3	1.0	1.2	−0.6	0.58	0.749	1.9
14	0.3	0.0	−0.1	0.2	0.3	0.14	0.162	0.4
15	−0.7	0.5	1.0	−0.9	1.0	0.18	0.823	1.9
16	−1.8	−1.0	−1.2	−1.1	−1.7	−1.36	0.326	0.8
17	0.2	−1.0	−1.6	1.0	−0.5	−0.38	0.909	2.6
18	−1.0	0.3	−0.2	−1.5	−0.5	−0.58	0.624	1.8
19	−0.3	−0.9	0.6	−0.1	−0.1	−0.16	0.480	1.5
20	0.0	0.2	−0.6	0.5	2.5	0.52	1.047	3.1
21	−1.0	−0.5	0.2	0.3	−0.2	−0.24	0.476	1.3
22	1.8	−0.1	0.1	0.0	−3.7	−0.38	1.802	5.5
23	−1.0	−0.9	0.4	1.1	0.3	−0.02	0.808	2.1
24	−0.1	−2.0	0.0	2.5	1.6	0.40	1.550	4.5
25	0.3	0.6	1.7	−0.9	0.7	0.48	0.835	2.6
						−0.24	20.664	56.2

$$\bar{\bar{X}} = \frac{\Sigma \bar{X}}{k} = \frac{-0.24}{25} = -0.0096; \qquad \bar{\sigma} = \frac{\Sigma \sigma}{k} = \frac{20.664}{25} = 0.927; \qquad \bar{R} = \frac{\Sigma R}{k}$$

$$= \frac{56.2}{25} = 2.248$$

Fig. 13-15. Data for the $\bar{X}$, σ, and R Charts

Thus the center line on the $\bar{X}$ chart, Figure 13-16 (a), is drawn at 2.9999904 in. or 3.0000 in. (rounded).

The control limits are then set at plus or minus three standard errors of the mean $(\sigma_{\bar{x}})$:

$$\text{UCL} = \bar{\bar{X}} + 3\sigma_{\bar{x}}$$
$$\text{LCL} = \bar{\bar{X}} - 3\sigma_{\bar{x}}.$$

The formula for $\sigma_{\bar{x}}$ is

$$\sigma_{\bar{x}} = \frac{\sigma'}{\sqrt{n}}.$$

The standard deviation of the universe (σ') is not known but must be estimated from $\bar{\sigma}$, the mean standard deviation of the samples. To get $\bar{\sigma}$, σ is computed for each sample. The formula,

$$\sigma = \sqrt{\frac{\Sigma(X - \bar{X})^2}{n}},$$

may be used. For sample 1, this is

$$(0.5 - 0.32)^2 = \quad (0.18)^2 = 0.0324$$
$$(-0.7 - 0.32)^2 = (-1.02)^2 = 1.0404$$
$$(1.0 - 0.32)^2 = \quad (0.68)^2 = 0.4624$$
$$(-0.1 - 0.32)^2 = (-0.42)^2 = 0.1764$$
$$(0.9 - 0.32)^2 = \quad (0.58)^2 = \underline{0.3364}$$
$$\Sigma (X - \bar{X})^2 = 2.0480$$

$$\sigma = \sqrt{\frac{2.048}{5}} = \sqrt{0.4096} = 0.640.$$

The standard deviations of the 25 samples are listed in column (4) of Figure 13-15. The mean standard deviation is

$$\bar{\sigma} = \frac{0.640 + 1.018 + \cdots + 0.835}{25} = 0.927.$$

Unfortunately, $\bar{\sigma}$ is not an unbiased estimator of σ'. Instead, $\bar{\sigma}$ must be multiplied by a correction factor, called c'. Figure 13-17 shows the factor

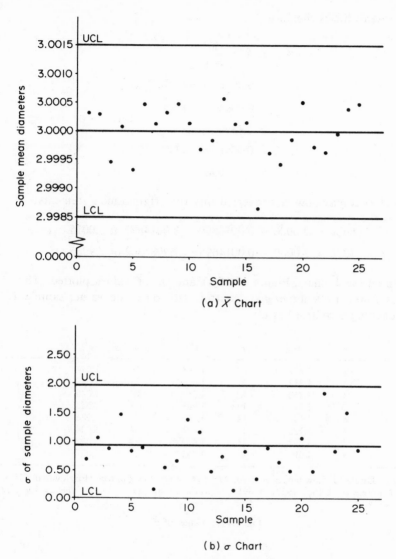

(a) $\bar{X}$ Chart

(b) σ Chart

Fig. 13-16. The $\bar{X}$ and σ Charts

c' for various values of n. (These values are also listed in Appendix F.) Therefore, σ' is computed

$$\sigma' = \bar{\sigma} c'$$
$$= (0.927)(1.1895)$$
$$= 1.1027.$$

The control limits then are

$$UCL = \bar{\bar{X}} + \frac{3\sigma'}{\sqrt{n}}$$
$$= 0.0096 + 3(1.1027)/\sqrt{5}$$
$$= 0.0096 + 1.4794$$
$$= 1.4890.$$
$$LCL = 0.0096 - 1.4794$$
$$= -1.4698.$$

These limits may now be converted into the original measurements:

$$UCL = 3.0000 + 0.0014890 = 3.0014890 \text{ or } 3.0015$$
$$LCL = 3.0000 - 0.0014698 = 2.9985302 \text{ or } 2.9985$$

drawn on the $\bar{X}$ chart, Figure 13-16(a), and the $\bar{X}$ values plotted. The $\bar{X}$ values appear to be under good control, with only one value, sample 16, approaching a control limit.

n	c'	n	c'	n	c'
2	1.772	10	1.084	18	1.044
3	1.382	11	1.075	19	1.042
4	1.253	12	1.068	20	1.040
5	1.190	13	1.063	21	1.038
6	1.151	14	1.058	22	1.036
7	1.126	15	1.054	23	1.034
8	1.108	16	1.050	24	1.033
9	1.094	17	1.047	25	1.031

SOURCE: Dudley J. Cowden, *Statistical Methods in Quality Control* (Englewood Cliffs, N.J.: Prentice-Hall, Inc., 1957), p. 691. (*Reproduced by permission of the author and publisher.*)

Fig. 13-17. Values of c'

Simplified Computation of Control Limits for the $\bar{X}$ Chart Based upon σ

The formula for the control limits is

$$CL = \bar{\bar{X}} \pm 3\sigma'_x$$
$$= \bar{\bar{X}} \pm \frac{3c'}{\sqrt{n}} \bar{\sigma}.$$

n	A_1	n	A_1	n	A_1
2	3.7599	10	1.0281	18	0.7384
3	2.3937	11	0.9727	19	0.7170
4	1.8800	12	0.9253	20	0.6974
5	1.5958	13	0.8842	21	0.6793
6	1.4100	14	0.8482	22	0.6625
7	1.2766	15	0.8162	23	0.6469
8	1.1750	16	0.7876	24	0.6324
9	1.0942	17	0.7618	25	0.6188

Source: Dudley J. Cowden, *Statistical Methods in Quality Control* (Englewood Cliffs, N.J.: Prentice-Hall, Inc., 1957), p. 693. (*Reprinted by permission of the author and publisher.*)

Fig. 13-18.   Values of A_1

The values for $3c'/\sqrt{n}$ can be computed and tabulated. These values are generally called A_1 and are listed in Figure 13-18 and in Appendix F. To compute the control limits by this method,

$$\text{UCL} = \bar{\bar{X}} + A_1 \bar{\sigma}$$

$$= 0.0096 + (1.5958)(0.927)$$

$$= 0.0096 + 1.4793$$

$$= 1.4889.$$

$$\text{LCL} = 0.0096 - 1.4793$$

$$= 1.4697.$$

The differences in the values obtained between the first and second methods are caused by rounding error.

The σ Chart

The σ chart is the companion chart to the $\bar{X}$ chart, and both are usually required for adequate analysis of the production process under study. Therefore, the σ chart is presented (Figure 13-16) together with the $\bar{X}$ chart.

The center line of the σ chart is $\bar{\sigma}$, in this case (from Figure 13-15),

$$\bar{\sigma} = \frac{0.640 + 1.818 + \cdots + 0.835}{25} = 0.927.$$

The control limits of the σ chart are

$$\text{UCL} = \bar{\sigma} + 3\sigma'/\sqrt{2n}$$
$$\text{LCL} = \bar{\sigma} - 3\sigma'/\sqrt{2n},$$

where $\sigma' = c'\bar{\sigma}.$

Therefore, $\text{UCL} = 0.927 + 3(1.1895)(0.927)/\sqrt{10}$

$$= 0.927 + 1.046$$
$$= 1.973.$$
$$\text{LCL} = 0.927 - 1.046$$
$$= -0.119 \text{ or LCL} = 0.$$

Since the LCL cannot be negative, it is set at zero, the control lines are drawn, and the σ values plotted—Figure 13-16(b). All points appear to be in satisfactory control.

Simplified Computation of Control Limits for the σ Chart

The formula for the control limits is

$$\text{CL} = \bar{\sigma} \pm 3\sigma'/\sqrt{2n}$$
$$= \bar{\sigma} \pm (3c'/\sqrt{2n})\bar{\sigma}.$$

n	B'	n	B'	n	B'
2	1.7843	10	0.7979	18	0.5948
3	1.4568	11	0.7608	19	0.5789
4	1.2617	12	0.7284	20	0.5642
5	1.1285	13	0.6998	21	0.5506
6	1.0301	14	0.6744	22	0.5380
7	0.9537	15	0.6515	23	0.5261
8	0.8921	16	0.6308	24	0.5151
9	0.8411	17	0.6120	25	0.5047

SOURCE: Computed by the author from the formula,

$$B' = \frac{3c'}{\sqrt{2n}}$$

Fig. 13-19. Values of B'

The values for $3c'/\sqrt{2n}$ are listed in Figure 13-19 and in Appendix F as B'. For $n = 5$, $B' = 1.1285$. Therefore, the control limits are

Quality Control Charts

225

$$UCL = \bar{\sigma} + B'\bar{\sigma}$$
$$= 0.927 + (1.1285)(0.927)$$
$$= 0.927 + 1.046$$
$$= 1.973.$$
$$LCL = 0.927 - 1.046$$
$$= -0.119 \text{ or } LCL = 0.$$

These limits agree with those previously computed.

Analysis of $\bar{X}$ and σ Charts

When points plotted on the $\bar{X}$ and σ charts fall outside the control lines, the causes should be corrected and investigated. Much more, however, may be learned from analyzing the charts than merely what points are out of control.

Six times the estimated value of the standard deviation of the universe, σ', indicates the range within which almost 100 per cent (99.73 per cent) of the product will fall as long as the present conditions of control are maintained. In this case

$$6\sigma' = 6c'\bar{\sigma}$$
$$= 6(1.1895)(0.927)$$
$$= 6.616 \quad \text{or} \quad 0.0066 \text{ in.}$$

Since the tolerance limits set by the engineer are 0.0060 in., some of the product must necessarily exceed these tolerances. The minimum of out-of-tolerance work will be produced when $\bar{\bar{X}}$ is held at exactly 3.0000 in. Under practical conditions, it will be extremely difficult to maintain $\bar{\bar{X}}$ at this exact value, because such things as tool wear, and so forth, tend to cause $\bar{\bar{X}}$ to vary. Thus the actual production of out-of-tolerance work will be more than the absolute minimum permitted by σ'.

The minimum amount of out-of-tolerance work (assuming the underlying distribution is normal) is shown by Figure 13–20. (The percentage of out-of-tolerance work may be computed by using the z transformation and the Table of Areas under the Normal Curve (Appendix C):

$$z = \frac{X - \bar{\bar{X}}}{\sigma'}$$
$$= \frac{3.0 - 0.0000}{1.104} = 2.7174,$$

where $\sigma' = c'\bar{\sigma} = (1.1895)(0.927) = 1.104.$

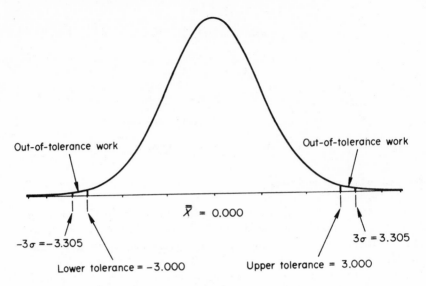

Out-of-tolerance work

Fig. 13-20. Out-of-Tolerance Work

According to Appendix C,

$$\Pr(\infty \geq z \geq 2.7174) = 0.99671.$$

The percentage of out-of-tolerance work at the high limit is

$$1.00000 - 0.99671 = 0.00329 \quad \text{or} \quad 0.33 \text{ per cent.}$$

Since the same out-of-tolerance work will occur at the low limit, the total such work will be

$$2(0.33 \text{ per cent}) = 0.66 \text{ per cent.}$$

Slightly more than one-half of 1 per cent bad work would usually be highly acceptable. In the event that this performance is unacceptable, however, either the method of processing or the tolerance limits would have to be changed. Note that in this case, work out of tolerance on the high side may be reworked, whereas such work on the low side is scrap.

When $6\sigma'$ is *less* than the total tolerance range, then $\bar{X}$ need not be centered so exactly. This condition is especially useful where tool wear results in a gradual increase of dimension size. The original setting of the tool brings the distribution down to the lower tolerance limit, and as the tool wears, the distribution gradually moves up to the upper tolerance limit. This condition is illustrated in Figure 13-21.

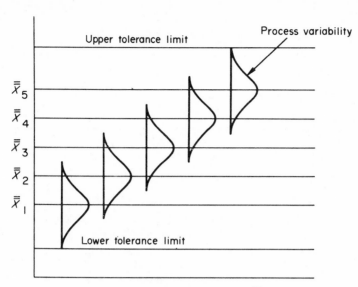

Fig. 13-21. Permissible Slippage of $\bar{\bar{X}}$

SEC. 13-7. THE $\bar{X}$ AND R CHARTS

The $\bar{X}$ and σ charts, because, of the laborious computations involved in computing σ, are less popular than are the $\bar{X}$ and R charts. Since σ' can be estimated from $\bar{R}$ as well as from $\bar{\sigma}$, the R charts can be effectively substituted. The R charts should, however, be used only for relatively small sample sizes, rarely more than 12 or 15 units. Therefore, for the large sample sizes ($n > 12$), the σ chart is to be preferred. R is the range between the smallest and largest readings of the sample. Once again the data from Figure 13-15 will be used. The values of R are listed in column (5), and $\bar{R}$ is computed as

$$\bar{R} = \frac{\Sigma R}{n} = \frac{1.7 + 2.8 + \cdots + 2.6}{25} = 2.248.$$

The $\bar{X}$ Chart Based upon $\bar{R}$

The technique of constructing the $\bar{X}$ chart based upon $\bar{R}$ is very similar to that based upon $\bar{\sigma}$. The difference lies in estimating σ'. Once again the center line, Figure 13-22(a), is drawn at $\bar{\bar{X}} = -0.0096$ (from the data of Figure 13-15). The control limits are set at

$$CL = \bar{\bar{X}} \pm 3\sigma_{\bar{x}},$$

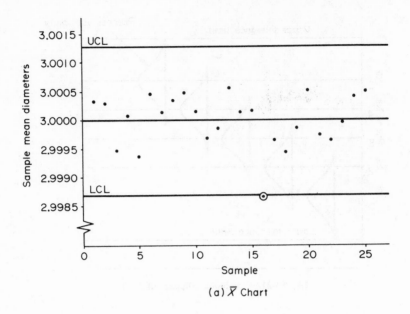

(a) $\bar{X}$ Chart

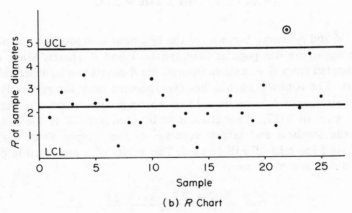

(b) R Chart

Fig. 13-22. The $\bar{X}$ and R Charts

where
$$\sigma_{\bar{x}} = \frac{\sigma'}{\sqrt{n}} \quad \text{and} \quad \sigma' = d'\bar{R},$$

since $\bar{R}$ is a biased estimator of σ', and d' is the correction factor. The values for d' are tabulated in Figure 13-23 and in Appendix F. Therefore,

$$\text{UCL} = \bar{\bar{X}} + 3d'\bar{R}/\sqrt{n}$$
$$= -0.0094 + 3(0.4299)(2.248)/\sqrt{5}$$

n	d'	n	d'	n	d'
2	0.8865	6	0.3946	10	0.3249
3	0.5907	7	0.3698	11	0.3152
4	0.4857	8	0.3512	12	0.3069
5	0.4299	9	0.3367		

SOURCE: Dudley J. Cowden, *Statistical Methods in Quality Control* (Englewood Cliffs, N.J.: Prentice-Hall, Inc., 1957), p. 691. (*Reprinted by permission of the author and publisher.*)

Fig. 13-23. Values of d'

$$= -0.0094 + 1.2966$$
$$= 1.2872.$$
$$LCL = -0.0094 - 1.2966$$
$$= -1.3060.$$

These values may be converted back into the original dimensions:

$$UCL = 3.0000 + 1.2872 = 3.0012872 \quad \text{or} \quad 3.0013$$
$$LCL = 3.0000 - 1.3060 = 2.998694 \quad \text{or} \quad 2.9987$$

drawn on the chart (Figure 13-22), and the values of $\bar{X}$ plotted. These limits are slightly narrower than those computed from $\bar{\sigma}$. This result is not the general rule, since neither $\bar{\sigma}$ nor $\bar{R}$, even after the correction factors are applied, are perfect estimators of σ'. Sample 16 is now slightly outside the control limits; whereas, using $\bar{\sigma}$, it appeared to be under control.

Simplified Computation of Control Limits for the $\bar{X}$ Chart Based upon $\bar{R}$

The formula for the control limits is

$$CL = \bar{\bar{X}} \pm 3\sigma'/\sqrt{n}$$
$$= \bar{\bar{X}} \pm (3d'/\sqrt{n})\bar{R}.$$

(The values for $3d'/\sqrt{n}$ are listed in Figure 13-24 and in Appendix F as A_2.) For $n = 5$, $A_2 = 0.5768$. Therefore the control limits are

$$UCL = \bar{\bar{X}} + A_2\bar{R}$$
$$= -0.0094 + (0.5768)(2.248)$$
$$= -0.0094 + 1.2966$$

n	A_2	n	A_2	n	A_2
2	1.881	6	0.4833	10	0.3082
3	1.023	7	0.4193	11	0.2851
4	0.7285	8	0.3726	12	0.2658
5	0.5678	9	0.3367		

SOURCE: Dudley J. Cowden, *Statistical Methods in Quality Control* (Englewood Cliffs, N.J.: Prentice-Hall, Inc., 1957), p. 693. (*Reproduced by permission of the author and publisher.*)

Fig. 13-24. Values of A_2

$$= 1.2872 \quad \text{or} \quad \text{(in terms of the original dimensions) } 3.0013.$$

$$\text{LCL} = -0.0094 - 1.2966$$

$$= -1.3060 \quad \text{or} \quad \text{(in terms of the original dimensions) } 2.9987.$$

The R Chart

The center line of the R chart is $\bar{R}$. From the data of Figure 13-15,

$$\bar{R} = 2.248$$

which is drawn on Figure 13-22. The control limits are

$$\text{CL} = \bar{R} \pm 3\sigma'_R.$$

Because the expressions for σ'_R are somewhat complicated, only the shortcut methods for computing the control limits will be considered. The formulas are

$$\text{UCL} = D_4\bar{R}$$

$$\text{LCL} = D_3\bar{R}.$$

n	D_3	D_4	n	D_3	D_4
2	0	3.267	8	0.136	1.864
3	0	2.575	9	0.184	1.816
4	0	2.282	10	0.223	1.777
5	0	2.115	11	0.256	1.744
6	0	2.004	12	0.284	1.716
7	0.076	1.924			

SOURCE: Dudley J. Cowden, *Statistical Methods in Quality Control* (Englewood Cliffs, N.J.: Prentice-Hall, Inc., 1957), p. 697. (*Reproduced by permission of the author and publisher.*)

Fig. 13-25. Values of D_3 and D_4

(The values of D_3 and D_4 are listed in Figure 13-25 and in Appendix F.) The computations of the control limits are

$$UCL = D_4\bar{R}$$
$$= (2.115)(2.248)$$
$$= 4.755.$$
$$LCL = D_3\bar{R}$$
$$= (0)(2.248)$$
$$= 0.$$

The limits are drawn on the control chart (Figure 13-22), and the R values plotted.

The control limits for the R chart in this particular example are narrower than were those for the σ chart. As explained previously, this is not a general condition; for in another example the control limits of the R chart could be wider than those of the σ chart made from the same data. The analysis of the $\bar{X}$ and R charts is similar to that discussed in Sec. 13-6 for the $\bar{X}$ and σ charts.

SEC. 13-8. THE THEORY OF RUNS

A point falling outside the control limits indicates an out-of-control condition which should be investigated. This statement can be made with a high degree of confidence because it will be false only about 3 out of 1000 times, on the average. There are, however, other indicators that may warn the analyst of out-of-control conditions.

The *center line* of the control chart is that line above which 50 per cent of the observations will fall and below which will be the other 50 per cent. Thus, the probability that a point will fall above the line is 0.5. The probability that two points in succession will fall above the line is $(0.5)(0.5) = 0.25$. Figure 13-26 shows the probabilities of a series of points falling on one side of the center line. Since the probability of a similar series falling on the other side of the center line would be the same, the probability of a given series of points falling on either side of the center line is double that shown in Figure 13-26. Thus a series of 9 points on either side of the center line would occur with a probability of $2(0.00195) = 0.00390$, or a probability slightly greater than that of a single point fall-

Number of Points	Probability
2	$(0.5)^2 = 0.25000$
3	$(0.5)^3 = 0.12500$
4	$(0.5)^4 = 0.06250$
5	$(0.5)^5 = 0.03125$
6	$(0.5)^6 = 0.01563$
7	$(0.5)^7 = 0.00781$
8	$(0.5)^8 = 0.00391$
9	$(0.5)^9 = 0.00195$
10	$(0.5)^{10} = 0.00098$
11	$(0.5)^{11} = 0.00049$

Fig. 13-26. Probabilities of a Series of Points Falling on One Side of the Center Line

ing outside the control limits. Therefore, a series of 9 points on one side of the center line would appear to indicate an out-of-control condition. Many authorities recommend that a series of 7 points be so regarded, even though the probability of such an occurrence is $2(0.00713) = 0.01426$, or about 5.2 times as great as that of a single point falling outside the control limits.

Other types of series may also be used. Figure 13-27 shows the probabilities of various series of points falling on one side of the line. Such points are distributed according to the binomial law,

$$(0.5 + 0.5)^n,$$

where n stands for the number of points under consideration. The computation for a series of 7 out of 8 points on one side of the line is (see Sec. 9-3 for an explanation of this computation):

$$\Pr(n) = nCm\, p^m q^{(n-m)}.$$
$$\Pr(7 \text{ of } 8 \text{ on one side}) = {}_8C_7(0.5)^7(0.5)^1$$
$$= 8(0.00781)(0.5)$$
$$= 0.0313.$$

Again, to compute the probability that a given series may occur on either side of the line, the probabilities shown in Figure 13-27 must be doubled. The probability of 12 of 13 points on one side of the center line occurring is $2(0.0016) = 0.0032$, or approximately the same as that of one point falling outside the control limits. Similarly, the probability of 14 out of 16 would be $2(0.0019) = 0.0038$; of 16 out of 19, $2(0.0018) = 0.0036$; and of 18 out of 22, $2(0.0017) = 0.0034$. Some authorities, however, recommend the use of 7 in a row, 10 out of 11, 12 out of 14, 14 out of 17, and 16 out

Number of Points	Probability
7 of 8	0.0313
8 of 9	0.0175
9 of 10	0.0097
10 of 11	0.0054
11 of 12	0.0030
12 of 13	0.0016
13 of 14	0.0008
10 of 12	0.0161
11 of 13	0.0095
12 of 14	0.0056
13 of 15	0.0032
14 of 16	0.0019
15 of 17	0.0011
13 of 16	0.0085
14 of 17	0.0052
15 of 18	0.0031
16 of 19	0.0018
17 of 20	0.0011
15 of 19	0.0074
16 of 20	0.0046
17 of 21	0.0029
18 of 22	0.0017
19 of 23	0.0011

Fig. 13-27. Probabilities of Given Series of Points

of 20 as bases for out-of-control action to be initiated. As can be seen from Figure 13-27, the probabilities of these series occurring are considerably greater than is that of a single point falling outside the control limits.

SEC. 13-9. SUMMARY OF CONTROL CHART FORMULAS

The *d* Chart

$$\text{Center line} = \bar{d} = \frac{\sum d}{k},$$

where $\bar{d}$ = number of defective units per sample

k = number of samples.

$$\text{Control limits} = \bar{d} \pm 3\sqrt{n\bar{p}\bar{q}},$$

where n = sample size

$$\bar{p} = \frac{\bar{d}}{n}$$

$$\bar{q} = 1 - \bar{p}.$$

The p Chart

$$\text{Center line} = \bar{p} = \frac{\sum d}{kn} \text{ for equal sample sizes}$$

$$= \bar{p} = \frac{\sum d}{\sum n} \text{ for unequal sample sizes,}$$

where n = sample size

d = number of defective units per sample

k = number of samples.

$$\text{Control limits} = \bar{p} \pm 3\sqrt{\frac{\bar{p}\bar{q}}{n}},$$

where n and $\bar{p}$ are the same as for the center line and $\bar{q} = 1 - \bar{p}$.

The c Chart

$$\text{Center line} = \bar{c} = \frac{\sum c}{n},$$

where c = number of defects per unit

n = number of units.

$$\text{Control limits} = \bar{c} + 3\sqrt{\bar{c}},$$

where $\bar{c}$ has the foregoing meaning.

The $\bar{X}$ Chart Based upon σ

$$\text{Center line} = \bar{\bar{X}} = \frac{\sum \bar{X}}{k},$$

where k = number of samples.

$$\bar{X} = \frac{\sum X}{n},$$

where X = the individual observation

n = the sample size.

$$\text{Control limits} = \bar{\bar{X}} \pm A_1\bar{\sigma},$$

where A_1 = tabulated values in Figure 13–18 and Appendix F

$$\bar{\sigma} = \frac{\sum \sigma}{k},$$

where k has the foregoing meaning and

$$\sigma = \sqrt{\frac{\sum (X - \bar{X})^2}{n}},$$

where X, $\bar{X}$, and n have the previous meanings.

The $\bar{X}$ Chart Based upon $\bar{R}$

$$\text{Center line} = \bar{\bar{X}} = \frac{\sum \bar{X}}{k},$$

where $k =$ number of samples

$$\bar{X} = \frac{\sum X}{n},$$

where $X =$ the individual observations

$n =$ the sample size.

$$\text{Control limits} = \bar{\bar{X}} \pm A_2 \bar{R},$$

where A_2 is listed in Figure 13-24 and Appendix F.

$$\bar{R} = \frac{\sum R}{k},$$

where $k =$ number of samples

$R =$ difference between largest and smallest observation.

The σ Chart

$$\text{Center line} = \bar{\sigma} = \frac{\sum \sigma}{k},$$

where $\sigma = \sqrt{\frac{\sum (X - \bar{X})^2}{n}},$

where $X =$ the individual observation

$$\bar{X} = \frac{\sum X}{n}$$

$n =$ the sample size.

$$\text{Control limits} = \bar{\sigma} \pm B' \bar{\sigma},$$

where B' is listed in Figure 13-19 and in Appendix F, and $\bar{\sigma}$ has the fore-going meaning.

The R Chart

$$\text{Center line} = \bar{R} = \frac{\Sigma R}{k},$$

where $R =$ the difference between the largest
            and smallest measurements of the sample

            $k =$ the number of samples.

$$\text{Control limits} = \text{UCL} = D_4\bar{R}$$
$$\text{LCL} = D_3\bar{R}$$

where D_3 and D_4 are listed in Figure 13-25 and Appendix F, and $\bar{R}$ has the foregoing meaning.

DISCUSSION QUESTIONS

13-1. Name some advantages to be gained by using control charts as compared to other quality control techniques.

13-2. What is meant by a *skewed* distribution? A *leptokurtic* distribution? A *platykurtic* distribution?

13-3. Under what circumstances is a d chart applicable?

13-4. What is meant by a *constant-cause system*?

13-5. What is the minimum desirable number of samples to be used in setting control chart limits?

13-6. Define the statistic d. According to what probability law is the statistic d distributed?

13-7. Explain the process of setting the center line and the control limits of the d chart.

13-8. Define the term *assignable cause*.

13-9. State a disadvantage of using a d chart where the samples vary in size.

13-10. Under what circumstances is a p chart applicable?

13-11. Why may the p chart be superior to the d chart?

13-12. Explain how to determine the center line and control limits of the p chart.

13-13. In what way is the p chart superior to the d chart when the samples vary in size?

13-14. Under what circumstances is the c chart applicable?

13-15. Explain how to determine the center line and the control limits of the c chart.

13-16. Under what circumstances are $\bar{X}$ and σ charts applicable?

13-17. Explain how to determine the center line and the control limits of the $\bar{X}$ chart based upon σ.

13-18. Explain how to determine the center line and the control limits of the σ chart.

13-19. What is the significance of a point falling outside the control limits? What action, if any, should be taken?

13-20. What information can be derived from σ', the estimated standard deviation of the underlying distribution?

13-21. Why is the R chart more popular than the σ chart?

13-22. Explain how to determine the center line and the control limits of the $\bar{X}$ chart based upon $\bar{R}$.

13-23. Explain how to determine the center line and the control limits of the R chart.

13-24. Discuss the theory of runs. State a basis for selecting runs as being indicative of out-of-control conditions.

PROBLEMS

13-1. The X Company inspects 100 per cent of Product A on a pass-or-fail basis. The following chart shows the results of the last 25 days' inspections. Each day's production was 250 units.
Required:
  a. Set up a d chart and plot the number of defectives.
  b. Eliminate any data which fall outside the control limits and compute new control limits.

Day	Number of Defectives	Day	Number of Defectives	Day	Number of Defectives
1	46	10	55	19	34
2	60	11	30	20	32
3	33	12	49	21	40
4	48	13	50	22	31
5	55	14	41	23	15
6	32	15	50	24	54
7	29	16	37	25	49
8	31	17	21		
9	40	18	38		

13-2. From the data of Problem 13-1,
  a. Set up a p chart and plot the daily percentage of defectives.
  b. Eliminate any data which fall outside the control limits and compute new control limits.

13-3. The X Company inspects 100 per cent of Product B on a pass-or-fail basis. The accompanying chart shows the results of the last 25 days' inspections. The daily production is 175 units. Set up a d chart and plot the daily number of defective units.

Day	Number of Defectives	Day	Number of Defectives	Day	Number of Defectives
1	11	10	9	19	14
2	10	11	15	20	12
3	15	12	15	21	10
4	11	13	9	22	12
5	5	14	12	23	14
6	13	15	12	24	10
7	13	16	12	25	7
8	19	17	13		
9	12	18	12		

13-4. From the data of Problem 13-3, set up a p chart and plot the daily percentage of defectives.

13-5. The X Company inspects 100 per cent of Product C on a pass-or-fail basis. The number of units of Product C produced each day varies widely. The following table shows data from the last 25 days' production. Set up a d chart and plot the data, along with appropriate control limits.

Day	Sample Size	Number of Defectives	Day	Sample Size	Number of Defectives	Day	Sample Size	Number of Defectives
1	742	46	10	195	8	19	222	15
2	62	3	11	330	23	20	618	37
3	285	20	12	646	42	21	173	9
4	201	12	13	942	50	22	78	4
5	953	52	14	91	5	23	830	47
6	356	25	15	754	49	24	356	17
7	46	3	16	737	44	25	870	45
8	236	16	17	234	16			
9	81	6	18	238	14			

13-6. From the data of Problem 13-5, set up a p chart and plot the daily percentage of defectives, along with appropriate control limits.

13-7. The Y Company manufactures steel sheets, 3ft × 4ft in size. Each sheet is inspected for surface defects. The following table shows the number of defects for the last 25 sheets inspected. Set up a c chart and plot the number of defects per sheet.

Sheet	Defects	Sheet	Defects	Sheet	Defects
1	19	10	14	19	8
2	15	11	11	20	6
3	8	12	11	21	7
4	12	13	9	22	8
5	6	14	11	23	15
6	7	15	10	24	7
7	11	16	6	25	12
8	13	17	6		
9	13	18	12		

Quality Control Charts

239

13-8. The Y Company manufactures a high-quality steel wire. In inspecting the wire for defects, it counts the number of defects per 100 ft of wire. The accompanying table shows the number of defects recorded for the last twenty-five 100-ft lengths. Set up a c chart and plot the number of defects per 100 ft of wire.

100ft Section	Defects	100ft Section	Defects	100ft Section	Defects
1	3	10	1	19	3
2	3	11	0	20	4
3	2	12	1	21	6
4	2	13	2	22	1
5	6	14	3	23	5
6	1	15	4	24	2
7	2	16	5	25	3
8	6	17	2		
9	6	18	3		

13-9. The Acme Orange Juice Company sells orange juice in 8-oz cans. It utilizes automatic filling equipment, and desires to maintain the nominal 8-oz filling within ± 0.3 oz. It takes a sample of five cans every three hours and measures the liquid in each of the five cans. The following table shows the variations from 8 oz of the last 25 samples. Set up an $\bar{X}$ and a σ chart and plot $\bar{X}$ and σ.

Sample	\multicolumn{5}{c}{Variations in Ounces}
	1	2	3	4	5
1	−0.11	0.01	0.02	−0.11	0.02
2	−0.17	0.00	0.03	−0.11	−0.01
3	0.04	0.13	−0.07	−0.16	−0.14
4	−0.18	0.10	0.04	0.20	−0.05
5	0.05	0.12	0.09	−0.10	−0.01
6	−0.10	−0.06	−0.08	−0.15	−0.08
7	−0.01	0.02	0.10	0.10	0.05
8	0.03	0.00	−0.18	−0.04	−0.01
9	0.00	−0.01	−0.10	−0.10	−0.01
10	0.00	−0.01	0.11	0.17	−0.09
11	0.01	0.18	0.03	−0.01	0.00
12	−0.06	−0.01	−0.01	0.06	0.04
13	0.04	0.01	−0.20	0.00	−0.03
14	0.25	0.00	0.00	0.08	0.03
15	−0.09	−0.38	0.25	−0.03	0.09
16	−0.05	−0.09	0.15	0.05	−0.09
17	0.01	−0.08	0.03	0.19	−0.03
18	0.03	0.03	0.06	−0.03	−0.01
19	0.10	0.13	0.12	0.11	−0.16
20	0.17	0.18	−0.06	0.03	−0.03
21	0.09	−0.03	0.02	0.09	−0.01
22	−0.03	0.01	0.02	−0.02	−0.09
23	0.21	0.23	−0.05	0.09	0.16
24	−0.06	−0.20	0.13	0.03	−0.03
25	−0.12	0.06	0.12	−0.03	−0.01

13-10. From the data of Problem 13-9, set up an $\bar{X}$ and an R chart and plot $\bar{X}$ and R.

13-11. The Z Chemical Company produces a solvent which must contain 3 per cent of alcohol. It tries to maintain the actual percentage at 3 per cent ± 0.3 per cent. It tests hourly in samples of five. The following table shows the results of the last 25 samples. Set up an $\bar{X}$ and a σ chart and plot $\bar{X}$ and σ.

	% Alcohol				
Sample	1	2	3	4	5
1	2.9	2.8	3.0	2.8	3.1
2	2.9	3.0	3.0	3.0	3.0
3	3.0	3.1	3.1	3.1	2.9
4	3.0	3.0	3.0	3.0	3.0
5	2.9	3.0	3.1	2.9	3.1
6	2.8	2.9	2.9	2.9	2.8
7	3.2	2.9	2.8	3.1	3.0
8	2.9	3.0	3.0	2.9	2.9
9	3.0	2.9	2.9	3.0	3.0
10	3.0	3.0	2.9	3.0	3.3
11	2.9	2.9	3.0	3.0	3.0
12	3.2	3.0	3.0	3.0	2.6
13	2.9	2.9	3.0	3.1	3.0
14	3.0	2.8	3.0	2.7	2.8
15	3.0	3.1	3.2	3.0	3.1
16	3.0	3.1	3.0	3.1	3.2
17	3.0	2.9	3.0	3.0	3.0
18	3.0	3.1	2.9	3.0	3.0
19	3.1	3.2	3.1	3.0	3.2
20	2.9	2.9	3.1	3.2	3.0
21	3.0	3.2	2.8	3.1	3.1
22	2.9	3.0	3.0	2.9	2.9
23	2.9	3.1	3.0	3.1	3.0
24	3.1	3.0	3.0	2.9	3.0
25	3.0	2.9	3.2	3.0	3.0

13-12. From the the data of Problem 13-11, set up an $\bar{X}$ and an R chart and plot $\bar{X}$ and R.

BIBLIOGRAPHY

American Standards Association, *Guide for Quality Control and Control Chart Method of Analyzing Data.* New York: American Standards Association, 1941.

Burr, Irving W., *Engineering Statistics and Quality Control.* New York: McGraw-Hill Book Company, Inc., 1953, pp. 84-295.

Cowden, Dudley J., *Statistical Methods in Quality Control.* Englewood Cliffs, N.J.: Prentice-Hall, Inc., 1957, pp. 154-282.

Grant, E. L., *Statistical Quality Control.* New York: McGraw-Hill Book Company, Inc., 1946, pp. 3-312.

Heide, John D., *Industrial Process Control by Statistical Methods*. New York: McGraw-Hill Book Company, Inc., 1952.

Moroney, M. J., *Facts from Figures*. Baltimore, Md.: Penguin Books, 1951, pp. 141-72.

Peach, Paul, *Industrial Statistics and Quality Control*. Raleigh, N.C.: Edwards & Broughton Co., 1947, pp. 27-149.

Schrock, Edward M., *Quality Control and Statistical Methods*. New York: Reinhold Publishing Corporation, 1950, pp. 32-154.

Shewhart, W. A., *Economic Control of Quality of Manufactured Product*. New York: D. Van Nostrand Company, Inc., 1931.

_____, *Statistical Method from the Viewpoint of Quality Control*. Washington, D.C.: Department of Agriculture, The Graduate School, 1939.

14

Work Sampling

SEC. 14-1. **STATEMENT OF THE PROBLEM**

The West Coast Aircraft Corporation employs 200 maintenance men who may be assigned jobs in any of three different buildings. Because of the nature of maintenance work, controlling the repair crew by realistically set time standards presented significant difficulties. Several of the executives, however, thought that too much of the repair crew's time was being spent unproductively and that it was imperative that the percentage of idle time be reduced. As a result, the executives asked for information about the amounts, causes, and types of nonproductive time. *Nonproductive time* was defined as any time other than that spent actually on the equipment being repaired.

The foremen, in consultation with the workers, decided that nonproductive time could be classified as follows:

1. Waiting for parts
2. Waiting for tools
3. Waiting for instructions
4. Conversation unrelated to the job
5. Personal time

It was agreed that the proportion of time spent in each of these categories would have to be obtained before any effective plan for reducing idle time could be devised.

As a means of measuring the proportion of time spent in each category, 100 per cent observation was considered. This method was rejected for two reasons: (1) it would be very costly, (2) the behavior patterns of the repair crews under continuous observation would undoubtedly differ from their normal behavior patterns. The use of work sampling was then proposed because (1) work sampling would be far less costly than would continuous observation; (2) the proportion of time spent in each category could be obtained with any desired degree of accuracy; (3) the work sampling observation techniques were such that the employees would tend to engage in their normal work patterns, even though they were fully informed that the observations were taking place. These arguments prevailed, and it was agreed to apply the work sampling approach.

SEC. 14-2. BASIC WORK SAMPLING CONCEPTS

Work sampling, as its name implies, is a statistical sampling technique and is therefore based upon statistical sampling theory. The basic work sampling techniques were developed in the early 1930's in England by L. H. C. Tippett who called the process *snap-reading*. It was introduced into the United States by R. L. Morrow, who applied the term *ratio delay* to the technique. In 1952, H. L. Waddell, editor of *Factory Management and Maintenance*, decided that the name *work sampling* would be more descriptive. Involved is the determination of a proportion, for example, in the illustrative problem, the proportion of time the employees spend for personal requirements. If all other time is classified into one category and personal time into another category, the two categories are mutually exclusive, and their sum represents unity. These, then, can be considered the terms of the binomial, where

$$p = \text{personal time}$$
$$q = \text{all other time.}$$

Each of the other categories (waiting for parts, and so forth) could be considered to be a different p, and all other time for each p would be the related q.

Usually a specified number of spot observations are made per day or per shift. In the following example, assume that five observations, at randomly selected times, are to be made each eight-hour day. Figure 14-1 represents fifteen such working days, with idle time indicated by the black segments. By measurement, the black segments (idle time) are 40 per cent of the total time. For the sake of simplicity in the illustration, time is measured in 15-minute blocks, and both working and idle time are represented in either single or multiple 15-minute blocks.

Of the 450 blocks available for work, 180 are designated as idle time, each block having been selected on a random basis. A total of 75 observations (5 per day for 15 days) were made. (See Sec. 14–5 for the method of

Day

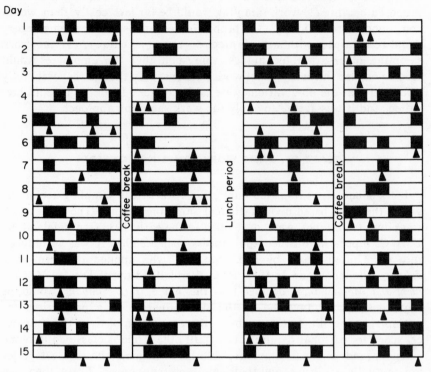

Fig. 14-1. Work Sampling Illustration

selection.) Each of the arrows in Figure 14-1 represents an observation. Thirty of the 75 observations were of "idle time" and 45 were of "working time." Thus, the sample proportion was exactly equal to the population proportion, namely, 40 per cent. This exact relationship must be regarded as purely coincidental, and another sample of 75 observations would very likely differ. In fact, according to Figure 11-3, 600 observations would be required to get plus or minus 10 per cent accuracy (that is, the sample proportion would be likely to range from 36 per cent to 44 per cent), and this with only a 95 per cent degree of confidence.

The distribution of the proportions of the fifteen samples of five observations each will illustrate that the number of five-observation samples taken (fifteen) is inadequate. According to the theory of the binomial distribution, the frequencies of the sample proportions should be distributed according to the expansion of the binomial (see Sec. 9-3 for the method of expanding the binomial), in this case,

$$(p + q)^5,$$

where $p = 0.4$ and $q = 0.6$. This expansion is

$$p^5 = (0.4)^5 = 0.01024$$
$$5p^4q = 5(0.4)^4(0.6) = 0.07680$$
$$10p^3q^2 = 10(0.4)^3(0.6)^2 = 0.23040$$
$$10p^2q^3 = 10(0.4)^2(0.6)^3 = 0.34560$$
$$5pq^4 = 5(0.4)(0.6)^4 = 0.25920$$
$$q^5 = (0.6)^5 = 0.07776.$$

The expected frequencies may now be compared with the actual sample frequencies:

Periods	Expected Frequencies	Actual Frequencies
0	$0.01024 \times 15 = 0.1536$	2
1	$0.07680 \times 15 = 1.1520$	2
2	$0.23040 \times 15 = 3.4560$	3
3	$0.34560 \times 15 = 5.1840$	6
4	$0.25920 \times 15 = 3.8880$	1
5	$0.07776 \times 15 = 1.1664$	0

Although the pattern is clearly evolving, many more samples of five observations each would be required before the observed frequencies will closely match the expected or computed frequencies. Therefore, if the actual proportion of idle time were not known, little confidence could be placed in the 40 per cent inference derived from the sample. In fact, at the 95 per cent confidence level, the probable range would be 0.4 plus or minus 28.3 per cent. That is, the range of the proportion would be from 28.68 per cent to 51.32 per cent—a range which would probably be considered to be too broad to be acceptable. Six hundred observations providing a range of from 36 per cent to 44 per cent may still be too broad, requiring more observations in order to obtain the desired accuracy. The number of required observations may be obtained from Figure 11-3 or computed as explained in the following section.

SEC. 14-3. COMPUTING THE NUMBER OF OBSERVATIONS

The number of work sampling observations is dependent upon three factors: (1) the degree of confidence desired, usually set at the 95 per cent level, (2) the proportion of occurrences in the population, (3) the accuracy required. One of these, the proportion of occurrences in the population, is unknown, for it is this very item which is to be determined by the work sampling technique.

Nevertheless, some preliminary estimate of the proportion of occurrences must be made. Generally, there are two methods available for making the preliminary estimates. The easier method is to make a guess based upon past experience. Such a guess, however, is usually subject to wide error, and hence may not be very effective in practice. The second and preferred method is to take a test sample of small size, say, 100–200 observations, and to use the sample proportion as the preliminary estimate.

The determination of the required accuracy is somewhat subjective, depending upon the use to which the results of the study are to be put. If the manager is merely seeking general information, the acceptable range may be fairly broad; whereas, if the results are to be used to set standards, a more narrow range will be required. In computing the number of observations, the range is expressed as the sample proportion plus or minus a specified percentage of that proportion. When the proportion is in the central area, such as 50 per cent, a plus or minus 10 per cent range will give an accuracy of from 45 per cent to 55 per cent, or a coverage of 10 percentage points. Such a range is, of course, quite broad for practical applications. When the proportion is 1 per cent, a plus or minus 10 per cent range will give an accuracy of from 0.9 per cent to 1.1 per cent, or a coverage of 0.2 percentage points. Thus a plus or minus 10 per cent could easily be too broad when the proportion is in the middle range, but fully acceptable when the proportion is small.

The best estimate of the proportion of occurrences in the population is the proportion of occurrences in the total sample. (Note that this is not the proportion in the daily sample.) A series of such samples taken from a given population is likely to result in different estimates of the proportion in the population. If an infinite number of such samples were taken, the resulting sample proportions would be distributed according to the binomial, with the n of the binomial equal to the size of the total sample. The normal distribution may, however, be satisfactorily substituted for the binomial when the n of the binomial is large, as it would be in this case. The true population proportion will be the mean of this distribution (see Figure 14-2). Thus approximately 95 per cent of the sample proportions will be within plus or minus 2 standard deviations of the population proportion. Conversely, given any sample proportion, it will, 95 per cent of the time, be within plus or minus 2 standard deviations of the population proportion. These standard deviations are called the *standard error of the proportion*, the symbol for which is σ_p.

The formula for σ_p is

$$\sigma_p = \sqrt{\frac{p'q'}{N}},$$

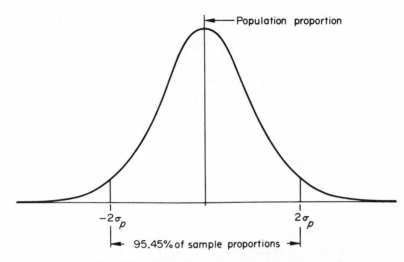

Fig. 14-2. Distribution of Sampling Proportions

where $\qquad$ $p' =$ the population proportion

$q' = 1 - p'$

$N =$ the total number of observations.

Since p' is not known, it must be inferred from successive accumulated samples. This formula may be converted to a formula for ascertaining the number of observations required by solving for N: First, square each side

$$\sigma_p^2 = \frac{p' q'}{N}.$$

Then cross-multiply and divide by σ_p^2:

(a) $\qquad\qquad\qquad\qquad N = \frac{p' q'}{\sigma_p^2}.$

However, σ_p in Eq. (a) is a straight numerical expression of the standard error of the proportion. In order to make the formula more useful, the standard error should be expressed as a percentage of p'. This percentage may be computed by dividing σ_p by p':

$$\sigma_p \text{ expressed as a percentage of } p' = \frac{\sigma_p}{p'}.$$

Since plus or minus 2 standard errors will take in approximately 95 per cent of all sample proportions, therefore,

The 95 per cent confidence limit $= 2\sigma_p$;

or (expressed as a percentage) $= \dfrac{2\sigma_p}{p'}$.

Now let $S =$ the 95 per cent confidence limit; hence,

$$S = \frac{2\sigma_p}{p'}$$

and

$$Sp' = 2\sigma_p$$

$$\sigma_p = \frac{Sp'}{2}$$

$$\sigma_p^2 = \frac{S^2(p')^2}{4}.$$

This value may now be substituted into Eq. (a):

(a)
$$N = \frac{p'q'}{\sigma_p^2}$$

$$= \frac{p'q'}{S^2(p')^2/4}.$$

(b)
$$N = \frac{4q'}{S^2p'},$$

where
$$q' = 1 - p'$$

$p' =$ the population proportion

$S =$ the percentage tolerance allowed

$N =$ the number of observations.

In practice, p' (the population proportion) is not known, since this is the value sought. Therefore a preliminary estimate of N is computed using the preliminary estimate of p', which was obtained as an experienced guess or from a small sample. As the sampling proceeds, and the cumulative number of observations increases, p' is again inferred from the sample p. If the new p' differs from the preceding p', a new N is computed. This procedure is repeated several times until the N required by the most recent computation is achieved.

Example, Part I.   After a preliminary sample of 200 observations, p' is inferred from the sample p to be 30 per cent or 0.3. The desired accuracy is $\pm$ 5 per cent or $\pm$ 0.05.

Using formula (b):

(b)
$$N = \frac{4q'}{S^2p'}$$

$$= \frac{4(0.7)}{(0.05)^2(0.3)} \text{ , since } q' = 1 - p'$$

$$= 3733 \text{ observations required.}$$

Example, Part II.   Another 500 observations, making a total of 700, have been taken, and a revised p' of 0.25 is inferred.
Again from (b):

$$N = \frac{4(0.75)}{(0.05)^2(0.25)}$$

$$= 4800 \text{ observations required.}$$

Example, Part III.   After 4800 observations, a revised p' of 0.26 is inferred:

$$N = \frac{4(0.74)}{(0.05)^2(0.26)}$$

$$= 4554 \text{ observations required.}$$

Since the 4800 observations exceed the 4554 required, an accuracy within the $\pm$ 5 per cent limits is assured at the 95 per cent confidence level. That is, there is 95 per cent certainty that p' actually lies between the limits of 24.7 per cent and 27.3 per cent.

Ascertaining the Accuracy at a Given Number of Observations

The work sampling analyst may desire to know the accuracy achieved at a given number of observations. For this purpose, formula (b) may be solved for S:

(b) $$N = \frac{4q'}{S^2 p'}$$

$$S^2 = \frac{4q'}{Np'}$$

(c) $$S = \sqrt{\frac{4q'}{Np'}}$$

Example.   In Sec. 14-2, 75 observations were made with a p of 0.4. Within what range is the true proportion, at the 95 per cent confidence level?
Using (c):

$$S = \sqrt{\frac{4q'}{Np'}}$$

$$= \sqrt{\frac{4(0.6)}{75(0.4)}}$$

$$= 0.2828.$$

Although the $p = 0.4$ of Sec. 14-2 is exactly equal to the true p', if the analyst were ignorant of the actual value of p', he could only infer that $p' = 0.4 \pm 28.3$ per cent of 0.4, or that, at the 95 per cent confidence level, p' lies within the range of 0.2868 to 0.5132.

The Graphical Approach to Obtaining N

Figure 14-3 shows a graph of the cumulative proportion of heads obtained from 200 tosses of a coin. On the first toss, the proportion of heads must either be 100 per cent or 0 per cent. During the first few tosses, the proportion of heads may fluctuate violently. In Figure 14-3, there was a run of three tails to start with, then a run of heads, and so forth. The larger the number of tosses, the smaller will be the effect of such runs—in fact, the more likely it will be that the current run merely offsets a previous run in the opposite direction. In practice, when the graph line has remained horizontal for some time and is fluctuating within the desired limits, the N may be considered to be sufficiently large. In Figure 14-3, the proportion has fluctuated between 52 per cent and 55 per cent from

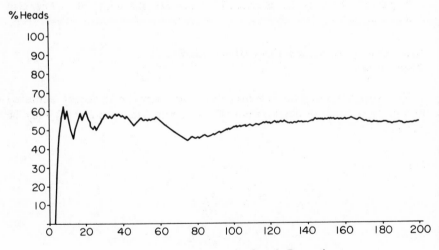

Fig. 14-3. Graphing Cumulative Sample Proportions

the one hundred and eleventh toss on. The inference is that the actual proportion is about 53.5 per cent. A horizontal trend has not, however, been sufficiently well established to put a high degree of faith in that figure. There is, nevertheless, initial evidence that the probability of heads or tails is not equal, and that the odds appear to favor getting a head rather than a tail. Does this evidence rule out the chance that the true proportion is 50 per cent? Using Eq. (c),

$$S = \sqrt{\frac{4q'}{Np'}}$$

$$= \sqrt{\frac{4(0.5)}{200(0.5)}}$$

$$= 0.1414.$$

Therefore, a sample with proportion p, sample size 200, taken from a universe with $p' = 0.5$, will fall, 95 per cent of the time, within the range $0.5 \pm (0.1414)(0.5)$ or from 0.4293 to 0.5707. A p of 0.535 (53.5 per cent) falls easily within this range. This points up the principal disadvantage of the graph of the cumulative sample proportions—it does not reveal to the analyst the true degree of accuracy attained by a specific N.

SEC. 14-4. SETTING THE SIZE OF THE DAILY SAMPLE

In setting the size of the daily sample, that is, the number of observations to make per day or shift, several factors must be considered. Among the more important of these are

1. The total number of observations required to achieve the desired accuracy.
2. The urgency of obtaining the sampling results.
3. Whether or not the events to be observed occur in a cyclical pattern.
4. The time required per observation round.
5. The number of observers available.

Total Number of Observations Required

The computation of the total number of observations required is treated in Sec. 14-3. The number of observations N is a function of three factors: (1) the degree of confidence required, usually set at the 95 per cent level, (2) the tolerance range within which the final results may lie, (3) the proportion of occurrence of the events.

The Urgency of Obtaining the Results

In the typical situation, once certain information is deemed to be desirable, there is a definite sense of urgency in obtaining that information. Such a demand for speed must, however, be tempered by the realization that speed may result in costs, such as extra wages, or in lack of accuracy of results. Very great speed may be obtained by taking all the required observations in one day. In such a case, great doubt would be cast upon the results, because no day can be considered to be a "typical" or "average" day. These averages are worked out by observing a large number of days, each of which varies from the other. As a result, although urgency points toward compressing the observations into a few days, the need for obtaining typical data suggests that the study should continue over a reasonably long period of time. The length of time required, however, is not easily subject to mathematical computation.

The Existence of Cyclical Patterns

In many cases, cyclical work patterns exist. For instance, work may be heavy at the beginning or ending of the week or month. Seasonal effects and holidays may have an important bearing on the work load. When cyclical patterns exist, the coverage of the cycle depends upon the information sought. Usually, average or typical data are desired, and therefore care must be exercised to extend the observations over one or more complete cycles. The beginning and ending of the observations should be at the same points in the cycle, otherwise bias will enter into the results. There is, of course, the possibility that the analyst may wish to compare slow periods in the cycle with busy periods. In this case, each segment of the cycle must be differentiated, and sufficient observations taken within each segment to obtain the accuracy required.

The Time Required per Observation Round

The time required per observation round will have an important bearing upon the number of observations that can be taken per observer per day. If the study is to be made in an office, where all employees are in full view, the observations may not take more than a very few minutes. If the observer must walk extensively, going from room to room, floor to floor, and building to building, the observation time per round can be quite long. The number of rounds to be made per day is equal to the number of observations per day divided by the number of stations to be observed.

It should be understood, however, that observations are "snap readings," and hence should be made instantaneously. Each observation should be made from a specified point, and the activity observed at the exact time of reaching that point should be recorded. The observer must not anticipate actions, but should record what is observed. It is true, nevertheless, that after the observation, the observer may need to investigate the activity further in order to record it. For example, in the terms of the illustrative problem, the observer may observe that the worker is idle, but he must then ascertain the cause of the idleness before recording the classification of the observation.

The Number of Observers

One of the major advantages of the work sampling technique is that trained industrial engineers are not required as observers. Almost any member of the organization may be easily trained for the task, and using the direct supervisors for the purpose is frequently the ideal solution. The number of observers required will depend upon the decisions concerning the other primary factors previously considered, and, of course, it is limited by the availability of personnel.

Summary

Basically, the number of observations per day is equal to the total number of observations required divided by the days desired to be covered by the study. If one observer cannot handle this number of observations per day, more observers will be needed. Each observer is limited as to the number of daily observation rounds by the number of stations to be observed and the distance between stations. If cyclical patterns are present, either whole cycles should be observed, or the cycles should be segregated into phases for separate observation.

SEC. 14-5. SCHEDULING THE DAILY OBSERVATIONS

Once the number of observation rounds per day has been determined, two types of schedules must be prepared: (1) the starting time for each round, (2) the sequence in which the observations are to be made. Sampling theory is based upon the concept that each event of the universe has an equal chance of appearing in the sample. This is called *random selection.* The events in a work sampling study to be selected at random are the minutes of the working day or shift, excluding lunch and scheduled rest periods. Therefore, the method used in scheduling the starting time of each round must give each minute of the working day an equal chance of being selected.

The use of a random digit table is one of the easier means of insuring the required randomness of selection. (See Sec. 11-2 for a discussion of tables of random digits.) A number of techniques of using the table are available. Some are easy to use but wasteful of random numbers, others better utilize the random digit table but are less easy to use. As an illustration, see the small table of random digits in Figure 14-4. Assume that five rounds are to be made per day, as in the example in Sec. 14-2.

One technique is to let two digits stand for the hour. For an eight-hour shift, with lunch from 12:00 to 1:00, the digits used would be: 08, 09, 10,

96407	81056	34862	39450	43084	39552	60541	03784	34490	75968
73810	91188	63405	63968	28905	98388	74508	37504	02651	92232
46242	65728	37976	27321	33498	72640	55514	41765	77281	70624
25472	65098	45175	31776	54872	06526	34150	30016	69143	40401
21819	55328	70650	65589	27303	98336	76081	07428	48298	27200

Fig 14-4. Table of Random Digits

11, 01, 02, 03, 04. All other combinations of two-digit numbers would be skipped. Thus, reading from left to right in Figure 14-4, the first acceptable two-digit number is 10, signifying that an observation round will be made between 10:00 A.M. and 11:00 A.M. It is now necessary to ascertain the minute, using numbers ranging from 00–59. The 56 following the 10 falls in this range, so one of the five rounds will start at 10:56 A.M. The hour for the second round is then selected. This turns out to be 04 for 4 P.M. and the minute is 30, so the exact starting time is 4:30 P.M. In the event that the round would take more than one-half hour to complete, the 4:30 starting time would be rejected, and the next time as determined by the table of random digits would be selected. A similar procedure would be used for times which would result in overlapping rounds. The starting times of the five rounds would be: 8:37, 10:11, 10:56, 3:43, and 4:30.

An alternative method, less wasteful of digits but more difficult to apply, is to use a three-digit number. Let the first digit stand for the shift hour, and the second two digits stand for the percentage of 60 minutes. The first three digits, 966, would be skipped because there are only eight hours. The second three would similarly be skipped. The third three, 105, would be converted into 8:03 A.M. That is, the 1 stands for the first hour, 8 o'clock, and the 05 for 5 per cent of 60 minutes. The resulting schedule would be: 8:03, 10:56, 1:02, 2:22, and 4:37. There are, of course, a number of other methods of using random digit tables to schedule the starting times of the observation rounds.

The path followed on the observation rounds should also be randomized. One technique for doing this is to have several possible starting points, and the starting point for each round determined by use of a random digit table. Another technique is to develop several alternative routes covering the same observation points. The route to be followed during a given round would then be selected by reference to the random digit table.

SEC. 14-6. PERFORMING THE DAILY OBSERVATIONS

In order adequately to perform the daily observations, the observer must be well instructed as to (1) what categories to observe; (2) how to make the observations; (3) he must also be provided with an adequate means of recording the observations as made.

The Categories to be Observed

In selecting the categories to be observed, the analyst must provide a category for every possibility, or the observer will encounter difficulty in recording his observations. This does not imply that there will always be a large number of categories in a given study. In the illustrative problem, two categories may suffice: working and idle. Since in this case it was desired to analyze the causes of idle time, the idle time was divided into five categories, making six categories in all. In the event that there are other categories of idle time, the recorded observations may be incorrect.

Making the Observations

The observer must neither anticipate activities nor misinterpret those he sees. He should make snap readings always from a given observation point. If it is necessary to question the employee or his foreman as to the specific category to be recorded, this should be done after the activity has been observed. Some authorities recommend that the observer be as unintrusive as possible and wait to record the observations until after leaving the observation area. The theory behind this is that the employee is less likely to vary his activities as a result of being observed. Nevertheless, these same authorities advise that the employees be fully informed of the study both with respect to its methods and its purposes.

Recording the Observations

Proper forms must be prepared in order to facilitate recording the observations. Usually standardized forms cannot readily be used because of the variability of the categories from one study to another. In designing the forms, simplicity and ease of recording are of utmost importance. Figure 14-5 illustrates a simple form that could be used for the illustrative problem. The assumption is that 5 observers are to be used, each observing 40 persons per observation round. The form provides enough spaces to record one day's observations of five rounds. The day's observations recorded in Figure 14-5 show that in 120 of the 200 observations, or 60 per cent, the employees were working. The remaining observations were 5 per cent, waiting for parts; $7\frac{1}{2}$ per cent, waiting for tools; $2\frac{1}{2}$ per cent, waiting for instructions; 15 per cent, unrelated conversation; and 10 per cent, personal time.

Date_____	Categories					
Observer_____	1. Working 2. Waiting for parts 3. Waiting for tools		4. Waiting for instructions 5. Unrelated conversation 6. Personal time				

Employee	Observation round					
	1st	2nd	3rd	4th	5th	
S. Jones	1	5	1	1	2	
B. Smith	1	6	1	1	1	
R. Day	1	5	1	6	1	
M. Brown	3	1	1	1	4	
L. Taylor	2	1	1	1	1	
P. Arrow	1	1	6	1	1	
J. Roberts	1	1	1	1	1	

Totals per category					
1	2	3	4	5	6
120	10	15	5	30	20

Fig. 14-5 Observation Sheet for Work Sampling

SEC. 14-7. USE OF CONTROL CHARTS IN WORK SAMPLING

Control charts such as are used in quality control work are also useful in work sampling (1) to detect nontypical sampling rounds resulting from assignable causes, (2) to help in setting valid p values, (3) to reveal trends in the operations as improvements are installed. Since the usual statistic involved in work sampling is the percentage or proportion of a certain activity in the universe of activities, the p chart is the most widely used.

Figure 14-6 shows a control chart for the sample problem based upon samples of 200 (40 observations for each of 5 observers). The center line, $\bar{p}$, is set after about 10 samples have been taken. The chart is drawn for the category "personal time," and the initial $\bar{p} = 0.10$; that is, $\bar{p}$ is equal to the average p of each of the first 10 samples. The control limits, both upper and lower, are set $3\sigma_p$ away from $\bar{p}$, where

$$3\sigma_p = 3\sqrt{\frac{\bar{p}(1-\bar{p})}{n}}.$$

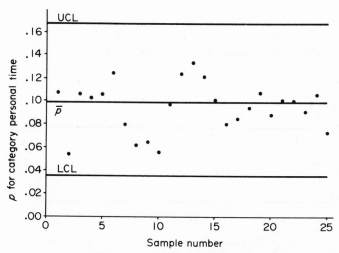

Fig. 14-6. Control Chart for Work Sampling

In this case, n = the number of observations per round. Therefore,

$$3\sigma_p = 3\sqrt{\frac{(0.1)(0.9)}{200}} = 0.06363$$

and   upper control limit = $0.1 + 0.064 = 0.164$

lower control limit = $0.1 - 0.064 = 0.036$.

After 25 rounds of observations, Figure 14-6 shows that no round has produced a p value falling beyond the control limits. The inference is that all the observation rounds produced unbiased estimates of p and that $\bar{p}$ is likely to be the best estimate of p' within the degree of accuracy permitted by the total number of observations N (in this case $N = 25 \times 200 = 5000$ observations).

Figure 14-7, however, shows three points which have fallen outside the control limits. Since $\pm 3\sigma_p$ takes in only 99.7 per cent of all p's, it is possible that a given observation falling outside the control limits is one of the remaining 0.3 per cent. But only 3 out of 1000 p's would normally be expected to exceed the $\pm 3\sigma_p$ limits. Thus the probability of a given p doing so is quite small, and the presumption therefore is that the p falling outside the limit is biased by some assignable cause and not one of the 3 out of 1000. Hence, each p falling outside the control limits is investigated in order to ascertain, if possible, what caused the abnormally high or low reading. If no such cause can be found, then the reading may really be one of those 3 out of 1000 cases.

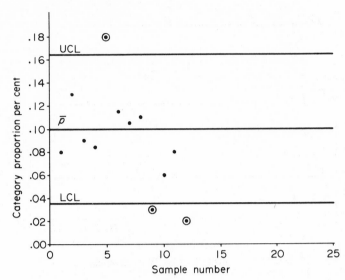

Fig. 14-7. Control Chart with Points Outside the Control Limits

If an assignable cause is found, the data from that observation round should be excluded from the computation of p', and an additional observation round made if necessary to satisfy the number of observations required for the desired accuracy. If no assignable cause is found, at least two possible interpretations of the out-of-control readings may be made: (1) the point is merely one of the 3 out of 1000 normal readings beyond the $\pm\ 3\sigma_p$ limits, (2) the point indicates that the $\bar{p}$ of the control chart is either too high (if the point is below the lower control limit) or too low (if the point is above the upper control limit).

In the first case, no action is required, and the control chart is continued with the $\bar{p}$ and the control limits unchanged. In the second case, a new $\bar{p}$ and control limits should be computed (including the out-of-control points in the computation), and the points replotted.

DISCUSSION QUESTIONS

14-1. How do work sampling concepts relate to the theory of statistical sampling?

14-2. What probability distribution forms the basis for work sampling theory?

14-3. Upon what factors do the number of sampling observations depend?

14-4. What factor required for computing the number of sampling observations is unknown, and how may this factor be estimated?

14-5. How is the required accuracy of the inferred proportion determined, and what effect does the value of p have upon this accuracy?

14-6. What is the *standard error of the proportion*, and what is the formula for computing it?

14-7. Explain how to compute the required number of observations.

14-8. Explain how to ascertain the accuracy achieved at a specified number of observations.

14-9. Describe the graphical approach to obtaining the required number of observations, and discuss the limitations of this method.

14-10. What are the important factors to be considered in setting the size of the daily sample? Discuss each of these factors.

14-11. Over how long a period should work sampling observations be made?

14-12. What effect does the existence of cyclical patterns have upon the work sampling observation plan?

14-13. Describe how the starting time for observation rounds are scheduled.

14-14. How may randomization be applied to the path followed in the observation rounds?

14-15. In what major areas should the observer be well instructed?

14-16. What difficulties would ensue if all possible categories were not provided for?

14-17. Discuss the preparation of data forms for the recording of observations.

14-18. What information may be obtained from control charts applied to work sampling data?

14-19. What type of control chart is most frequently used in work sampling?

14-20. Discuss how $\bar{p}$ is set, and under what circumstances it should be changed.

14-21. What limits are used to determine sample proportions out of control? What interpretation may be placed upon such proportions, and what actions should be taken?

PROBLEMS

14-1. It is desired to ascertain the down time on a bank of automatic screw machines. It is estimated that the down time is 25 per cent. Compute the number of observations required to obtain $\pm$ 10 per cent accuracy.

14-2. After 500 observations, the down time of Problem 14-1 appears really to be 30 per cent. Compute the number of observations required to obtain $\pm$ 10 per cent accuracy.

14-3. After 900 observations, the down time of Problem 14-1 was computed to be 31.5 per cent. Determine the number of additional observations required to obtain $\pm$ 10 per cent accuracy.

14-4. Two thousand observations have been made, and p' is computed as 16 per cent. Ascertain the degree of accuracy obtained.

14-5. Ascertain the degree of accuracy obtained after 3600 observations and a p' of 2 per cent.

14-6. Ten observation rounds per day are to be scheduled. Each round takes 15 minutes, and there are 15-minute breaks at 10:00 and 2:30, and lunch from 12:00 to 1:00. Prepare schedules of starting times for 3 days.

14-7. The company in Problem 14-6 is planning a different work sampling project requiring 30 rounds per day. Each round requires 3 minutes. Prepare schedules for the first 2 days.

14-8. The company in Problem 14-6 has 3 different routes planned for its observation rounds. Prepare a schedule showing which of the 3 routes will be used for each of the 10 rounds.

14-9. The company in Problem 14-7 has 5 different routes planned for its observation rounds. Prepare a schedule showing which of the 5 routes will be used for each of the 30 rounds.

14-10. Lay out a control chart with upper and lower control limits where $\bar{p} = 0.2$ and the daily sample size = 150.

14-11. Lay out a control chart with upper and lower control limits where $\bar{p} = 0.45$ and the daily sample size = 75.

BIBLIOGRAPHY

Barnes, Ralph M., *Work Sampling*, 2nd ed. New York: John Wiley & Sons, Inc., 1957.

_____, *Motion and Time Study*, 4th ed. New York: John Wiley & Sons, Inc., 1958, pp. 498-527.

Brisley, C. L., "How You Can Put Work Sampling to Work," *Factory Management and Maintenance* (July, 1952), 83-89.

Hansen, Bertrand L., *Work Sampling for Modern Management*. Englewood Cliffs, N.J.: Prentice-Hall, Inc., 1960.

Heiland, Robert E., and Wallace J. Richardson, *Work Sampling*. New York: McGraw-Hill Book Company, Inc., 1957.

Morrow, R. L., *Time Study and Motion Economy*. New York: The Ronald Press Co., 1946, pp. 175-99.

Niebel, Benjamin W., *Motion and Time Study*, 3rd ed. Homewood, Ill.: Richard D. Irwin, Inc., 1962, pp. 414-39.

Tippett, L. H. C., "Statistical Methods in Textile Research. Uses of the Binomial and Poisson Distribution. A Snap-Reading Method of Making Time Studies of Machines and Operatives in Factory Surveys," *Journal of Textile Institute Transactions* 26 (February, 1935), 51-55.

_____, *Technical Applications of Statistics*. New York: John Wiley & Sons, Inc., 1950.

15

PACE—
Performance and Cost Evaluation

SEC. 15-1. STATEMENT OF THE PROBLEM TO BE SOLVED

As a result of its work sampling experiment (see Sec. 14-1), the West Coast Aircraft Corporation found that its maintenance crew spent too much time in idleness. It was quite surprised, however, to learn that much of the idle time was caused by failure on the part of the supervisors, rather than by deliberate slacking off on the part of the employees. Idle time, such as waiting for parts, tools, and instructions, was caused at least to some degree by the lack of adequate planning.

What was needed, it was reasoned, was some method of controlling the inputs into the system. Thus, if the inputs were properly controlled, the outputs would more likely be satisfactory. The Northrop Corporation had recently devised a method for controlling the inputs of the human factor. It calls the method Performance And Cost Evaluation or PACE. The West Coast Aircraft Corporation decided to install the PACE program, to be used not only as a means of controlling its maintenance department, but also to be used generally throughout its operations, including production, office work, engineering, and research and development.

SEC. 15-2. BACKGROUND CONCEPTS OF PACE

The speed of operations of highly automated or assembly line industries is determined largely by the functioning of the machines, and the tempo of the workers tends to be geared to the speed of these machines. Controls of the kind supplied by PACE are thus relatively unnecessary.

261

In the airframe and missile industries (and all others neither highly automated nor using assembly line techniques), however, the speed of operations tends to be set by the performance of people. It was to control this type of operation that PACE was developed by the Norair Division of the Northrop Corporation. The techniques utilized in PACE and discussed here are those developed by the Northrop Corporation. The reader interested in a more detailed discussion of the subjects developed in this chapter is referred to the multivolume text, to be entitled *P.A.C.E.*, currently being written by D. N. Petersen, Director of the PACE Services Section at the Norair Division of the Northrop Corporation and to be published by that company.

PACE is a statistical analytical method based largely upon work sampling and effort rating. These and other work measurement techniques, such as time and motion studies, and so forth, are usually aimed at measuring the individual. PACE, however, is a device to measure the effectiveness of a group in performing an assigned task. It is used as a means of controlling the input of the human factor in the production equation.

PACE is divided into two major components. The first is PACE measurement, which is an index based upon four factors: (1) persons assigned to the task, (2) persons idle, (3) persons out of the task area, (4) the group effort rating. The second is the PACE program, which is a graphical analysis showing the PACE measurement index and five related indices, namely, (1) personnel requirements, (2) budget realization, (3) scheduling, (4) quality control, (5) parts shortages. The indices to be included as a part of the PACE program may be all or part of the foregoing five, or other indices may be substituted where such indices are found to be more pertinent to the specific situation.

PACE makes no attempt to determine or apply direct costs to product. No measurement is made of individuals nor do individual names appear on any PACE records. Instead the objective is to control those two factors which appear to permit the greatest improvement, namely, the human effort factor and idle time of employees. An analysis of the chart showing the six major components of the PACE program (see Figure 15-14) affords management an almost instantaneous view of current performance and performance trends, and permits a pinpointing of those factors causing "out-of-control" conditions, that is, conditions outside the limits considered to indicate satisfactory performance.

The PACE measurement index is based upon work sampling techniques quite similar to those discussed in Chapter 14. In this case, however, because of the effort rating factor involved, the observers must be highly qualified industrial engineers who have received additional training in PACE observational methods. This training, including the indoctrination of the supervisory personnel involved, takes about five weeks. The installation of the PACE program takes another five weeks; thus ten weeks are required before PACE is fully operational.

SEC. 15-3.   PACE MEASUREMENT INDEX

Basic to PACE is the PACE measurement index. The formula for the index is

$$\text{PACE index} = \frac{[N \pm L - (I + A)]}{N \pm L} \times E \times 100,$$

where
N = number assigned
L = number loaned
I = number idle
A = number absent
E = group effort rating.

The number available for the task is the basic number assigned plus or minus any persons temporarily transferred to or from the basic group (number loaned). From the number available is deducted the sum of those idle (that is, not specifically working at the task) and those physically out of the task area. This figure is the number actually working at the moment of observation. The number actually working divided by the number available $(N \pm L)$ gives the proportion of those available who are producing. This value, however, still lacks significance, since the tempo of the group may range from extremely slow to abnormally fast. The figure for the proportion working is therefore modified by the group effort rating, and the resulting figure is multiplied by 100 in order to convert the decimal into a percentage.

Three of the values in the PACE index are at least to some degree subjective, and hence might be challenged by those being measured. These are (1) the number idle, (2) the number out of area, (3) the group effort rating. The first two, however, can be fairly sharply defined.

The Idle Time Index

At least two definitions of persons idle may be used, and each results in a different index. In fact, both definitions and both indices may be profitably used. In both cases, an individual is classified as being idle only if he is in the assigned work area. A person out of the area is not classified as being idle regardless of his activity.

According to the first definition, a person is considered to be idle only if he is engaged in some activity not related to the job, such as horseplay, idle conversation, loafing, and so forth. This is the usual concept of idleness. Idleness is not necessarily caused by a desire on the part of the employee not to produce, but may be the result of waiting for parts, instructions, and so forth. Whatever the cause, employees will frequently be idle from 10 per cent to 40 per cent of the time. Column (6) of Figure

Week (1)	No. Assigned (2)	No. on Loan (3)	% Personnel (4)	Average No. Idle (5)	% Idle (6)	Average No. Observed (7)	% Out of Area (8)	Average % Effort (9)	% PACE (10)
1	120	0	100	12	10	110	8	80	65
2	120	10	108	42	32	117	10	83	48
3	120	11	101	45	34	122	7	79	46
4	120	8	98	9	7	123	4	70	62
5	120	7	99	15	12	119	6	70	57
6	120	2	96	7	6	118	3	75	68
7	120	0	98	8	7	118	2	80	73
8	120	−4	97	6	5	114	2	76	71
9	116	−6	95	3	3	106	4	77	72
10	110	−8	93	5	5	99	3	85	78
11	102	−5	94	8	8	95	3	86	77

Fig. 15-1. PACE Observation Data—First Eleven Weeks

15-1 shows the percentage idle for each of the first eleven weeks of observation. This percentage is computed by the formula:

$$\text{idle time index} = \frac{\text{average no. idle}}{\text{no. assigned} \pm \text{loans}} \times 100.$$

For the first week, this is

$$\text{idle time index} = \frac{12}{120 + 0} \times 100 = 10 \text{ per cent.}$$

The PACE Measurement Factors are graphically illustrated in Figure 15-2, and the weekly per cent idle is shown plotted on the basic PACE chart (Figure 15-3). This concept of per cent idle is the one used as a component of the PACE measurement index.

Notice that the lower 5 per cent of Figure 15-3 is shaded. The objective is to maintain the per cent idle index at 0 per cent. Such perfection can rarely be achieved, however, for practical purposes, a weekly reading falling within the shaded area (5 per cent or less) is regarded as being in control. When the weekly reading falls above the shaded area, there

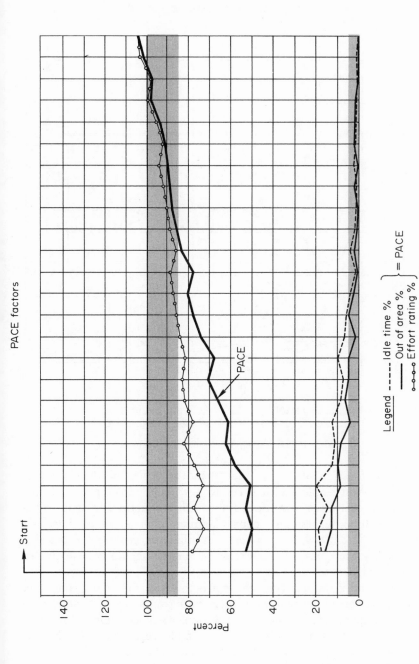

Fig. 15-2. PACE Measurement Factors

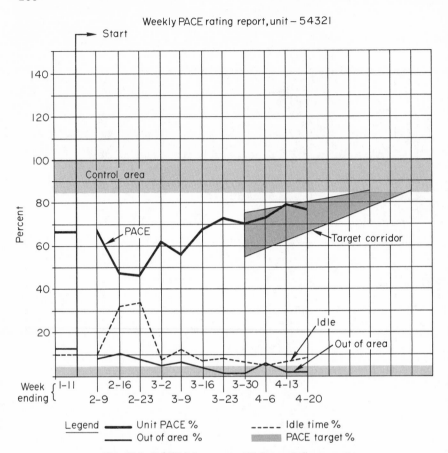

Fig. 15-3. PACE Measurement Index and Components

is probably an assignable cause other than the desire of the employees to slack off. Most employees, it is believed, want to do a good job and will produce well when conditions favor such production. Excessive idleness may well be the result of poor planning, such as parts shortages, inadequate instructions, and so forth. A high per cent idle index is a warning that the cause of the excessive idleness should be investigated and corrected.

A refinement of the idle-time concept is that referred to as *adding value realization*. A person is considered to be adding value only if he is physically working on the product of the group, such as typing (for office personnel) or tightening a bolt (for plant employees). For this purpose, receiving instructions from the supervisor is considered to be working, but is not adding value directly to the product. Thus, manual, oral, or visual work not directly related to physically adding value to the product would not be counted. The formula for the adding value index is

$$\text{adding value index} = \frac{\text{no. adding value}}{\text{no. assigned} \pm \text{loans}} \times 100.$$

The average number of employees adding value to the product for the ninth through twenty-fourth weeks is shown in Figure 15-4. The computation for the ninth week is

$$\text{adding value index} = \frac{58}{116 - 6} \times 100 = 53 \text{ per cent.}$$

The adding value percentages are graphed as vertical bars on Figure 15-14. The adding value index is *not* a component of the PACE measurement index.

The ideal adding value index is 100 per cent. This ideal can rarely, if ever, be reached. Therefore, any value falling within the range 85 per cent to 100 per cent (the shaded area in the center of Figure 15-14) is considered to be in control. Any value falling below the shaded area is cause for investigation, since the employees are spending an excessive amount of time in manual, oral, or visual activity not directly pertaining to the physical product of the group.

Week	No. Assigned	No. on Loan	No. Adding Value	% Adding Value
9	116	−6	58	53
10	110	−8	56	55
11	102	−5	54	56
12	97	−3	56	60
13	94	−2	58	63
14	92	−1	59	65
15	91	−2	55	62
16	89	−3	54	63
17	86	−2	57	68
18	84	−1	60	72
19	83	0	63	76
20	83	0	66	80
21	83	−1	68	83
22	82	0	69	84
23	82	−1	70	87
24	81	−1	71	89

Fig. 15-4. Data for Adding Value Index

The Out of Area Index

Employees may be out of their assigned area for a number of reasons, such as going to parts storage, going to the engineering department, away on personal business, and so forth. Except for personal business, many such out of area trips may be caused by poor planning on the part of the supervisors. The job can, perhaps, be planned so that parts are brought to the place of work, needed engineering advice is at hand, and so forth. Therefore, all absences from the job are counted as out of area. The only exceptions are those occasions when the employee is officially authorized to perform an assigned task at some other location. The formula for the out of area index is

$$\text{out of area index} = 100 - \frac{\text{no. of workers observed}}{\text{no. assigned} \pm \text{loans}} \times 100.$$

The per cent out of area for the first eleven weeks is listed in column (8) of Figure 15-1. The computation for the first week is

$$\text{out of area index} = 100 - \frac{110}{120 + 0} \times 100 = 8 \text{ per cent.}$$

The out of area index is shown graphed on Figure 15-3; it is one of the components of the PACE measurement index.

Once again, the lower shaded area (0 per cent to 5 per cent) represents readings in control. Any readings outside that area (over 5 per cent) offer excellent opportunities for improvement, particularly in relation to job planning. The goal is to bring everything possible to the group so that members of the group do not need to leave the assigned area in order to locate supplies, directives, and so forth.

The Group Effort Index

The counting of people idle or out of area is based upon reasonably objective facts. The PACE measurement index would have relatively little significance, however, if it were based only on these two factors. They are, therefore, modified by the somewhat more subjective factor of effort expended, or what the industrial engineer calls *tempo*. This rating is generally applied to an individual during the time study of a production operation. Here, the tempo of the entire group is to be rated. This is merely the average of the tempo of the individual members. A 100 per cent effort rating is based upon the commonly accepted norm of a man walking without a load and on level ground at a rate of 3 miles per hour. Thus with a four-man group, if the individual ratings are

Man	Rating (%)
1	110
2	84
3	100
4	70
	364

The group effort rating computation is

$$\text{group effort rating} = \frac{364}{4} = 91 \text{ per cent.}$$

In measuring the group effort, only individuals working are considered; persons idle are not part of the group effort rating.

It can readily be seen that unless the group effort ratings are made by highly trained men, and made on a very consistent basis, the PACE measurement index will have relatively little significance. For this reason only experienced industrial engineers who have undergone additional training in PACE observation procedures are used as observers. This training is largely concentrated on the measuring of group effort. The industrial engineer, as a result of his time study work, usually has a wide experience in the effort rating of individuals. This ability must first be applied to the effort rating of several individuals and finally to rating the effort of a composite group. The technique used is the observation of motion pictures of individuals and groups working with varying degrees of effort. The training is continued until the observers rate the groups consistently at predetermined levels. When the observers are assigned to observation areas, their work is periodically checked by supervisors of the PACE observation group. When the observer's ratings appear to be off-standard, he is subjected to additional training. Any observers unable to achieve acceptable effort rating standards are transferred to other duties.

The average group effort ratings for the first eleven weeks' observations are listed in column (9) of Figure 15-1 and graphed in Figure 15-3. The group effort index is the third and final component of the PACE measurement index.

Since all the components of the PACE measurement index have now been determined, the per cent PACE may be computed. These values are listed in column (10) of Figure 15-1 and graphed in Figure 15-3. The computation for the first week is

$$\text{PACE index} = \frac{[N \pm L - (I + A)]}{N \pm L} \times E \times 100$$

$$= \frac{[120 + 0 - (12 + 10)]}{120 + 0} \times 80 \times 100$$

$$= 65 \text{ per cent.}$$

Making the Observations

The observations are made in accordance with the rules of work sampling discussed in Chapter 14. In the beginning, each observer makes about 15 rounds per day and is able to observe from 300 to 700 people per round. When all PACE program indices are under control, the number of rounds per day may be reduced. Several possible routes should be developed, and the round for each route selected by a random process. The starting times for each route must also be selected by a similar random process. (Suggested techniques are discussed in Sec. 14-5.)

The Target Corridor

The PACE measurement index is considered in control when it is in the 85 per cent to 100 per cent range. The 85 per cent lower range is derived from a 5 per cent error allowance for each of the three components of the PACE index, namely idle time, out of area, and effort rating. Few establishments will have an initial PACE index in the control area when the program is first established. Nor can the index be expected to go immediately to 85 per cent or above. Improvement will be gradually achieved as weak spots are revealed by excessive idle time and out of area indices and by a too low effort index. As the supervisors attack and eliminate these weak spots, the PACE index will trend toward the control area. After about eight weeks of observations, the strength of this trend will be quite evident. At this time an upper and lower control line may be drawn on the basic PACE chart (see Figure 15-3) leading into the control area. These control lines should follow the trend so far obtained, leading into the control area at around fourteen to sixteen weeks. The area between the two control lines is called the *target corridor*. PACE readings falling outside the corridor call for special investigation. Those falling below the lower control line mean that improvements are not being made as fast as they should, and perhaps special correctional efforts may be required. Readings falling above the upper control line should be investigated to find how this exceptional performance was achieved so as to be able to continue it.

SEC. 15-4. THE PERSONNEL INDEX

The PACE measurement index and its components, the idle time, out of area, and group effort indices, can be used very advantageously in the analysis and control of the human factor in the production equation. The value of the PACE index is improved considerably when it is combined with all or some of the five other indices which together constitute the

PACE program. The first of these five indices to be considered is the *personnel index*. The personnel index is closely related to the components of the PACE index.

If all employees performed with a 100 per cent effort rating and were never idle or out of the area, the group assignment would be performed with the minimum personnel requirement. Therefore, as the PACE index trends upward and approaches the 100 per cent limit, the number of employees required should approach the minimum requirement.

The personnel index is the ratio between the number of employees in the group this week and the similar number last week expressed as a percentage. The formula for the personnel index is

$$\text{personnel index} = \frac{\text{group size this week}}{\text{group size last week}} \times 100.$$

The personnel index values for the first eleven weeks are listed in column (4) of Figure 15-1, and are graphed in Figure 15-5. The computation for the index value for the second week is

$$\text{personnel index} = \frac{120 + 10}{120 + 0} \times 100 = 108 \text{ per cent.}$$

An index value over 100 per cent means that the group size has increased. Unless the assigned task has correspondingly increased, a personnel index value over 100 per cent should be investigated for a possible assignable cause. Clearly, the components of the PACE index (idle time, out of area, and group effort) would be the logical place for the initial investigation. Since the personnel index is plotted on the same chart with PACE and its components, the specific area for investigation may be immediately apparent.

A horizontal personnel index trend at 100 per cent should occur only with the PACE index well within the control area and also trending horizontally. When the PACE index is climbing, there should be a horizontal personnel index at 100 per cent only if the task assignment is also increasing. In most cases, particularly during the early phases of the program, the PACE index will be trending upward, and the personnel index will be below 100 per cent. Notice that the slope of the personnel index is not the criterion to check. A 95 per cent horizontal trend would indicate a 5 per cent reduction in group size every week—a very enviable achievement, given that the task size remains constant. Similarly, a 105 per cent horizontal trend would indicate a 5 per cent weekly increase in group size.

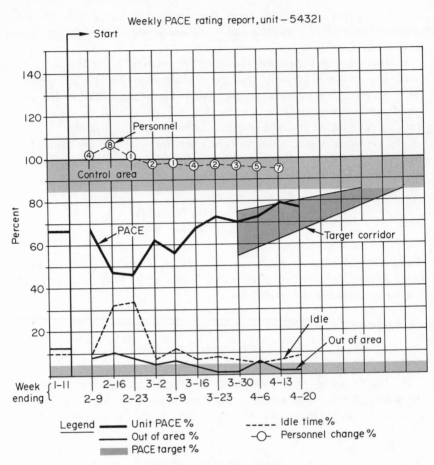

Fig. 15-5. The Personnel Index

SEC. 15-5. THE BUDGET INDEX

Budgetary control provides one of the more commonly used control functions. The usual practice is to prepare detailed budgets for both the departmental operations and for the job or function. The budgeted figures are then compared to those actually expended. The budget may be in terms of hours or cost or both. For the purpose of the PACE program, the budget must be prepared in terms of hours by job and function as related to the group being measured. The budget index then may be computed weekly as follows

$$\text{budget index} = \frac{\text{budgeted hours}}{\text{actual hours}} \times 100.$$

The values for the first eleven weeks' observations are listed in Figure 15-6, and graphed in Figure 15-7. The computation for the first week is

$$\text{budget index} = \frac{3460}{4800} \times 100 = 72 \text{ per cent.}$$

The significance of the relationship between budgeted and actual performance is dependent upon two factors: (1) The accuracy with which the budget is prepared; that is, how close would perfect performance coincide with budgetary predictions, (2) how well did the group actually perform in relation to its best potential performance. A budget index of 100 per cent does not necessarily mean that both the budgetary prediction and the actual performance were perfect. It only means that the two values were equal.

Week	Budgeted Hours	Actual Hours	Budget Index
1	3460	4800	72
2	3460	5200	67
3	3250	5240	62
4	3640	5120	71
5	3150	5080	62
6	4000	4880	82
7	4320	4800	90
8	4180	4640	90
9	4140	4400	94
10	3700	4080	91
11	3800	3880	98

Fig. 15-6. Data for the Budget Realization Index

If, before the installation of the PACE program, the budget figures were geared to a presumably inferior performance, the budget index would start at around 100 per cent. Then as the PACE index trends toward the control area, the budget index should also rise, but would be in excess of 100 per cent. A continued budget index in excess of 100 per cent indicates that the job has been overbudgeted. On the other hand, if the budget were geared to expected satisfactory performance, at the beginning of the PACE program the budget index would be low, probably not too far from the PACE index. As PACE improves so will the budget index. When PACE is well into the control area, the budget index should hover around a 100 per cent horizontal trend. A horizontal budget line below 100 per cent would tend to indicate that the project had been underbudgeted.

In many of the industries to which the PACE program would be applicable (those not highly automated nor under rigid assembly line

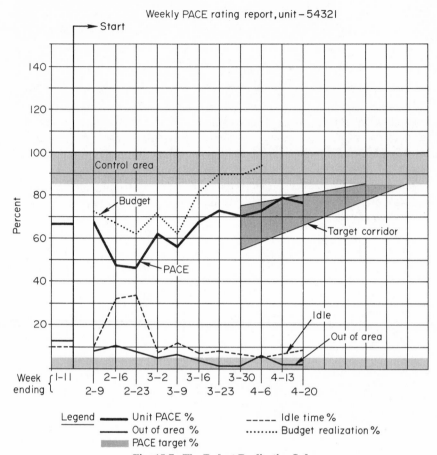

Fig. 15-7. The Budget Realization Index

conditions) the budget should be prepared using learning curve concepts. (The learning curve is discussed in Chapter 8.)

SEC. 15-6. THE SCHEDULE INDEX

In the usual manufacturing situation, the production of components and assemblies is scheduled to achieve a smooth flow of the product through the plant and to achieve deliveries on the required dates. Failure to maintain the schedule in any given department can raise havoc with the scheduling in the remainder of the plant. If one department drops behind schedule, the parts it supplies to the next department will not be available when needed. This can set up a chain reaction of shortages from department to department. The opposite condition (being ahead of schedule), although usually not as serious, can also create difficult problems, particularly those pertaining to storage.

Week	Units Scheduled	Units Produced	Schedule Index
1	250	210	84
2	250	193	77
3	235	188	80
4	263	221	84
5	228	194	85
6	289	266	92
7	312	324	104
8	302	336	111
9	299	323	108
10	267	294	110
11	275	300	109

Fig. 15-8. Data for the Schedule Index

The *schedule index* is a device to measure the degree to which the production schedule is being maintained. The index is based upon the ratio of items produced per unit of time to items scheduled to be produced per that unit of time. For the purposes of PACE, the convenient time unit is one week. The formula is

$$\text{schedule index} = \frac{\text{actual units produced}}{\text{units scheduled to be produced}} \times 100.$$

The data for the units scheduled and produced for the first eleven weeks are listed in Figure 15-8, and graphed in Figure 15-9. The computation for the first week is

$$\text{schedule index} = \frac{210}{250} \times 100 = 84 \text{ per cent.}$$

An index of 100 per cent indicates that production is occurring right on schedule. A continuing index above 100 per cent is evidence that the group size should be reduced. When the index is running below 100 per cent, the components of PACE should be checked as well as the parts shortage index (see Sec. 15-8). If one or more of these indices are out of control, an investigation should be made and the cause corrected. If all indices are within the control range, then very likely the group size will have to be increased.

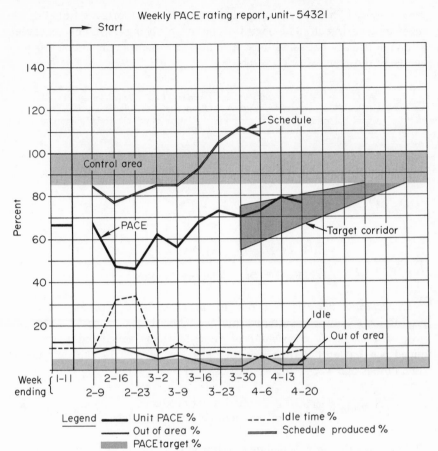

Fig. 15-9. The Schedule Index

SEC. 15-7. THE QUALITY INDEX

The quality index was devised to combat the fear that as the group effort increases, the quality of the product is likely to suffer. A company wishing to use the quality index must also be using a statistical inspection system. Records must be kept as to the percentage defective in the case of small units, or as to number of defects per unit in the case of large assemblies. The percentage defective for the preceding ten or twelve weeks is used to estimate $\bar{p}$, the expected average percentage defective.

The quality index is based upon the p control chart (see Sec. 13-4). The deviation of this week's per cent defective, p, from the average per cent defective is

$$\text{deviation} = p - \bar{p}.$$

This deviation is then divided by the standard error of the percentage in order to express the deviation in terms of standard errors:

$$\text{deviation in terms of standard errors of } \% = \frac{p - \bar{p}}{\sigma_{\bar{p}}},$$

where

$$\sigma_{\bar{p}} = \frac{\sqrt{\bar{p}(1 - \bar{p})}}{\sqrt{n}}$$

$n = $ number of units this week.

The true average percentage defective, p', is within the range $\bar{p} \pm 3\sigma_{\bar{p}}$ with a probability of 0.9973. Since the standard error is in terms of per cent, the range would be $\pm$ 3 per cent. However, the control limit is set at 15 per cent (that is, at 85 per cent to 100 per cent). In order to bring the 3 per cent to a value of 15 per cent (the width of the control area), the value of the deviation in terms of standard errors of the percentage is multiplied by five; thus,

$$\text{quality index} = 100 - \frac{5(p - \bar{p})}{\sigma_{\bar{p}}}$$

$$= 100 - \frac{5(p - \bar{p})}{\sqrt{\bar{p}(1 - \bar{p})} / \sqrt{n}}$$

$$= 100 - \frac{5\sqrt{n}(p - \bar{p})}{\sqrt{\bar{p}(1 - \bar{p})}},$$

the adjusted value is then subtracted from 100 so that the trend will increase as quality increases, and the out of control point will be the 85 per cent level rather than the 15 per cent level.

Note that $\bar{p}$, the past average percentage defective, is now set at 100 per cent. Thus the 100 per cent line is the center line of a p control chart (see Sec. 13-4), and the lower control limit is at 85 per cent. The upper control limit would be at 115 per cent, but is not drawn on the chart. The quality index may be subjected to the usual control chart analysis, including the theory of runs (see Sec. 13-8).

The data for the quality index for the first eleven weeks' observations are shown in Figure 15-10, and the index is graphed on Figure 15-11. The computation for the first week is

$$\text{quality index} = 100 - \frac{5\sqrt{n}(p - \bar{p})}{\sqrt{\bar{p}(1 - \bar{p})}}$$

$$= 100 - \frac{5\sqrt{210}(0.08 - 0.05)}{\sqrt{(0.05)(0.95)}}$$

$$= 90 \text{ per cent.}$$

Week	Number Produced	Number Defective	Percentage Defective	Quality Index
1	210	17	8.0	90
2	193	7	3.7	104
3	188	18	9.8	85
4	221	17	7.9	90
5	194	19	9.7	85
6	266	8	2.9	108
7	324	15	4.5	102
8	336	11	3.3	107
9	323	27	8.4	86
10	294	16	5.5	98
11	300	21	7.0	92

$$\varepsilon = \overline{70.7}$$

$$\bar{p} = \frac{70.7}{11} = 6.4\%*$$

*Average percentage defective, preceding 10 weeks = 5 per cent.

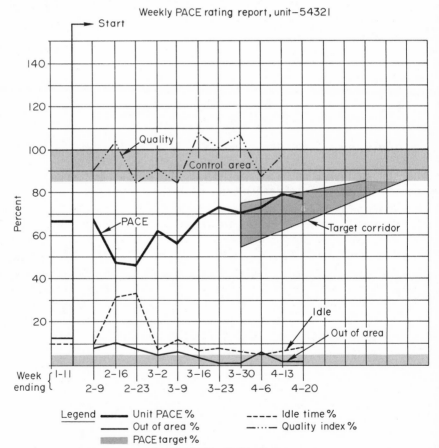

Fig. 15-11. The Quality Index

SEC. 15-8. THE SHORTAGE INDEX

In order to maintain a given manufacturing schedule, it is absolutely necessary that parts be available when and where needed. Parts usually come from two sources: (1) within-plant production and (2) procured from outside suppliers. Maintenance of all schedule indices at 100 per cent should help assure that the parts produced within the plant flow in such a manner as to eliminate parts shortages from that source, assuming that all required parts are properly scheduled. An effective system of inventory control is required to assure that parts procured from outside suppliers are on hand when needed. Even under well-controlled conditions, however, parts shortages will occur.

The effects of such shortages permeate many of the indices so far discussed. The idle time index will go up if the employees have to wait for parts. In those cases where employees are laid off when parts shortages exist, they soon learn to stretch out the work using the parts remaining. This, of course, will be reflected in the effort ratings and PACE indices.

In order to isolate the causes of these effects on other indices, a shortage index is highly useful. The base of the shortage index is the ratio of the number of shortages to the total number of parts. This ratio will approach zero as the number of shortages decreases. At no time, however, is the ratio likely to be very large. For those indices where a declining trend indicates an improvement, the 0 per cent to 5 per cent range represents the area considered to be in control. Therefore the ratio regarded as the control limit in a given department must be adjusted so the index, when graphed, will at that point graph as 5 per cent. Departments vary as to the criticalness of parts shortages. For some departments, the critical ratio will be 0.1 per cent or less. Other departments may function well with ratios of 1 per cent or more. To bring the 0.1 per cent ratio up to a 5 per cent index, the ratio must be multiplied by a factor of 50. Similarly, for a 1 per cent critical ratio, the factor will be only 5. Thus the formula for the shortage index is

$$\text{shortage index} = \frac{\text{no. of parts out of stock}}{\text{no. of parts in dept.}} \times \text{shortage factor} \times 100.$$

The data for the shortage index for the first eleven weeks are listed in Figure 15-12 and graphed on Figure 15-13. The computation for the first week is

$$\text{shortage index} = \frac{203}{3273} \times 5 \times 100 = 31 \text{ per cent.}$$

The shortage index is an extremely important one from the viewpoint

Week	Parts in Dept.	No. of Shortages	Shortage Factor	Shortage Index
1	3273	203	5	31
2	3273	242	5	37
3	3273	255	5	39
4	3273	144	5	22
5	3273	216	5	33
6	3273	98	5	15
7	3273	85	5	13
8	3273	72	5	11
9	3273	65	5	10
10	3273	85	5	13
11	3273	79	5	12

Fig. 15-12. Data for the Shortage Index

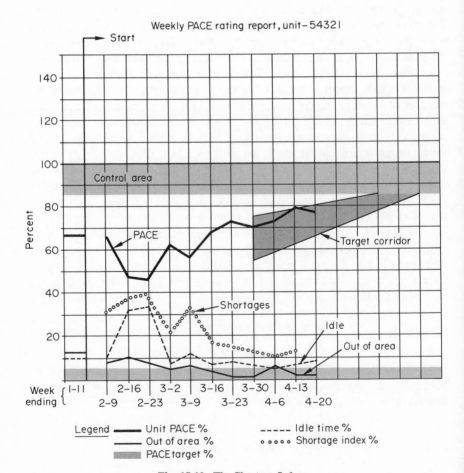

Fig. 15-13. The Shortage Index

of the department. Low effort and PACE indices and high idle time and out of area indices may be traceable to a high shortage index. The head of a department experiencing poor ratings caused by the failure of other officials to perform is likely to apply lateral pressure on those officials. Parts shortages may, of course, be caused by being ahead of schedule in the department in which the shortages have occurred. This would be indicated by a too high schedule index, and a possible remedy would be to reduce the size of the group involved. On the other hand, given a schedule index of 100 per cent or below, the shortage could be caused by a failure of the supplying department to meet its schedule. This would be indicated by a low schedule index in that department. Other possible causes of the parts shortage are (1) failure of the scheduling department to schedule the parts properly, (2) failure of the inventory control department to request the parts, (3) failure of the purchasing department to process the purchase order, (4) failure of the supplier to meet promised delivery dates. The head of a department with a high shortage index is likely to exert pressure to have the reasons for the shortages investigated and eliminated.

SEC. 15-9. COMPARATIVE ANALYSIS OF THE PACE PROGRAM

Figure 15-14 shows graphed on one chart all the indices so far discussed (except for the group effort index which, after the first few weeks tends to follow closely the PACE index). A chart of this nature is submitted weekly to each departmental manager and to his superiors. The chart shows at a glance the present position and the trend of each index, and the interrelationship existing between all of the indices. An analysis of the situation at the end of the eleventh week may be helpful in further illustrating this relationship.

The PACE index is on a generally rising trend, well within the target corridor, although it is down slightly from last week. One of its components, the idle time index is out of control, up from a marginally controlled position last week. The other graphed component, out of area, is just at the control limit, having been under satisfactory control for several weeks. The schedule index has been following a horizontal trend around 110 per cent; the personnel index is similarly horizontal at about 96 per cent; the quality index has been fluctuating within the ± 15 per cent control area, that is, between 85 per cent and 115 per cent; the budget index has been rising and is nicely within the control area; the shortage index has not yet reached control, but is on a declining trend.

The question is, Are there any areas requiring immediate attention? PACE is still low, but has been satisfactorily following the target corridor.

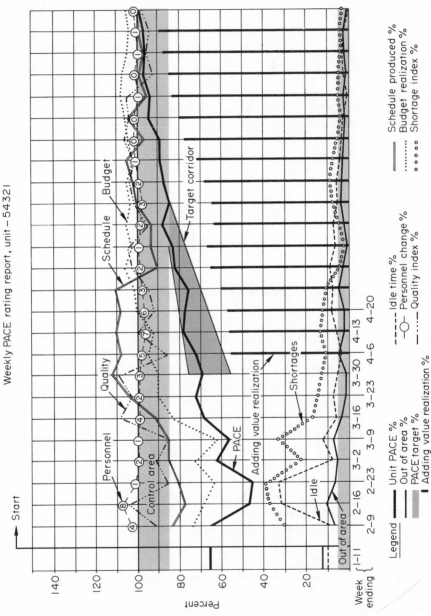

Fig. 15-14. Weekly PACE Program Report Chart

Nevertheless, the low level of PACE shows that there is definitely room for improvement, and that the reasons for failure to perform up to standard should be carefully investigated and rectified. Since the out of area component of PACE is and has been well under control, little improvement can be expected; hence, managerial pressures should be exerted elsewhere. The idle time index has been running close to, or above, the control limits, showing that some improvement can yet be achieved.

A glance at the shortage index reveals that at least some of the excess idle time has been caused by parts shortages, and that shortages would therefore offer a fruitful area for investigation. The schedule index, which has been running at around 110 per cent for several weeks, indicates, however, that some of the shortages were very likely caused by being ahead of schedule. The schedule index may be lowered by reducing the size of the group. The chain effect would then be (1) a reduced group size would tend to reduce the schedule index to normal (that is, 100 per cent); (2) with the schedule at normal, the number of shortages should decrease, possibly bringing the shortage index into the control area; (3) with the reduction in parts shortages, the amount of idle time should be reduced, and both the idle time and group effort indices improved; (4) an improvement in the idle time and group effort indices will also show up in an improved PACE index.

Figure 15-14 graphically portrays the gradually improved performance since the introduction of the PACE program. Inspection of the quality index reveals that no points have fallen outside the control area. This indicates that quality has been satisfactorily maintained in spite of the greatly improved production picture. An impression of the reduction in costs so far obtained can be gained from the trend of the budget index. At the start of the program, the budget realization was in the 60 per cent to 70 per cent area. The index has improved to the extent that it has fallen within the control area for the past five weeks, with a present reading of 98 per cent.

DISCUSSION QUESTIONS

15-1. Under what conditions is the PACE program applicable?

15-2. Upon what two work measurement techniques is PACE measurement based?

15-3. What is the major objective of the PACE program?

15-4. What are the two major components of the PACE program?

15-5. Upon what four factors is the PACE measurement index based?

15-6. Name the indices which together comprise the PACE program.

15-7. State the formula for the *PACE measurement index*.

15-8. Define the term *idle time* as used in the idle time index.

15-9. State the formula for the *idle time index*.

15-10. Discuss the concept of *adding value realization*.

15-11. State the formula for the *adding value index*.

15-12. Define the concept of *out of area* as used in the out of area index.

15-13. State the formula for the *out of area index*.

15-14. Discuss the concept of *group effort rating*.

15-15. What effect does persons idle have upon the group effort rating?

15-16. Why are experienced industrial engineers used as PACE observers, and what additional training must they undergo?

15-17. What is meant by the term *target corridor*? Discuss the method of constructing the target corridor.

15-18. State the formula for the *personnel index*.

15-19. Discuss the meanings of personnel index values at, above, and below 100 per cent.

15-20. State the formula for the *budget realization index*.

15-21. Discuss the significance of various budget realization values.

15-22. State the formula for the *schedule index*.

15-23. Discuss the significance of various schedule index values.

15-24. State the formula for the *quality index*.

15-25. Why is an adjustment factor of *five* used in the quality index?

15-26. What is the relationship of the quality index to control chart theory?

15-27. State the formula for the *shortage index*.

15-28. Why is a *shortage factor* required in the shortage index formula? Describe how to derive the shortage factor.

15-29. Discuss the interrelationships between the various indices of the PACE program.

PROBLEMS

15-1. Following are data from the first eight weeks of PACE observations:

Week	No. Assigned	No. on Loan	Average No. Idle	Average No. Observed	Average % Effort
1	250	0	50	225	70
2	250	13	70	243	75
3	250	8	55	227	74
4	250	0	38	228	76
5	250	0	44	235	76
6	250	−5	31	228	80
7	245	−6	26	229	78
8	239	−2	19	225	83

Graph:
a. Idle time index
b. Out of area index
c. Group effort index
d. PACE index
e. The target corridor

15-2. The following data are from the first eight weeks of PACE observations:

Week	No. Assigned	No. on Loan	Average No. Idle	Average No. Observed	Average % Effort
1	540	0	162	432	80
2	540	54	207	517	75
3	540	84	156	517	70
4	540	84	174	561	77
5	540	95	127	546	82
6	540	75	43	584	80
7	540	75	62	597	75
8	540	44	88	520	80

Graph:
a. Idle time index
b. Out of area index
c. Group effort index
d. PACE index
e. The target corridor

15-3. From the data in problem 15-1, graph the personnel index.

15-4. From the data in problem 15-2, graph the personnel index.

15-5. From the following data, related to the data of problem 15-1, graph a budget realization index.

Week	Budgeted Hours	Actual Hours
1	5,500	10,000
2	5,050	10,520
3	5,470	10,320
4	5,700	10,000
5	5,400	10,000
6	5,880	9,800
7	5,740	9,560
8	5,970	9,480

15-6. From the following data, related to the data of problem 15-2, graph a budget realization index.

Week	Budgeted Hours	Actual Hours
1	9,720	21,600
2	11,880	23,760
3	12,710	24,920
4	11,960	24,920
5	14,480	25,400
6	13,530	24,600
7	15,010	24,600
8	14,720	23,360

15-7. From the following data, related to the data of problem 15-1, graph a schedule index.

Week	Units Scheduled	Units Produced
1	550	413
2	505	404
3	547	427
4	570	490
5	540	432
6	588	517
7	574	540
8	597	567

15-8. From the following data, related to the data of Problem 15-2, graph a schedule index.

Week	Units Scheduled	Units Produced
1	486	403
2	594	463
3	636	528
4	598	538
5	724	608
6	677	630
7	751	713
8	736	736

15-9. From the following data, related to the data of problem 15-1, graph a quality index.

Week	Number Produced	Number Defective*
1	413	17
2	404	19
3	427	9
4	490	30
5	432	22
6	517	32
7	540	29
8	567	26

*Average per cent defective, preceding 10 weeks = 5 per cent.

15-10. From the following data, related to the data of problem 15-2, graph a quality index.

Week	Number Produced	Number Defective*
1	403	21
2	463	21
3	528	60
4	538	38
5	608	36
6	630	34
7	713	57
8	736	53

*Average per cent defective, preceding 10 weeks = 8 per cent.

15-11. From the following data, related to the data of problem 15-1, graph a shortage index.
a. Basic number of parts in the department = 250.
b. Critical percentage of shortages = 2 per cent.

Week	No. of Shortages	Week	No. of Shortages
1	88	5	75
2	100	6	63
3	80	7	58
4	85	8	38

15-12. From the following data, related to the data of problem 15-2, graph a shortage index.
a. Basic number of parts in the department = 2360.
b. Critical percentage of shortages = 0.5 per cent.

Week	No. of Shortages	Week	No. of Shortages
1	590	5	637
2	543	6	472
3	708	7	425
4	590	8	378

15-13. Graph all the indices from Problems 15-1, 15-3, 15-5, 15-7, 15-9, and 15-11 on one graph paper. Then write a comprehensive analysis concerning index trends and conditions as of the end of the eighth week.

15-14. Repeat Problem 15-13, but graph the indices from Problems 15-2, 15-4, 15-6, 15-8, 15-10, and 15-12.

BIBLIOGRAPHY

Close, Gilbert C., "PACE, an Effective Cost Reduction Tool for Management," *Modern Machine Shop*, 31 (January, 1959) 98-111.

King, Warren J., "[PACE] Gives Over-all Work Effort Picture," *Factory*, 116 (December, 1958), 107-08.

Loebelson, Robert M., "Northrop's Management Tools for Cost Control," *Space/ Aeronautics*, 33 (March, 1960), 40-41.

Nolan, R., "Performance and Cost Evaluation at Northrop," *Aircraft and Missiles Manufacturing*, 1 (December, 1958), 6-11.

Petersen, D. N., "PACE—A New Industrial Engineering Technique for Management," *The Journal of Industrial Engineering*, XI (July-August, 1960), 304-12.

Smith, Alice L., "Northrop's PACE Program: New Cost-Cutting Tool for Management," *Dun's Review and Modern Industry*, 73 (February, 1959), 52-61.

Willatt, Norris, "Northrop Develops New Management Tool," *American Business*, (April, 1960), 7-10.

16

PERT—
Program Evaluation
and Review Technique

SEC. 16-1. STATEMENT OF THE PROBLEM TO BE SOLVED

The West Coast Aircraft Corporation has received a U.S. Navy contract to research and design a revolutionary new carrier-based pursuit
plane. The basic requirement of the contract is designing and building
the prototype of a supersonic jet fighter plane capable of landing on and
taking off from aircraft carrier flight decks.

The Navy requires that all its prime contractors and also all significant
subcontractors possess PERT capability. The West Coast Aircraft Corporation has accordingly developed a PERT group within its planning
department. In addition to meeting the Navy contract requirement, West
Coast hopes to achieve the many advantages which result from using PERT
as a tool in planning and controlling research and development programs.

SEC. 16-2. BACKGROUND CONCEPTS OF *PERT*

PERT was developed by the Special Projects Office of the Bureau of
Naval Weapons with the cooperation of Booz, Allen & Hamilton. The
group was assigned the Program Evaluation Review Task (PERT). Upon
the successful completion of the mission, the meaning of the initials was
changed to Program Evaluation and Review Technique.

The first phase of the development became known as PERT/Time, since
the time element rather than the cost element of program planning was
the primary consideration. A second phase, called PERT/Cost, has since
been developed. This chapter is concerned largely with PERT/Time,
although PERT/Cost will receive some consideration.

The development of a PERT program requires a series of operations, namely:

1. Creation of the network
2. Estimation of time requirements
3. Development of critical and slack paths
4. Setting initial schedules
5. Transferring resources from slack areas to critical areas in order to meet scheduling requirements

The network is created in order to set forth important and definite points of development, called *events*, and to portray these events graphically in relation to their predecessor and successor events. This requires a high degree of specificity in planning and is believed by many to be the most significant advantage offered by PERT.

In setting up the network, the events are distinct points in time. The events are connected by lines, called *activities*. Although activities ordinarily represent the passage of time, the measurement or estimation of time estimates are completely disregarded when setting up the original network. Not until all important events have been isolated and their relationships to other events graphically portrayed is time considered. The next step is obtaining time estimates, normally from those who will be in direct charge of the work.

PERT was designed as an aid to planning and controlling research and development work and is most useful in one-time operations. Operations of this nature are, however, notorious for the difficulty of making time estimates. For this reason PERT requires three, namely, (1) an optimistic time, (2) a most likely time, (3) a pessimistic time.

These estimates are combined statistically in order to develop expected activity times and the probabilities of meeting specific scheduled dates. The expected activity times are used to reveal critical and slack paths in the network. (These terms are defined in Sec. 16-5.) When the computed probabilities of meeting scheduled dates are low, the program manager is likely either to change the scheduled dates if this is possible, or to transfer resources from slack-path activities to critical-path activities in order to increase the computed probabilities of maintaining the program on schedule. It is also sometimes possible to operate in parallel some activities originally set up as being sequential in the network. In extreme cases, some activities may even be dropped in order to achieve scheduling requirements.

SEC. 16-3.   SETTING UP THE *PERT* NETWORK

Basic to PERT programming is the creation of the network. The *network* is defined as

A flow plan consisting of all the activities and events that must be accomplished to reach the project objectives, showing the sequences in which they are planned to be accomplished and their interdependencies and interrelationships.[1]

Thus the network consists of events and activities:

Event. A specific definable accomplishment in a project plan, recognizable at a particular instant in time. Events do not consume time or resources and are normally represented in the network by circles or rectangles.

Activity. An element of a project which is represented on a network by an arrow. An activity cannot be started until the event preceding it has occurred. An activity may represent: (1) a process, (2) a task, (3) a procurement cycle, or (4) waiting time. In addition, an activity may simply represent a connection or interdependency between two events on the network.

Events and activities are represented on the network as shown in Figure 16-1.

There are a number of approaches to planning the network. The first step in each method, however, is to define in very specific terms the last

Fig. 16-1. Network Representation of Events and Activities

or "objective" event. This event represents the culmination of the project. For West Coast's contract, the objective event might be "final acceptance by the U.S. Navy." One of the more popular, and perhaps the preferred, approach to planning the network is the so-called *backward* method. According to this technique, the first operation is to place at the far right of the paper (a large sheet of butcher paper is ideal for the purpose) the objective event. Then to the left of the objective event is placed that event which immediately precedes the objective event. If more than one event immediately precedes the objective event, then these events are placed in a column to the left of the objective event. In either case, the preceding event(s) is/are connected to the objective event by an arrow, which represents the activity which must be carried out in order for the project to proceed from the preceding to the succeeding event. A similar procedure is carried out successively going backward until the initial event is reached. In the West Coast's case, this may well be "contract awarded." The back-

[1]The definitions used in this chapter are those adopted by the Department of Defense and the National Aeronautics and Space Administration as published in the *DOD* and *NASA Guide PERT COST Systems Design* (Washington, D.C.: Government Printing Office, June, 1962).

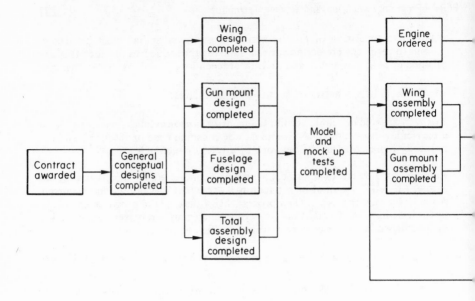

ward method tends to assure that no significant events are left off the network.

A second approach is known as the *forward* method. Here the initial event is the first event to be placed on the paper. Nevertheless, the objective event must previously have been explicitly stated. The approach is similar to the backward method in that each succeeding (instead of preceding) event is placed as the planning proceeds from the initial event to the objective event.

A third approach is merely to list all events as they occur to the planners. When the list is considered to be complete, the events are then inserted into their proper places in the network. When using this method, the planners will almost invariably find that there are gaps in the network which must be filled in by events which had not occurred to them during the listing.

A highly simplified (and perhaps completely unrealistic) network for West Coast's contract appears in Figure 16-2. In practice such a network would contain from several hundred to possibly several thousand events. The objective event, "final acceptance by Navy," was placed first. The Navy's acceptance procedures cannot begin, however, until West Coast has completed its final tests. Hence, the event "final testing completed" is placed on the chart as the next preceding event. Similarly, the final testing cannot take place until the plane is completely assembled. Since West Coast manufactures only the airframe, the final assembly is contingent

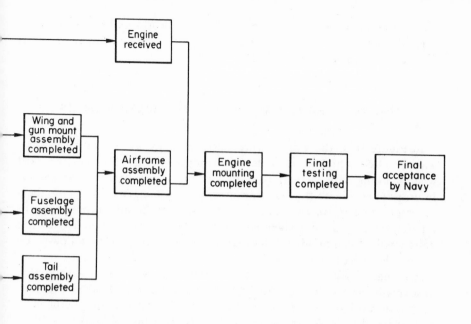

upon the two events: "airframe assembly completed" and "engine received."
Stepping back one more phase in time, completion of the airframe assembly
is dependent upon the occurrence of three events, namely: (1) "wing and
gun mount assembly completed," (2) "fuselage assembly completed," (3)
"tail assembly completed." Similar reasoning is used to carry the network
back to the initial event "contract awarded."

It should be reemphasized that the network in Figure 16-2 is unrealis-
tically simple. The reader undoubtedly will think of many events which
should appear on the network. Those pertaining to the landing gear and
to the arresting gear could be cited as examples. A realistic network is
not presented because it would be too complex to be useful as an instruc-
tional device.

When PERT is to be used for relatively simple projects, one level of
network may serve for all levels of management. When, however, the project becomes more complex, several levels of networks are required. Each
level of network should be drawn so as to meet the needs of the level of
management which is to use it. At the top level of management, the network will consist of events covering broad areas of achievement. For
example, the completion of important subcontracts may appear as single
events at this level. Single activities or small groups of activities at the
top level will be expanded into more detailed networks for the next level.
For example, the subcontractor, whose completed task appeared as a single
event on the prime contractor's top level network, will have a semi-

detailed network of his own project. These networks will continue to be expanded down the levels of management until there is sufficient detail for the use of the operating levels.

SEC. 16-4. ESTIMATING THE ACTIVITY TIME REQUIREMENTS

In Figure 16-2, the events were designated by a descriptive phrase. This practice is highly desirable, but using the phrases becomes awkward when working with the activities, that is, the arrows between the events. In order to eliminate this awkwardness, it is customary to assign numbers as well as descriptive phrases to the events. Then for all purposes except reports, the events are designated by their numbers, and activities are designated by two numbers—by that of the preceding event followed by that of the succeeding event.

Although Figure 16-2 is an overly simplified network, it is too complex for explanatory use in this and the succeeding sections. Instead the very simple network of Figure 16-3 will be used. Several possible methods of numbering the events present themselves. Numbering backwards is illustrated in Figure 16-3, with the objective event being numbered 1. Similarly, the initial event could be numbered 1, with the numbering proceeding in a forward direction. The objective of these systems would be to give order to the numbers assigned to an activity. That is, for the backward system, the preceding event would have a number larger than the succeeding event, and vice versa for the forward system. In a complex network, however, this objective cannot be easily achieved just by reading

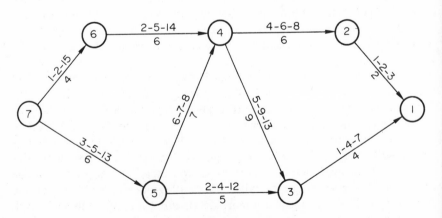

Fig. 16-3. Network with Time Estimates

from the network because of the interdependencies that exist among the various events. Therefore, many authorities feel that a random assignment of numbers is satisfactory, so that the order of number magnitude has no particular significance. For those desiring to use either the forward or backward numbering systems, a technique for converting a random numbering system into either the forward or backward system is discussed in Sec. 16-5.

After the network has been created to the satisfaction of the group involved, time estimates must be assigned to each activity. The individual or group selected to make each time estimate should be that individual or group most closely connected with, and responsible for, the activity under consideration. The difficulty in making these time estimates has already been noted, along with the resulting need for three time estimates; namely,

Optimistic Time Estimate (a). The time in which the activity can be completed if everything goes exceptionally well. It is estimated that an activity would have no more than one chance in a hundred of being completed within this time.

Most Likely Time Estimate (m). This is the most realistic estimate of the time an activity might consume. This time would be expected to occur most often if the activity could be repeated numerous times under similar circumstances.

Pessimistic Time Estimate (b). The time required for an activity under adverse conditions, barring acts of God. It is estimated that an activity would have no more than one chance in a hundred of exceeding this amount of time.

These three time estimates (a, m, and b) are then combined statistically in order to develop the expected elapsed time, t_e, (that is the *mean*) of the activity, and the standard deviation, σ, of the time estimate. It has been assumed (without rigorous proof) that the three time estimates will tend to conform to the end points and mode of the beta distribution as shown in Figure 16-4(a). Simplified approximations to the mean and standard deviation of the beta distribution (using the values a, m, and b) have been developed as follows:

$$t_e \text{ (the expected elapsed time)} = \frac{a + 4m + b}{6}$$

$$\sigma^2_{t_e} = \left(\frac{b - a}{6}\right)^2.$$

Figure 16-4 shows that $t_e = m$ when the distribution of the time estimate is symmetrical as in (c) and (d). Further, $t_e > m$ when the distribution is skewed to the right as in (a), and $t_e < m$ when the distribution is skewed to the left as in (e).

When $t_e \neq m$, then t_e falls one-third the distance from m to the midrange. This may be shown as follows (see Figure 16-5):

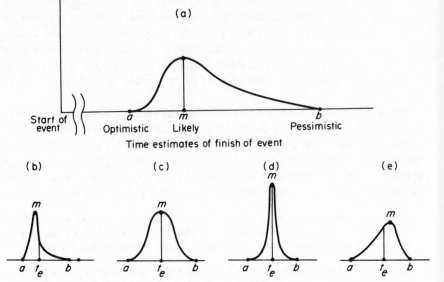

Fig. 16-4. **Assumed Distributions of Activity Time Estimates.** *Source*: PERT Summary Report Phase I (Special Projects Office, Bureau of Naval Weapons, Department of the Navy, Washington, D. C., 1958), pp. 6-7.

$$\text{midrange} = \frac{a+b}{2}$$

$$\text{distance from } m \text{ to midrange} = \frac{a+b}{2} - m$$

$$\text{one-third distance of } m \text{ to midrange} = \frac{1}{3}\left(\frac{a+b}{2} - m\right)$$

$$= \frac{a+b}{6} - \frac{m}{3}.$$

Fig. 16-5. **Location of t_e Between m and the Midrange**

The most likely time, m, plus one-third the distance from m to the midrange is

$$m + \left(\frac{a+b}{6} - \frac{m}{3}\right)$$

$$= \frac{6m + a + b - 2m}{6}$$

$$= \frac{a + 4m + b}{6}$$

but

$$t_e = \frac{a + 4m + b}{6}.$$

Therefore, t_e is one-third the distance from the most likely estimate (m) to the midrange of the optimistic and pessimistic estimates $(a + b)/2$.

Assume that the time estimates $(a, m,$ and $b)$ are as shown above the lines in Figure 16-3. That is, the times for activity 7–6 are

$$a = 1$$
$$m = 2$$
$$b = 15.$$

The expected elapsed time may be computed by the formula,

$$t_e = \frac{a + 4m + b}{6}$$

$$= \frac{1 + 4(2) + 15}{6}$$

$$= 4.$$

The t_e values are shown under the lines in Figure 16-3.

SEC. 16-5. CRITICAL AND SLACK PATH ANALYSIS

The first step in critical and slack path analysis is to determine the earliest expected date for each event:

Earliest Expected Date (T_E). The earliest date on which an event can be expected to occur. The T_E value for a given event is equal to the sum of the statistically calculated *expected elapsed times* (t_e) for the activities on the longest path from the beginning of the project to the given event.

Figure 16-6 shows the expected elapsed time values (t_e) on the activity lines. The initial event, 7, is given a T_E value of 0, that is, the present time. The T_E value of event 6 is the T_E of 7 plus the t_e of activity 7-6, that is, $0 + 4 = 4$. The T_E of event 5 is similarly $0 + 6 = 6$. Event 4, however, has two activities leading into it. Going by way of event 6, the T_E of event 4 would be $4 + 6 = 10$. But going by way of event 5, the T_E of event 4 becomes $6 + 7 = 13$. *When multiple activities lead into an event, the T_E of that event is always the largest sum of the preceding t_e's.* Therefore, the T_E of event 4 is 13. This process is continued until the objective event is reached, which has a T_E, in this case, of 26. The next step is to calculate the latest allowable dates:

Latest Allowable Date (T_L). The latest date on which an event can occur without creating an expected delay in the completion of the project. The T_L value for a given event is calculated by subtracting the sum of the *expected elapsed times* (t_e) for the activities on the longest path from the given event to the *end* event of the project from the latest date allowable for completing the project. T_L for the end event in a project is equal to the directed date (T_D) of the project. If a directed date is not specified, $T_L = T_E$ for the end event.

First a completion date must be assigned to the end or objective event, 1. This date may be prior to, equal to, or later than, the date specified by the T_E for the objective event (referred to as T_{E_O}). If T_{L_O} is later than T_{E_O} the likelihood of completing the project by T_{L_O} is quite high. On the other hand, if T_{L_O} is prior to T_{E_O}, the likelihood of completing the project by T_{L_O} is relatively small, or perhaps even impossible. The method of computing the probability of meeting T_{L_O} is discussed in Sec. 16-6.

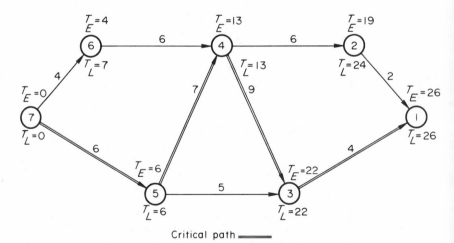

Critical path ══════

Fig. 16-6. Network with T_E and T_L Times

In Figure 16-6, T_{L_O} is set equal to T_{E_O}, that is, $T_{L_O} = 26$. The event T_L's are then computed in a manner similar to computing the T_E's, except that the starting point is T_{L_O}, and the progression is backward toward the initial event. Again, since event 4 can be reached by two routes [1-2-4, for which $T_L = 26 - (2 + 6) = 18$, and 1-3-4, for which $T_L = 26 - (4 + 9) = 13$], the *smaller* of the possible T_L values is chosen, in this case $T_L = 13$.

Critical and Slack Path Analysis by Hand Computation

When the project has many events and activities, the critical and slack path analysis is usually performed by a computer. For relatively small networks, however, computation by hand is entirely feasible. In addition, an understanding of hand processing will help in understanding what the computer does, since the techniques are quite similar.

The first step in hand computation is to list the activities by predecessor—successor event in an order such that if an event precedes another event in the network, that event will be listed before the succeeding event. Such a listing would be easy to prepare from the simple network of Figure 16-6. For more complicated networks, the following method may be used.

Prepare a card for each event in the network and place an event number at the top center of each card. In a column on the left of the card list all events directly preceding the event for which the card is numbered, and in a column to the right list all directly succeeding events. Then stack the cards in numerical order by event number. Figure 16-7 shows the seven cards for the network of Figure 16-6. This stack is called *stack number one*. Now remove the initial event card, 7, from stack number one and place it in stack number two, face up. Working on the uppermost card in stack number two (in this case card 7), the card for the event at the top of the right column (card 5) is located in stack number one, and a check mark is made next to the number 7 in the left column of card 5. Since all events in the left column of card 5 have been checked, card 5 is removed from stack number one and placed at the *bottom* of stack number two.

Returning to card 7 in stack two, the next event listed in the right column is 6. Card 6 is located in stack one, event 7 at the left checked off, and since no unchecked events remain at the left, card 6 is placed at the bottom of stack two. Again returning to card 7 in stack two, all event cards indicated in the right column have been checked off in stack one. Therefore, card 7 is removed from stack two and placed at the *bottom* of stack number three. In this case, of course, card 7 is the *only* card in stack number three.

Returning to stack two, card 5 is now the top card. Event 4 is the first

Fig. 16-7. Event Card Stack Number One

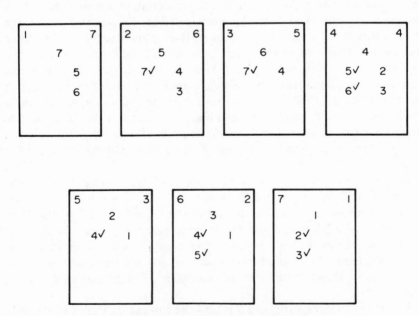

Fig. 16-8. Event Card Stack Number Three

listed on the right, and event 5 is checked in the left column of card 4. Since, however, not all events in the left column of card 4 are checked, card 4 is *not* removed from stack one. This process is continued until *all* the cards are in stack number three. They are then in the proper sequence. For the network under consideration, the cards will be in the order shown on Figure 16-8. For those desiring to use either the forward or backward numbering systems, the network events may now be renumbered according to their positions in stack three. For the forward system, the numbers in the upper left-hand corner of the cards in Figure 16-8 would be substituted for the event numbers in the upper center of the cards. For the backward system, the number in the upper right-hand corner would be similarly substituted.

The information from stack three is now listed as in columns (1) and (2) of Figure 16-9. From the first card, the preceding event is 7, and the succeeding events are 5 and 6. Thus activities 7–5 and 7–6 are placed first and second on the list. Columns (3), (4), (5), and (6) are used to compute the t_e values according to the formula,

$$t_e = \frac{a + 4m + b}{6}.$$

Column (7) is computed by the formula,

$$\sigma_{t_e}^2 = \left(\frac{b - a}{6}\right)^2.$$

Pred. Event (1)	Suc. Event (2)	a (3)	m (4)	b (5)	t_e (6)	$\sigma_{t_e}^2$ (7)	T_E (8)	T_L (9)	$T_L - T_E$ (10)
7 ✓	5	3	5	13	6	2.78	6	6	0
7 ✓	6	1	2	15	4	5.44	4	7	3
5 ✓	4 ✓	6	7	8	7	1.11	⑬	13	0
5 ✓	3 ✓	2	4	12	5	2.78	11	22	11
6	4 ✓	2	5	14	6	4.00	10	13	3
4 ✓	2	4	6	8	6	4.44	19	24	5
4 ✓	3 ✓	5	9	13	9	1.78	㉒	22	0
2	1 ✓	1	2	3	2	1.11	21	26	5
3	1 ✓	1	4	7	4	2.00	㉖	26	0

Critical and Slack Path Analysis

0	3	5	11
7	7	4	5
5	6	2	3
4	4	1	
3			

Fig. 16-9. Computation of Critical and Slack Paths. (The significance of column (7) is discussed in Sec. 16-6.)

The next step is to compute the T_E values in column (8). First inspect column (2) for event numbers appearing more than once. Place a check mark alongside any such numbers. In Figure 16-9, events 4, 3, and 1 all appear twice and are checked. Then the T_E for the first activity listed is computed. In this case activity 7–5 has a T_E of 6. Continuing down the list, activity 7–6 has a T_E of 4. These, of course, are merely equal to the t_e's for the activities since each predecessor event is also the initial event. For the third activity, 5–4, the T_E is computed by adding the t_e of 5–4, that is, 7, to the T_E of event 5, namely, 6. The sum, 13, is placed in column (8). Notice, however, that event 4 is checked in column (2). Therefore event 4 may or may not have a $T_E = 13$.

Continuing, activity 5–3 will have a $T_E = 6 + 5 = 11$. Then the activity 6–4 has a $T_E = 4 + 6 = 10$. This is the second and last event 4 in column (2). Activity 5–4 has a T_E of 13, and 6–4 of 10. Since $13 > 10$, event 4 is assigned the T_E of 13. This is indicated by circling the 13 in column (8). The T_E of activity 4–2 is then computed by adding the T_E of event 4 (13) to the t_e of 4–2 (6) to obtain a $T_E = 19$. This process is continued until the objective event is reached. Note that, for each event checked in column (2), the largest T_E obtained in column (8) for that event is circled and used for further computations.

The T_L's of column (9) are computed in a similar manner, but in reverse order. First check in column (1) any events appearing more than once. Thus in Figure 16-9, events 7, 5, and 4 are checked. The directed date for the objective event is placed in column (9) for activity 3–1.

Directed Date for an Event (T_D). A time commitment for a specific accomplishment.

The T_D for T_{L_0} for Figure 16-9 is set equal to $T_{E_0} = 26$. Since, however, event 1 is checked in column (2), the value 26 is inserted in column (9) opposite each 1 in column (2). In this case, a 26 is placed opposite activity 2–1. Moving up to the next activity, 4–3, it is noted that event 3 is *not* checked in column (1). Therefore the T_L for event 3 is equal to the T_L for 1 (26) minus the t_e for 3–1 (4), which equals 22. But event 3 is checked in column (2), so the 22 is placed in column (9) opposite each 3 in column (2).

Next find the T_L for event 2. Since event 2 is not checked in column (1), the T_L for 2 equals the T_L for 1 (26) minus the t_e for 1–2 (2) which equals 24. The 24 is placed in column (9). Moving upward again, the T_L for event 4 is to be computed. But event 4 is checked in column (1), and is listed twice. Therefore, there are two ways to compute the T_L of event 4, and the lesser of the two values is the one desired. Arriving at 4 via 3, $T_L = 22 - 9 = 13$; and via 2, $T_L = 24 - 6 = 18$. Since 13 is the lesser value, it is placed in column (9) opposite *both* event 4's in column (2). The process is continued until the initial event is reached.

The *activity slack values* may now be computed by the subtraction, $T_L - T_E$. These are listed in column (10) of Figure 16-9. Notice that there are several different $T_L - T_E$ values: four 0's, two 3's, two 5's, and one 11. This shows that there are four different paths with varying amounts of slack or leeway. These paths are listed on Figure 16-9. Thus the path going through events 7, 5, 4, 3, and 1 has zero slack. Should slippage occur in any one of the activities along this path (that is, should any of the activities take more time than that specified by their t_e's), then the directed date, T_D, of the objective event will not be achieved, unless there is a corresponding reduction in time of one or more of the other activities on this path. If the T_D had been set at 24 instead of 26, this path would have had a slack value of -2. Similarly, if the T_D had been set at 28, the slack value of the path would have been $+2$. This path is referred to as the *critical path*.

Critical Path. That particular sequence of activities that has the greatest negative (or least positive) activity slack.

All other paths are referred to as *slack paths*. Note, however, that a slack path contains slack only in relation to the critical path. A slack path may have negative, zero, or positive slack.

SEC. 16-6. COMPUTING THE PROBABILITY OF ACHIEVING THE COMPLETION DATE

The project manager is vitally interested in the likelihood of meeting the scheduled completion date (T_D) of the project. He would prefer that this likelihood be expressed quantitatively in terms of probability. Standard PERT procedures provide this information.

The restricting path of the network is, of course, the critical path. The variances, $\sigma_{t_e}^2$, of this path are summed, and the square root taken to obtain the standard deviation of T_E:

$$\sigma_{T_E} = \sqrt{\sum_{\substack{\text{for c.p.} \\ t_e}} \sigma_{te}^2} \ .$$

The difference between the earliest expected completion date T_{E_0} and the scheduled completion date T_{D_0} is divided by σ_{T_E} in order to express the difference in σ_{T_E}'s, thus,

$$z = \frac{T_{E_O} - T_{D_O}}{\sigma_{T_E}}.$$

Since the T_{E_O} is the sum of a series of means of probability distributions, T_{E_O} will tend to be distributed according to the normal probability distri-

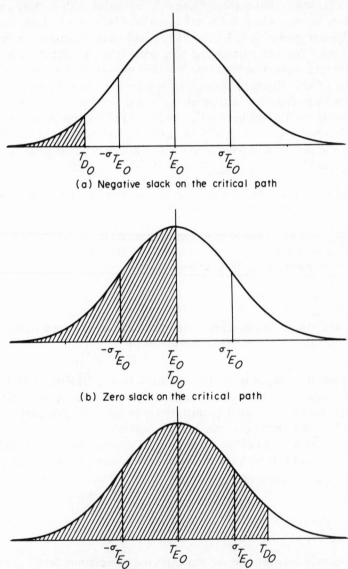

(a) Negative slack on the critical path

(b) Zero slack on the critical path

(c) Positive slack on the critical path

Fig. 16-10. Estimating the Probability of Meeting Scheduled Dates

bution, and the z computed earlier will be the z transformation discussed in Sec. 10–4. (This can be evaluated by using the Table of Areas under the Normal Curve in Appendix C.)

Figure 16-10 shows that the most likely estimate of T_{E_O} is the mean of a normal curve. However, T_{E_O} may fall any place on the curve. The question is, What is the probability that T_{E_O} and T_{D_O} will coincide? Three cases are presented: Case (a) shows the existence of negative slack, or the case where T_{D_O} precedes T_{E_O}. The probability that T_{E_O} will actually fall at T_{D_O} is the area under the curve from $-\infty$ to T_{D_O}. This area is found by entering the table in Appendix C with z as previously computed. If z is negative, as it will be for case (a), the probability value is equal to $1 -$ (the value in the table). Thus the probability of meeting the scheduled completion date will be less than 0.5.

Case (b) shows the existence of zero slack. Since z is equal to zero, the probability of meeting the scheduled date equals 0.5. For case (c), positive slack, the probability will be greater than 0.5. The project manager may use these probabilities in evaluating the feasibility of his schedule. The objective should be to have the probability close to 0.5. Probabilities ranging far from 0.5 in either direction tend to indicate that changes should be made. If the probability is below 0.5, at least two actions may be taken: (1) the scheduled date, T_{D_O}, may be moved back sufficiently far to bring the probability within an acceptable range, (2) resources may be transferred from activities within slack paths to activities on the critical path. Such a shift of resources will require reestimates of times affected and a recomputation of critical and slack paths. It is quite possible that such a shift will result in one or more other paths becoming critical, whereas the original critical path may now possess slack.

A probability much above 0.5, may indicate that too many resources have been devoted to the project. If other projects are available, the project manager should consider the desirability of shifting resources to the other projects. Again, such a shift requires new time estimates and new critical and slack path analysis. One desirable feature of PERT is that such changes may be "simulated" by introducing them into the PERT network. Thus the potential results of the changes may be studied before actually ordering the changes to be made. Since the original networks are still available, it is a simple task to reject such proposed changes when they do not appear to be feasible after the new networks have been studied.

As the various activities are completed, since some will be ahead of schedule, some on time, and others behind, the PERT program must be continuously updated and revised when necessary. The various managers must be kept informed as to the progress of the project. The project will be kept on schedule largely by the transference of resources from ahead-of-schedule activities to behind-schedule activities.

SEC. 16-7. *PERT/COST*

The PERT/Cost system is based upon a PERT network similar to that discussed under PERT/Time (see Sec. 16–3). The time element in the PERT/Cost system may be either the three estimate type used in the PERT/Time system or it may be a single estimate. In the latter case, the most likely time is the one to be used. In all subsequent computations, the single time estimate is substituted for the t_e used in the preceding sections.

The over-all project is broken down into cost segments called *work packages.*

> *Work Package.* The *unit* of work required to complete a specific job, such as a report, a design, a drawing, a piece of hardware, or a service, which is within the responsibility of one operating unit in an organization.

A work package may be represented on the network by one or more activities. Since the collection of costs must be performed by the regular accounting system, each work package is assigned a *charge number.* Among the reasons that the work package may include more than one network activity are (1) reducing the expense of a too detailed cost accounting system, (2) avoiding unrealistic cost allocations.

After the network has been developed and the project broken into work packages, the costs per work package are estimated. In the three time estimate method, t_e is used as the basis for cost estimating. In the single time estimate system, the most likely time is used. In both cases it has been found desirable to use a single time as the basis for cost estimates because of the time relationships frequently involved in costs, and because the complexities of multiple cost estimates become too great to handle. The cost estimates include costs of manpower, material, and other resources. These estimates are then used as a comparison to the actual costs experienced.

Figure 16-11 shows the PERT network with the cost estimates. The numbers under the costs are the t_e or the most likely time estimates. When the network and estimates have been accepted, the project is begun, and time and cost expenditures accumulated. These are periodically compared with the original estimates. Figure 16–12 shows one such comparison.

Activity 7–6 has been completed on both the time and cost schedules. Activity 7–5 has been completed on time and has a cost underrun of $2000. Activity 6-4 has not yet been completed, but both time and cost schedules appear to be under control. Activity 5-4, however, appears to be in considerable trouble. It has not been completed, but already is one week behind its time allotment and has a cost overrun of $5000. It is, in

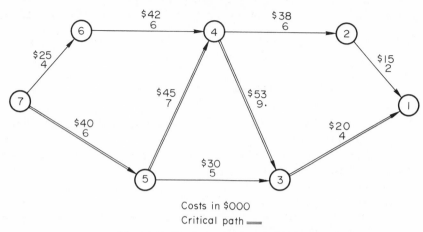

Costs in $000
Critical path ═══

Fig. 16-11. Network with Cost Estimates

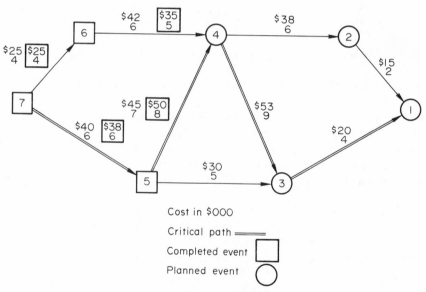

Cost in $000
Critical path ═══
Completed event ☐
Planned event ◯

Fig. 16-12. Cost and Time Estimates Compared to the Actual Figures

addition, on the critical path, and therefore places the completion date of the entire project in jeopardy.

Estimates of time and costs necessary to complete both activities 6–4 and 5–4 are required at this point. Although 6–4 appears to be proceeding according to schedule, the time and cost estimates to complete the activity could reveal some danger points. Activity 5–4 may require replanning, with possible changes being the transfer of resources to the activity or the carrying on, in parallel, of some activities originally conceived of as being sequential.

DISCUSSION QUESTIONS

16-1. What are the basic steps to be followed in developing a PERT program?

16-2. Define the term *event*.

16-3. What are some of the actions a program manager may take in order to increase the probability of meeting scheduled dates?

16-4. Define the term *network*.

16-5. Define the term *activity*.

16-6. Describe the process of setting up the network. What is the *backward method*? The *forward method*?

16-7. Describe the various methods of numbering the events.

16-8. Describe the method of making time estimates. By whom should the estimates be made?

16-9. State the formula for estimating the *expected elapsed time* (t_e).

16-10. State the formula for estimating the variance of the expected elapsed time ($\sigma^2_{t_e}$).

16-11. Explain where t_e falls in the distribution of the time estimates.

16-12. Define the term *earliest expected date* (T_E).

16-13. Explain how to compute the *earliest expected time* (T_E).

16-14. Define the term *latest allowable date* (T_L).

16-15. Explain how to compute the *latest allowable date* (T_L).

16-16. Describe the card technique of ordering events.

16-17. Describe the method of hand computation of the critical and slack path analysis.

16-18. Define the term *directed date for an event* (T_D).

16-19. Explain how computing the T_L's differs from computing the T_E's.

16-20. Define the term *activity slack value*.

16-21. Explain how to ascertain the paths associated with the several slack values.

16-22. Define the term *critical path*.

16-23. Define the term *slack path*.

16-24. Describe the method of computing the probability of achieving the completion date.

16-25. What three probability situations can result from the computations considered in Question 16-24? Discuss the meaning of each and the appropriate actions to be taken.

16-26. Describe the technique of keeping the project on schedule.

16-27. Define the term *work package*. Why is the work package concept used in PERT/Cost rather than the activity concept?

16-28. Describe the PERT/Cost method of allocating costs and of analyzing expenditures.

PROBLEMS

16-1. Using the network of Figure 16-3, assume the following time estimates:

Activity	a	m	b
7–5	2	4	10
7–6	2	3	9
5–4	5	8	10
5–3	1	5	10
6–4	3	5	9
4–2	4	5	7
4–3	5	7	9
2–1	2	5	6
3–1	1	4	8

Set $T_{L_O} = T_{E_O}$.
Required
1. Compute
   a. t_e
   b. $\sigma^2_{t_e}$
   c. T_E
   d. T_L
   e. $T_L - T_E$
2. Critical and slack path analysis.

16-2. Repeat Problem 16-1, using the following data:

Activity	a	m	b
7–5	1	5	12
7–6	1	4	8
5–4	5	7	8
5–3	3	4	9
6–4	2	7	8
4–2	4	9	11
4–3	1	3	5
2–1	6	10	15
3–1	8	10	14

Set $T_{L_O} = 33.0$.

16-3. Repeat Problem 16-1, using the following data:

Activity	a	m	b
7–5	3	4	8
7–6	1	3	11
5–4	2	6	9
5–3	4	5	10
6–4	3	6	10
4–2	5	7	13
4–3	2	8	10
2–1	6	10	14
3–1	4	8	16

Set $T_{L_O} = 25.0$.

16-4. Compute the probability of achieving the T_{L_O} in Problem 16-1. Analyze the significance of this probability.

16-5. Repeat Problem 16-4, using the data of Problem 16-2.

16-6. Repeat Problem 16-4, using the data of Problem 16-3.

16-7. Given the following network and time estimates:

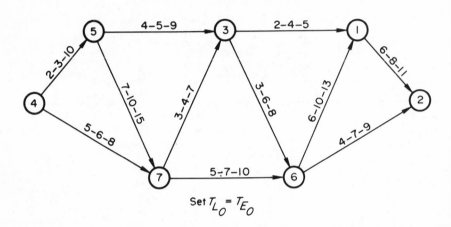

Set $T_{L_O} = T_{E_O}$

Required

1. Renumber the events according to (a) the forward method, and (b) the backward method.
2. Compute
   a. t_e
   b. $\sigma_{t_e}^2$
   c. T_E
   d. T_L
   e. $T_L - T_E$
3. Critical and slack path analysis.

16-8. Repeat Problem 16-7, using the following data:

Activity	a	m	b
4–5	10	12	14
4–7	8	10	13
5–3	6	11	14
5–7	5	8	16
7–3	3	10	12
7–6	9	11	15
3–1	10	13	20
3–6	8	11	16
6–1	7	10	14
6–2	6	9	14
1–2	8	12	15

Set $T_{L_O} = 65.00$.

16-9. Repeat Problem 16-7, using the following data:

Activity	a	m	b
4–5	7	15	20
4–7	10	14	16
5–3	11	13	17
5–7	9	12	18
7–3	14	17	20
7–6	6	9	13
3–1	3	11	14
3–6	12	16	21
6–1	8	14	16
6–2	13	16	18
1–2	5	9	13

Set $T_{L_0} = 80.00$.

16-10. Compute the probability of achieving the T_{L_0} in Problem 16-7. Analyze the significance of this probability.

16-11. Repeat Problem 16-10, using the data of Problem 16-8.

16-12. Repeat Problem 16-10, using the data of Problem 16-9.

16-13. Number the events of Figure 16-2 according to (a) the forward method, (b) the backward method.

BIBLIOGRAPHY

DOD and NASA Guide PERT COST, The Office of the Secretary of Defense and the National Aeronautics and Space Administration. Washington, D.C.: Government Printing Office, June, 1962.

General Information Manual PERT, International Business Machines Corporation, Publication No. E20-8067-01. White Plains, N.Y.: n.d.

Miller, Robert W. "How to Plan and Control with PERT," *The Harvard Business Review*, 40 (March-April, 1962), 93-104.

NASA PERT and Companion Cost System Handbook, National Aeronautics and Space Administration. Washington, D.C.: Government Printing Office, Oct. 30, 1962.

NASA PERT Handbook, National Aeronautics and Space Administration. Washington, D.C.: Government Printing Office, Sept. 1, 1961.

PERT Data Processing Lesson Plan Handbook for Technicians, rev. ed., Department of the Navy, Bureau of Naval Weapons, Special Projects Office. Washington, D.C.: Government Printing Office, November, 1960.

PERT Summary Report Phase 1, Department of the Navy, Bureau of Naval Weapons, Special Projects Office. Washington, D.C.: Government Printing Office, July, 1958.

PERT Summary Report Phase 2, Department of the Navy, Bureau of Naval Weapons, Special Projects Office. Washington, D.C.: Government Printing Office, September, 1958.

Pocock, J.W., "PERT as an Analytical Aid for Program Planning—Its Payoff and Problems," *Operations Research*, 10 (November-December, 1962), 893-903.

Stilian, Gabriel, *et al. PERT: A New Management Planning and Control Technique.* New York: American Management Association, 1962, pp. 9-144.

Stirres, David M., and Maurice M. Murphy, *Modern Management Methods PERT and CDM.* Boston: Materials Management Institute, 1962, pp. 1-115.

17

CPM—
The Critical Path Method

SEC. 17-1. STATEMENT OF THE PROBLEM TO BE SOLVED

The West Coast Aircraft Corporation is planning to construct a new plant facility. Its experience with PERT (see Chapter 16) has convinced it that critical path scheduling will be useful in areas other than research and development projects. In fact, it thinks that the concept appears to be applicable in any planning and scheduling situation involving many sequences of operations with complex interrelationships.

West Coast has therefore assigned to its PERT group the task of developing an acceptable network and resulting schedule for the construction of the new plant facility. The PERT group, however, has heard of a method closely related to PERT called CPM (the Critical Path Method). CPM, it understands, is more useful to a construction program than is PERT for the following reasons:

1. CPM uses a single time estimate for each activity; whereas PERT uses three. In the construction industry an activity, such as building a brick wall, can be estimated both as to time and cost with a fairly high degree of accuracy.
2. Both normal program and crash program times and costs (both being relatively easy to estimate) can be used to develop a direct-cost curve.
3. The direct-cost curve may be combined with an indirect-cost curve and perhaps with a market-loss and penalty-cost curve to derive an optimum time-cost schedule.

These factors will be clarified in the following sections.

SEC. 17-2.   BACKGROUND CONCEPTS OF CPM

Although the concepts of PERT and CPM are closely related, there are several significant differences which will become clear as the discussion proceeds. Nevertheless, the development of CPM concepts will be built upon the PERT concepts already covered in Chapter 16.

The development of CPM actually preceded that of PERT by about one year. The two men most responsible for the basic development were J. E. Kelley, Jr., and Morgan R. Walker. In the intervening years other people have made useful contributions to the method. As a result of its great usefulness and relative ease of application, the Critical Path Method has become increasingly popular and is now in fairly widespread use.

Although many of the concepts of CPM are either identical with, or very similar to, the concepts of PERT, much of the terminology is different. For example, the network of CPM, almost identical to that of PERT, is referred to as an *arrow diagram*, events as *nodes*, slack as *total float*, and so forth. The terms used in CPM will be defined in the chapter at the point where they enter into the discussion. Their relation to PERT terms will be considered at the same time.

To develop a CPM program the following steps are required.

1. Prepare the network or arrow diagram.
2. Prepare estimates for (a) normal time and normal costs, (b) crash time and crash costs.
3. Prepare a schedule using all normal times and costs.
4. Prepare a schedule using all crash times and costs.
5. Prepare a least-cost schedule having the same time element as the schedule in (4).
6. Prepare a least-cost schedule with a time element between the schedule in (3) and the schedule in (4), but with the time closer to the time in (4) than that in (3).
7. Construct a direct-cost curve from the schedules in (3), (4), and (6).
8. Construct an indirect-cost curve.
9. Construct a market-loss and penalty-cost curve, if applicable.
10. Sum the curves constructed in (7), (8), and (9) to form a total-cost curve.
11. Select the lowest point of the total-cost curve, which point represents the least-cost time.
12. Prepare the least-cost schedule.

These steps will now be discussed in detail.

SEC. 17-3.   THE ALL-NORMAL AND ALL-CRASH SCHEDULES

The network or arrow diagram is prepared using the techniques described in Sec. 16-3. A number of the existing computer programs for

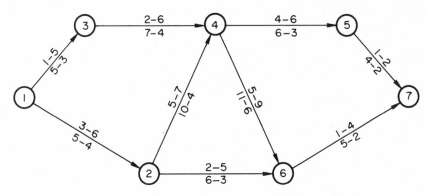

Fig. 17-1. The CPM Arrow Diagram

processing CPM require that the events or nodes be numbered by the forward method. That is, each activity is identified by two numbers, the first representing the preceding node and the second the following node, and in every case, the first number must be less than the second. This may be achieved by the method described in Sec. 16-27. The network shown in Figure 17-1 will be used as a basis for the discussion.

Estimating Times and Costs

Most activities can be accomplished in a wide variety of ways. Associated with each way is an activity time and cost. Frequently each activity may be accomplished in a given time in several different ways and hence with several different costs. The least cost for each time would, if graphed, tend to form a curve similar to that shown in Figure 17-2. Consider, for example, a task requiring 40 hours of work on a rented machine. Two machines are available, one (A) at $5 and one (B) at $7 per hour. Operators are available at $3 per hour. Extra second and third shift expenses are $3 and $5 per hour respectively.

The task can, of course, be completed in a large number of ways using different shift combinations and different mixes of machines A and B. Figure 17-3 shows a number of these ways, including two ways each for completion in 5, 4, 3, or 2 days, and one way for completion in 1 day. For example, the task could be completed in 5 days using machine A on first shift only at a cost of $320. It could similarly be completed in 5 days using machine B. The cost using the latter method would, however, be $400. These costs are plotted on Figure 17-2. A curve is drawn through the lower cost (or lowest, where more than two costs can be computed). This direct-cost curve tends to bend upward as the time period for the task is reduced. Note, however, that a straight

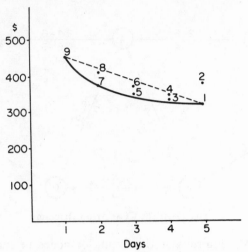

Fig. 17-2. Activity Direct-Cost Curve

line drawn from point 1 to point 9 approximates the curve fairly well. For this reason, CPM uses only those two points. Point 1 is called the *normal* time and cost, and Point 9 is called the *crash* time and cost. As used in CPM, these terms are defined:

Normal Cost. The lowest direct investment required to complete an activity.
Normal Time. The minimum time associated with the normal cost.
Crash Time. The minimum time required to complete an activity.
Crash Cost. The minimum cost associated with the crash time.

In Figure 17-1, the crash times and normal times are shown in that order above the line; the crash costs and normal costs, below the line; thus,

$$\textcircled{i}\ \frac{T_c - T_n}{C_c - C_n}\ \textcircled{j}; \qquad i < j.$$

The slope of each activity cost line (using the straight-line approximation) is found by the formula:

$$\text{slope of activity cost line} = \frac{C_c - C_n}{T_n - T_c}.$$

The slope is expressed in costs per unit of time in which the activity is expressed, usually in weeks and tenths of weeks. This is the ordinary concept of the slope of a linear equation (see Figure 17-4). The slope states, in effect, the cost increase associated with every unit of time decrease.

Plotted Points	Days	Machine	Shift	Hours	Rate	Cost
1	5	A	1	40	8.00	$320.00
2	5	B	1	40	10.00	$400.00
3	4	A	1	32	8.00	
		B	1	8	10.00	$336.00
4	4	A	1	32	8.00	
		A	2	8	11.00	$344.00
5	3	A	1	24	8.00	
		B	1	16	10.00	$352.00
6	3	A	1	24	8.00	
		A	2	16	11.00	$368.00
7	2	A	1	16	8.00	
		B	1	16	10.00	
		A	2	8	11.00	$376.00
8	2	A	1	16	8.00	
		A	2	16	11.00	
		A	3	8	13.00	$408.00
9	1	A	1	8	8.00	
		B	1	8	10.00	
		A	2	8	11.00	
		B	2	8	15.00	
		A	3	8	13.00	$456.00

Fig. 17-3. Times and Costs for Completing the Illustrative Task

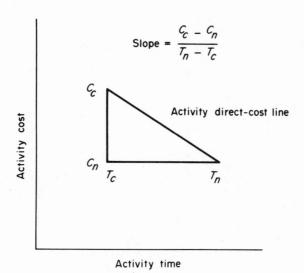

$$\text{Slope} = \frac{C_c - C_n}{T_n - T_c}$$

C_c

Activity direct-cost line

C_n T_c T_n

Activity cost

Activity time

Fig. 17-4. Slope of the Activity Direct-Cost Line

Setting up the Normal-times, Normal-costs Schedule

The normal-times, normal-costs schedule for the illustrative problem is shown in Figure 17-5. The data for columns (1) through (6) are taken from the arrow diagram of Figure 17-1. Column (7) is computed by the formula,

$$\text{slope} = \frac{C_c - C_n}{T_n - T_c}.$$

For activity 1–2, this becomes

$$\text{slope} = \frac{5-4}{6-3} = \frac{1}{3};$$

that is,

one-third of $1000 or $333.

This means (on a straight-line, direct-cost curve basis) that it will cost $333 extra for each week that the time for activity 1–2 is shortened. Columns (1)–(7) will be used as a basis for obtaining all the other required schedules. For the normal-time, normal-cost schedule, columns (8) and (9) are a repeat of columns (3) and (5), respectively. Columns (10) and (11) show the earliest times (T_E) and the latest times (T_L) that the activities can be completed. The data in these columns are computed as described in Sec. 16–5. Column (12) is computed by the formula,

$$\text{total float} = T_L - T_E.$$

Activity		Cost ($000)		Time (weeks)		$/Week Cost to Expedite	Normal-times, Normal-costs Schedule				
Pred. (1)	Suc. (2)	N (3)	C (4)	N (5)	C (6)	(7)	Cost (8)	Time (9)	T_E (10)	T_L (11)	Float (12)
1✓	2	4	5	6	3	333	4	6	6	6	0
1✓	3	3	5	5	1	400	3	5	5	7	2
2✓	4✓	4	10	7	5	3,000	4	7	⑬	13	0
2✓	6✓	3	6	5	2	1,000	3	5	11	22	9
3	4✓	7	7	6	2	750	4	6	11	13	2
4✓	5	3	6	6	4	1,500	3	6	19	24	5
4✓	6✓	6	11	9	5	1,250	6	9	㉒	22	0
5	7✓	2	4	2	1	2,000	2	2	21	26	5
6	7✓	2	5	4	1	666	2	4	㉖	26	0
Totals		31	59				31				

Slack Path Analysis

0: 1-2-4-6-7   Total time required: 26 weeks
1: 1-3-4   Total cost: $31,000
5: 4-5-7
9: 2-6

Fig. 17-5. The Normal-Times, Normal-Costs Schedule

Note that *total float* in CPM is the same as *activity slack* in PERT. In this case, the critical path has a slack of 0, and there are three slack paths with 2, 5, and 9 weeks of slack, respectively. The total time required by the normal-time, normal-cost schedule is 26 weeks, and the direct costs are $31,000. These are plotted as point *a* on Figure 17-11.

The Crash-times, Crash-costs Schedule

The crash-times, crash-costs schedule is shown in Figure 17–6. Columns (1)–(7) are taken directly from Figure 17-5. Columns (8) and (9) are from columns (4) and (6) respectively. Columns (10), (11), and (12) are obtained as previously explained. The slack path values have changed to 0, 1, 5, and 8; and the required time has been reduced to 14 weeks. Since all times used are crash times, this is the shortest time in which the total project can be completed. The direct costs, however, have risen from $31,000 to $59,000. The 14-week time and $59,000 cost are plotted on Figure 17-11 as point *d*.

SEC. 17-4. THE LEAST-COST CRASH AND LEAST-COST INTERMEDIATE SCHEDULES

A glance at the all-crash schedule of Figure 17-6 should be convincing that crashing all activities will result in wasted expenditures. For example, activity 5–7 was speeded up from two weeks normal time to one week

Activity		Cost ($000)		Time (Weeks)		$/Week Cost to Expedite	Crash-times, Crash-costs Schedule				
Pred. (1)	Suc. (2)	N (3)	C (4)	N (5)	C (6)	(7)	Cost (8)	Time (9)	T_E (10)	T_L (11)	Float (12)
1 ✓	2	4	5	6	3	333	5	3	3	3	0
1 ✓	3	3	5	5	1	400	5	1	1	6	5
2 ✓	4 ✓	4	10	7	5	3,000	10	5	⑧	8	0
2 ✓	6 ✓	3	6	5	2	1,000	6	2	5	13	8
3	4 ✓	7	6	6	2	750	7	2	3	8	5
4 ✓	5	3	6	6	4	1,500	6	4	12	13	1
4 ✓	6 ✓	6	11	9	5	1,250	11	5	⑬	13	0
5	7 ✓	2	4	2	1	2,000	4	1	13	14	1
6	7 ✓	2	5	4	1	666	5	1	⑭	14	0
Totals		31	59				59				

Slack Path Analysis

0: 1–2–4–6–7   Total time required: 14 weeks
1: 4–5–7   Total cost: $59,000
5: 1–3–4
8: 2–6

Fig. 17-6. The Crash-Times, Crash-Costs Schedule

crash time. This speed-up cost an extra $2000. But the slack path analysis shows that activity 5-7 is on a path which has a slack of one week. Thus, if activity 5-7 is returned to its normal time of two weeks, the total schedule can still be accomplished in the crash time of 14 weeks and at a saving of $2000.

Figure 17-7 shows a schedule which can be accomplished in 14 weeks, but all unneeded expediting costs have been removed. In preparing the schedule, columns (1)–(7) are again copied from Figure 17-5. Then columns (8) and (9), for all activities having zero slack in Figure 17-6, are copied directly from Figure 17-6. The 5 and 3 from columns (8) and (9) are transferred to Figure 17-7. Activities 2-4, 4-6, and 6-7 receive similar treatment.

Activity		Cost ($000)		Time (Weeks)		$/week Cost to Expedite	Least-cost, Crash-times Schedule				
Pred. (1)	Suc. (2)	N (3)	C (4)	N (5)	C (6)	(7)	Cost (8)	Time (9)	T_E (10)	T_L (11)	Float (12)
1√	2	4	5	6	3	333	5	3	3	3	0
1√	3	3	5	5	1	400	4.6	2	2	2	0
2√	4√	4	10	7	5	3,000	10	5	⑧	8	0
2√	6√	3	6	5	2	1,000	3	5	8	13	5
3	4√	4	7	6	2	750	4	6	8	8	0
4√	5	3	6	6	4	1,500	6	4	12	12	0
4√	6√	11	9	5	1,250	11	5	⑬	13	0
5	7√	2	4	2	1	2,000	2	2	14	14	0
6	7√	2	5	4	1	666	5	1	14	14	0
	Totals	31	59				50.6				

Slack Path Analysis

All zero except   Total time required: 14 weeks
5: 2–6   Total cost: $50,600

Fig. 17-7. The Least-Cost, Crash-Time Schedule

Next the activities on the path with one week slack are examined. These are activities 4–5 and 5–7. One week can be added to either of these activities without increasing the total project time of 14 weeks. If the week is added to activity 4–5, $1500 [from column (7)] will be saved. If, however, the week is added to activity 5–7, $2000 will be saved. Therefore, the slack path with one week slack is lengthened by adding one week to activity 5–7. Hence, the 1 of column (9) is changed to a 2. But, as a result, the cost of $4000 in column (8) is changed to $2000 reflecting the cost reduction of $2000. Since no more slack exists in the path formerly having one week of slack, the cost and time for activity 4–5 are transferred to columns (8) and (9) respectively.

The activities on the path with 5 weeks slack are now inspected. Activity 3–4 has an expediting cost of $750 per week, which is more than the $400 of activity 1–3. The time of activity 3–4 can be increased only 4 weeks, since this will bring the duration up to its normal time of 6 weeks. Therefore, the 2 in column (9) is replaced with a 6. The savings resulting from stretching out activity 3–4 by 4 weeks is 4 × $750 = $3000. Thus the 7 in column (8) is replaced with a 4. The remaining one week of slack is then taken up by extending the time of activity 1–3 and recording the resulting reduction in cost of $400. Finally, activity 2–6 is extended 3 weeks to its normal time of 5 weeks and the cost reduced 3 × $1000 = $3000. Columns (10), (11), and (12) are now completed in the usual manner. Note that all slack has been taken up except that in activity 2–6. The remaining slack cannot be removed because activity 2–6 is now at its normal time. The cost reduction resulting from these changes comes to $8400 bringing the total cost down to $50,600. The time of 14 weeks and cost of $50,600 are plotted on Figure 17-11 as point c.

The Least-cost, Intermediate-time Schedule

In order to obtain a third point on the project direct-cost curve (Figure 17-11), a least-cost, intermediate-time schedule is developed. The time chosen is one between the all-normal–schedule time (26 weeks in this case) and the all-crash–schedule time (14 weeks in this case). Since the project direct-cost curve tends to bend upward more sharply in the left portion, the time chosen should be closer to the all-crash time than to the all-normal time. A time of 17 weeks (one-quarter of the total time difference) has been arbitrarily chosen. The preparation of the least-cost intermediate-time schedule is more easily understood if the schedule is derived in several stages.

The first stage, Figure 17-8, is derived from the least-cost crash-time schedule (Figure 17-7). The 14-week schedule is to be expanded into a 17-week schedule. The time of the activity which will produce the greatest cost savings is first expanded. This is activity 2–4 with a cost savings of $3000 per week. Only 2 weeks, however, can be added to activity 2–4 without exceeding its normal time. Therefore, the normal cost and the normal time for activity 2–4 are inserted in columns (8) and (9) respectively. All other normal times and costs in columns (8) and (9) of Figure 17-7 are transferred to columns (8) and (9) of Figure 17-8, since the times of these activities cannot be increased without exceeding their normal times. So far, the time has been increased only from 14 to 16 weeks. One more week is needed; the activity affected must be on the same path as activity 2–4 and also should provide the maximum cost-savings possible. Activity 5–7 would meet these criteria if it were not already at its normal

Activity		Cost ($000)		Time (Weeks)		$/Week Cost to Expedite	Intermediate-time, Schedule—I				
Pred. (1)	Suc. (2)	N (3)	C (4)	N (5)	C (6)	(7)	Cost (8)	Time (9)	T_E (10)	T_L (11)	Float (12)
1✓	2	4	5	6	3	333	5	3	3	3	0
1✓	3	3	5	5	1	400	4.6	2	2	4	2
2✓	4✓	4	10	7	5	3,000	4	7	⑩	10	0
2✓	6✓	3	6	5	2	1,000	3	5	8	16	8
3	4✓	4	7	6	2	750	4	6	8	10	2
4✓	5	3	6	9	4	1,500	4.5	5	15	15	0
4✓	6✓	6	11	9	5	1,250	11	5	⑯	16	1
5	7✓	2	4	2	1	2,000	2	2	⑰	17	0
6	7✓	2	5	4	1	666	5	1	16	17	1
Totals		31	59				43.1				

Slack Path Analysis

0: 1-2-4-5-7
1: 4-6-7
2: 1-3-4
8: 2-6

Total time required: 17 weeks
Total cost: $43,100

Fig. 17-8. Intermediate-Time Schedule–I

time. Therefore the next lower choice is made—activity 4–5 with savings of $1500. One week is added to activity 4–5 bringing its time to 5 weeks; and $1500 is subtracted from its cost, bringing its cost down to $4500. This provides a total saving of $(2 \times \$3000) + (1 \times \$1500) = \$7500$. The rest of columns (8) and (9) are filled in directly from Figure 17-7, and columns (10), (11), and (12) are computed in the usual manner.

Figure 17-8 is inspected to ascertain whether any further savings may be obtained without affecting the total project time of 17 weeks. Such savings may be obtained only in paths having more than zero slack, and in which at least one activity-time is less than its normal time. The maximum savings obtainable would result from expanding activity 4–6—an expansion of one week with savings of $1250. The time of $5 + 1 = 6$ weeks and the cost of $\$11,000 - \$1250 = \$9750$ are inserted in columns (9) and (8) of Figure 17-9. All other figures from columns (8) and (9) of Figure 17-8 are transferred to Figure 17-9, and columns (10), (11), and (12) are computed. Figure 17–9 reveals that only one activity (activity 1–3) meets both of the required conditions; that is, has an activity-time less than normal and is on a path with more than zero slack. The new time of $2 + 2 = 4$ and the new cost of $\$4600 - \$800 = \$3800$ are inserted in columns (9) and (8) of Figure 17-10. All other figures from columns (8) and (9) of Figure 17-9 are transferred to Figure 17-10, and columns (10), (11), and (12) are computed. The only remaining activity with non-zero slack is 2–6. Its time cannot be lengthened without exceeding its normal time. The resulting least-cost schedule for the intermediate time of 17 weeks is $41,050. These values are plotted on Figure 17-11 as point b.

Activity		Cost ($000)		Time (Weeks)		$/Week Cost to Expedite	Intermediate-time, Schedule—II				
Pred. (1)	Suc. (2)	N (3)	C (4)	N (5)	C (6)	(7)	Cost (8)	Time (9)	T_E (10)	T_L (11)	Float (12)
1✓	2	4	5	6	3	333	5	3	3	3	0
1✓	3	3	5	5	1	400	4.6	2	2	4	2
2✓	4✓	4	10	7	5	3,000	4	7	⑩	10	0
2✓	6✓	3	6	5	2	1,000	3	5	8	16	8
3	4✓	4	7	6	2	750	4	6	8	10	2
4✓	5	3	6	9	4	1,500	4.5	5	15	15	0
4✓	6✓	6	11	9	5	1,250	9.75	6	⑯	16	0
5	7✓	2	4	2	1	2,000	2	2	17	17	0
6	7✓	2	5	4	1	666	5	1	17	17	0
Totals		31	59				41.85				

Slack Path Analysis

0: 1–2–4–5–7 or 1–2–4–6–7   Total time required: 17 weeks
2: 1–3–4   Total cost: $41,850
8: 2–6

Fig. 17-9. Intermediate-Time Schedule—II

Activity		Cost ($000)		Time (Weeks)		$/week Cost to Expedite	Least-cost, Intermediate-time Schedule				
Pred. (1)	Suc. (2)	N (3)	C (4)	N (5)	C (6)	(7)	Cost (8)	Time (9)	T_E (10)	T_L (11)	Float (12)
1✓	2	4	5	6	3	333	5	3	3	3	0
1✓	3	3	5	5	1	400	3.8	4	4	4	0
2✓	4✓	4	10	7	5	3,000	4	7	⑩	10	0
2✓	6✓	3	6	5	2	1,000	3	5	8	16	8
3	4✓	4	7	6	2	750	4	6	10	10	0
4✓	5	3	6	9	4	1,500	4.5	5	15	15	0
4✓	6✓	6	11	9	5	1,250	9.75	6	⑯	16	0
5	7✓	2	4	2	1	2,000	2	2	17	17	0
6	7✓	2	5	4	1	666	5	1	⑰	17	0
Totals		31	59				41.05				

Slack Path Analysis

All zero except   Total time required: 17 weeks
8: 2–6   Total cost: $41,050

Fig. 17-10. Least-Cost, Intermediate-Time Schedule

SEC. 17-5.   THE PROJECT TOTAL-COST CURVE

The project total-cost curve is the summation of two, and sometimes three, other curves, namely, (1) the project direct-cost curve, (2) the project indirect-cost curve, (3) perhaps a market-loss and penalty-cost curve.

The *project direct-cost curve*, shown on Figure 17-11, is constructed from the four points obtained from (1) the all-normal schedule (point *a*), (2) the all-crash schedule (point *d*), (3) the least-cost crash schedule (point

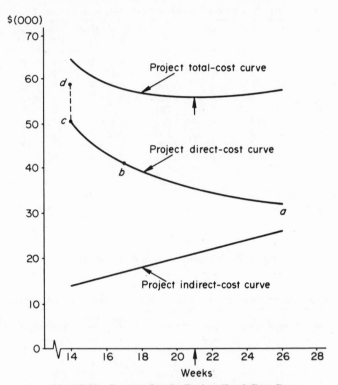

Fig. 17-11. Constructing the Project Total-Cost Curve

c), (4) the least-cost, intermediate-time schedule (point b). The *project* direct-cost curve is not the same curve as the *activity* direct-cost curve shown in Figure 17-2. The two concepts should be carefully distinguished. To construct the curve, a smooth line is drawn through points a, b, and c.

Next, the *project indirect-cost curve* is graphed. Indirect costs tend to be a function of time, and as a result, the indirect-cost curve tends to be a straight line. When curvilinear effects do exist, the curvature tends to be slight within the effective range of the curve. If such conditions do exist, the indirect-cost curve may be expressed in costs per week. In Figure 17-11, the indirect costs per week are considered to be $1000. To plot the curve, only two points are required: (1) the costs at 14 weeks are 14 × $1000 = $14,000; (2) the costs at 26 weeks are 26 × $1000 = $26,000. These two points are then connected with a straight line.

Although only direct and indirect costs are considered to exist in the example of Figure 17-11, other types of costs could be applicable. For example, assume that the contract date for the project completion is 20 weeks. Assume further that a bonus of $2000 per week is to be received for each week that is cut off the 20 weeks and that a penalty of $1000 per week is to be charged for each week of delay after the twentieth week. A curve reflecting these facts would also be plotted on Figure 17-11. Or assume that a market loss results from each week that the project remains uncompleted. All costs affecting the project should be utilized in constructing the project total-cost curve.

When all direct, indirect, bonus, penalty, market-loss, and so forth, curves applicable to the project are graphed, the total-cost curve is constructed by summing the other curves. On Figure 17-11, sufficient points are summed to permit the new curve to be clearly discernible. For example, the point at 14 weeks is the sum of the direct cost of $50,600 and the indirect cost of $14,000, or $64,600.

The total-cost curve will usually assume a U-shaped appearance. In any case, the low point of the curve represents the time duration of the project if all costs are to be minimized. In this case, the low point (indicated by the arrow on Figure 17-11) is 21 weeks. A schedule for 21 weeks is then prepared using the techniques discussed in Sec. 17–4 for preparing the least-cost, intermediate-time schedule. The preparation of the 21-week schedule is left as an exercise for the reader.

DISCUSSION QUESTIONS

17-1. Why may CPM be more useful than PERT in planning and controlling a construction project?

17-2. What is the CPM equivalent for the PERT term *network?* For *event?*

17-3. State the steps required to prepare a CPM program.

17-4. What is a common *node numbering system* for CPM?

17-5. Define the following terms and explain how to derive the required values:
a. Normal cost
b. Normal time
c. Crash time
d. Crash cost

17-6. Why is a straight-line function used for the *activity cost line?* What is the formula for developing the *slope* of the line?

17-7. Why are weeks and tenths of week recommended as the basic units of time?

17-8. Describe the method of setting up the *Normal-times, Normal-costs* schedule.

17-9. Define the term *total float.* What is the corresponding term used in PERT?

17-10. How are *total-time* and *total direct costs* determined for the Normal-times, Normal-costs schedule?

17-11. Describe the method of setting up the *Crash-times, Crash-costs* schedule.

17-12. How is the *Least-cost, Crash-times* schedule derived from the Crash-times, Crash-costs schedule?

17-13. What is the purpose of the *Least-cost, Intermediate-time* schedule? How is it derived?

17-14. How should the *time* for the *Least-cost, Intermediate-time* schedule be chosen? Why?

17-15. Describe how to construct the *project direct-cost curve.*

17-16. Discuss the planning and construction of the *project indirect-cost curve.* What is its usual shape, and why is this shape to be expected?

17-17. Discuss the need for, and construction of, *bonus, penalty,* and *market-loss curves.*

17-18. Explain how to construct the *project total-cost curve.*

17-19. Explain how to obtain the *time* for the *least-total-cost curve.*

17-20. Describe how to prepare the *schedule* for the *least-total-cost curve.*

PROBLEMS

17-1. Using the arrow diagram of Figure 17-1, assume the following time and cost estimates:

	Cost		Time	
Activity	Normal	Crash	Normal	Crash
1–2	1	9	9	6
1–3	4	6	7	2
2–4	7	9	12	6
2–6	7	12	10	8
3–4	6	7	12	8
4–5	5	8	6	2
4–6	7	18	7	1
5–7	3	5	14	4
6–7	4	7	8	5

Required
  a. Normal-times, normal-costs schedule
  b. Slack path analysis
  c. Total time required
  d. Total cost

17-2. Using the data of Problem 17-1, prepare
  a. Crash-times, crash-costs schedule
  b. Slack path analysis
  c. Total time required
  d. Total cost

17-3. Using the data of Problem 17-1, prepare
  a. Least-cost, crash-times schedule
  b. Slack path analysis
  c. Total time required
  d. Total cost

17-4. Using the data of Problem 17-1, prepare
a. Least-cost, intermediate-time schedule of 24 weeks
b. Slack path analysis
c. Total cost

17-5. Using the data of Problems 17-1 through 17-4, and assuming that indirect costs are $800 per week, construct a project total-cost curve.

17-6. Using the data of Problems 17-1 through 17-5, prepare a least-cost schedule.

17-7. Repeat Problem 17-1, using the following time and cost estimates:

Activity	Cost		Time	
	Normal	Crash	Normal	Crash
1–2	2	8	10	5
1–3	3	7	6	3
2–4	5	11	13	5
2–6	8	11	14	8
3–4	5	9	10	7
4–5	3	10	7	3
4–6	8	17	6	2
5–7	2	7	13	5
6–7	5	10	9	7

17-8. Repeat Problem 17-2, using the data of Problem 17-6.

17-9. Repeat Problem 17-3, using the data of Problem 17-6.

17-10. Repeat Problem 17-4, using the data of Problem 17-6.

17-11. Repeat Problem 17-5, using the data of Problems 17-7 through 17-10, and assuming that indirect costs are $1000 per week.

17-12. Repeat Problem 17-6, using the data of Problems 17-6 through 17-11.

17-13. Prepare the least-cost, 21-week schedule as discussed in Sec. 17-5.

BIBLIOGRAPHY

Backer, F., Jr., *et al.*, "Least-Cost Estimating and Scheduling," *Oil and Gas Journal*, 59 (Nov. 13, 1961), 170-71.

Berman, Herbert, "The Critical Path Method for Project Planning and Control," *The Constructor*, 43 (September, 1961), 24-5, 27, 29.

_____, "Try Critical Path Method to Cut Turnaround Time 20 Per Cent," *Hydrocarbon Process and Petroleum Refiner*, 41 (January, 1962), 135-38.

"Better Plans Come from Study of Anatomy of an Engineering Job," *Business Week*, (Mar. 21, 1959).

Christiansen, Borge M., "Network Models for Project Scheduling," *Machine Design*, 34 (May 10, 1962), 114-18; (May 24, 1962), 173-77; (June 7, 1962), 132-38; (June 21, 1962), 155-60; (July 5, 1962), 105-11; (July 19, 1962), 136-40.

Jacobs, R. T., and L. L. Meyers, *Critical Path Scheduling of ETR and MTR Reactor Shutdowns.* U.S. Atomic Energy Commission, AEC Research and Development Report IDO-16738. Washington, D.C.: U.S. Department of Commerce, Office of Technical Services, Jan. 10, 1962.

Levy, F. K., G. L. Thompson, J. D. Weist, *Critical Path Method—A New Tool for Management.* Office of Naval Research Memorandum No. 97. Carnegie Institute of Technology, Graduate School of Industrial Administration, May 25, 1962.

Sayer, J. S., J. E. Kelly, Jr., and Morgan R. Walker, "Critical Path Scheduling," *Factory,* 118 (July, 1960), 74–77.

Stilian, Gabriel N., *et al., PERT: A New Management Planning and Control Technique.* New York: American Management Association, 1962, pp. 147–63.

Stires, David M., and Maurice M. Murphy, *Modern Management Methods PERT and CPM.* Boston: Materials Management Institute, 1962, pp. 117–63.

18

Line of Balance

SEC. 18-1. STATEMENT OF THE PROBLEM TO BE SOLVED

The West Coast Aircraft Corporation, the low bidder, was named as the prime contractor to produce the T-7000 combat training plane (see Sec. 8-1). Utilizing the learning curve techniques discussed in Chapter 8, West Coast developed the delivery schedule shown in Figure 18-1.

The Air Force accepted the schedule as a part of the contract. To date, however, West Coast has not been able to maintain the planned schedule. Eight planes were to be delivered in April: actual deliveries— none. In May, instead of the required fourteen, only five were delivered, in June another seven, and in July, thirteen more, making a total of twenty-five against a scheduled number of fifty-nine.

A number of techniques for bringing production up to schedule were considered. After the advantages and disadvantages of each method were discussed, it was decided that a Line of Balance study would be the most likely to reveal where the difficulties were, and furthermore, Line of

Month	Number of Planes to be Delivered	Cumulative Deliveries
April	8	8
May	14	22
June	17	39
July	20	59
August	24	83
September	25	108
October	27	135
November	30	165
December	32	197
January	35	232
February	18	250

Fig. 18-1. Contract Schedule of Plane Deliveries

Balance could be used to continue to monitor the system to assure management that all production components keep in step with scheduled delivery requirements.

SEC. 18-2. BACKGROUND CONCEPTS OF LINE OF BALANCE

Line of Balance is a managerial tool applying the concept of management by exception to ascertaining and maintaining a balance in the components of the production process. The method was developed by the U.S. Navy during World War II and was used to maintain control of the multitudinous production contracts which were then, and have continued to be, in existence.

In applying the Line of Balance technique, a study is made as of a given point of time. The purpose of the study is to determine (1) where all phases of production should be at that point if the projected delivery schedule is to be maintained, (2) where all phases of production actually are, and to compare the two in order to find those phases requiring attention. Thus, the principle of management by exception comes into play, since those phases of the production process which are in step with the required delivery schedules require no corrective action. Managerial energy, therefore, is not unnecessarily spent investigating such operations, but may be concentrated on those areas which are current or potential trouble spots.

Corrective action, of course, is taken immediately. This, however, does not end the utility of the Line of Balance technique. Repeat studies may then be made periodically, monthly, for example, to ascertain that all phases of the production process have in fact been pulled into balance and continue to remain in balance. The initial Line of Balance study of any given project is the most expensive and time-consuming to make. The succeeding periodic studies, fortunately, are relatively simple and require much less time, effort, and skill.

A Line of Balance study consists of four principal operations:

1. The objective is ascertained. The *objective* is basically the delivery schedule of the end object (the product) graphed cumulatively; that is, each period's deliveries are added to all preceding deliveries.
2. A plan of operation is developed. The plan must show all principal and limiting events in the production process. The plan expresses graphically the lead time of each of these events. Setting up the plan is by far the most difficult of the Line of Balance operations.
3. A progress chart is prepared. The progress chart shows two things:
   a. The current status of each of the principal and limiting factors shown on the plan of operations. This is ordinarily a cumulative inventory count, specifying all items *completed* to the date of the study.

b. A Line of Balance showing the level at which each of the principal and limiting factors should be as of the date of the study.

4. The Line of Balance of each of the principal and limiting factors is compared with the current position of those factors. Those factors out of balance are revealed by a glance at the progress chart. Out-of-balance factors are investigated to ascertain the cause of the out-of-balance condition, and corrective steps are taken.

Each Line of Balance operation is described in detail in the following sections.

SEC. 18-3. THE OBJECTIVE CHART

The first step in the Line of Balance method is to develop and chart the cumulative delivery schedule of the end object (usually the finished product). The cumulative delivery schedule is often a straight-line function, since the company can turn out so many items per week or month. To graph such a schedule, the line starts at the origin and proceeds upward and to the right with a slope equal to the units produced per period of time, ordinarily one month. When conditions are present (such as a large amount of hand work) for learning to be possible, the cumulative delivery schedule function will be curvilinear. This latter condition is shown in Figure 18-2, which is based upon the delivery schedule of Figure 18-1. The schedule in turn is based upon the 80 per cent learning curve frequently experienced in the airframe industry.

The vertical axis represents accumulated scheduled deliveries and the horizontal axis, time expressed in 22-day months. The 22-day month is based upon an eight-hour day, five working days per week. The number of working days per month should be kept constant through all the operations of the Line of Balance method. Thus if in fact a seven-working day week is being used, suitable adjustments must be made.

The Schedule of Actual Deliveries

The schedule of actual deliveries is drawn on the same objective chart as the contract schedule. Several things are immediately apparent from an examination of the two lines thus graphed (see Figure 18-2): (1) the vertical distance between the lines shows the difference between the scheduled and actual deliveries; (2) the horizontal distance shows the time lag between the scheduled and actual deliveries; (3) the relative slopes of the two lines show whether they are tending to separate or to converge. In the present case, deliveries are (1) 36 planes under schedule; (2) the schedule is lagging by slightly less than two months; (3) the current trend of production is causing the two schedules to diverge,

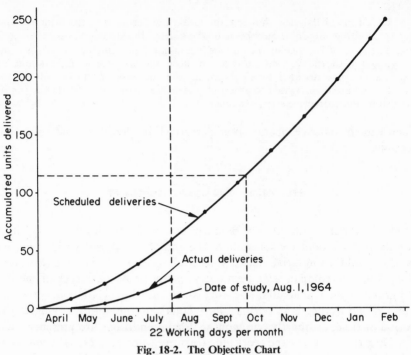

Fig. 18-2. The Objective Chart

indicating that, unless important changes are made, there is little likelihood that the original schedule will be achieved.

SEC. 18-4. THE PLAN OF OPERATIONS

The plan of operations for the T-7000 trainer (highly simplified) is shown in Figure 18-3. The two basic requirements for preparing the plan are (1) a bill of materials for the end product, (2) an intimate knowledge of the movement of the materials through the production processes. The second requirement implies ability to select those points in the processes which are principal and/or limiting. It should be reemphasized that the Line of Balance method makes no attempt to monitor all points in the production process, but only the principal and limiting points.

The bill of material for the end product is usually readily available, since its preparation is a standard procedure during the engineering of the product. From the bill of material must be selected those critical items which require lead time to obtain and which are purchased or produced only according to need.

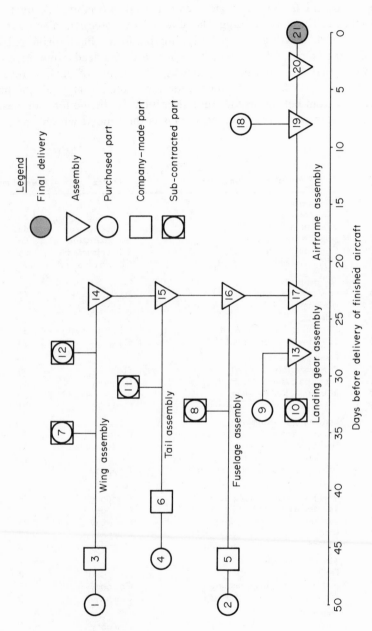

Fig. 18-3. The Plan of Operations

To develop a list of the principal and limiting factors in the production processes, the following is one recommended procedure. A detailed tour is made of the plant tracing the flow of the product. The tour is made backward, starting at the shipping platform. Each principal or limiting point is carefully noted, together with its lead time in days before the actual shipment of the product. The result of such a tour is shown in Figure 18-4. The bottom points were noted first, and the progression was from bottom to top. In determining lead time for purchased or subcontracted parts, the number of days is the time at which the part

No. on Prod. Plan	Principal or Limiting Factor	Source	Lead Time
	Wing assembly		
1	Raw material received	Purchased	50
3	Wing assembly started	Company	46
7	Ailerons received	Subcontracted	35
12	Gun mounts received	Subcontracted	28
14	Wing assembly completed	Company	23
	Tail assembly		
4	Raw material received	Purchased	46
6	Horizontal stabilizers and elevators started	Company	41
11	Vertical stabilizer and rudder received	Subcontracted	31
15	Tail assembly completed	Company	23
	Fuselage assembly		
2	Raw materials received	Purchased	50
5	Fuselage assembly started	Company	46
8	Instrumentation received	Subcontracted	33
16	Fuselage assembly completed	Company	23
	Landing gear assembly		
9	Wheels received	Purchased	33
10	Hydraulic gear received	Subcontracted	33
13	Landing gear subassembly completed	Company	28
17	Landing gear assembly completed	Company	23
	Airframe assembly		
14	Wing assembly completed	Company	23
15	Tail assembly completed	Company	23
16	Fuselage assembly completed	Company	23
17	Landing gear assembly completed	Company	23
19	Airframe assembly completed	Company	8
	Aircraft assembly		
18	Engine received	Purchased	8
19	Airframe assembly completed	Company	8
20	Aircraft assembly completed	Company	3
	Shipment		
20	Aircraft assembly completed	Company	3
21	Shipment made	Company	0

Fig. 18-4. The Principal and Limiting Events in the Production Processes

must be available on the production floor. The lead time for company-made parts, on the other hand, is the time at which production must be started. In the case of company-made subassemblies, the lead time is the completion date; that is, the date at which the subassembly must be ready for incorporation into the next phase of production.

The information from the schedule of principal and limiting points is transferred directly to the plan of operations. Each point must be placed in its correct time position and in its correct relationship to preceding and succeeding points. A time line is first drawn and scaled so as to cover the longest lead time, in this case 50 days. The zero point of the line is at the right. A legend showing distinctive marks for each type of point or event is prepared. Such a distinctive mark is an important aid in interpreting the plan of operations.

Directly above day zero is placed that item from the event schedule with a lead time of zero, in this case the "Delivery of the Aircraft." The next smaller time(s) is/are noted on the event schedule. In this case "Aircraft Assembly Completed," lead time, 3 days. The event is inserted on the chart using the proper mark. Next there are two events with lead time of 8 days. The problem arises as to which of these two events should be placed on the same line as the two events already recorded. It is evident that the event "Airframe Assembly Completed" is preceded by the events "Wing," "Tail," "Fuselage," and "Landing Gear Assemblies." Thus the event "Airframe Assembly Completed" is placed on the line with the event "Engine Received" placed above it at the same lead-time position. The four events with lead time of 23 days are then placed in a vertical line allowing sufficient space for the main subassembly events to be placed on horizontal lines to the left. The procedure is continued until all events have been placed on the plan of operations.

Numbering the Events

The events on the plan of operations are then numbered starting from left to right and from top to bottom. The leftmost event is numbered 1. If more than one event has the same lead time, the uppermost receives the lower number, and so forth. Inspection of the numbering on Figure 18-3 will clarify this concept.

SEC. 18-5.   THE PROGRESS CHART

The third step in the Line of Balance operations is the preparation of a progress chart containing two classes of information: (1) the current status of each item on the plan of operations; (2) a Line of Balance showing where each item should be.

The Current Status of Each Item

A chart is prepared (see Figure 18-5) with the vertical axis representing units and scaled the same as the vertical axis of the objective chart. In fact, it is convenient to place both of these charts on the same sheet of paper with the vertical axes in alignment as is shown in Figure 18-6. The horizontal axis has a place for a vertical bar representing each of the items on the plan. The item numbers are listed starting at the left and proceeding to the right. The vertical bars represent the accumulated finished units of the item represented by that number. The term *accumulated finished units* includes all units finished to date—those on end objects already delivered as well as those currently in inventory. In those cases where there are units currently in production but nearly finished, say, in excess of 90 per cent, these units may be shown on the progress chart with a hollow bar. This technique is demonstrated in item 14, Figure 18-5. The accumulated finished units are usually easily determined directly from the inventory records.

Striking the Line of Balance

The vertical bars on the progress chart represent the items on the plan of operations *as they presently are* in terms of accumulated finished units. The Line of Balance on the progress chart represents these same items *as they should be* at this point in time. In striking the Line of Balance, the lead time of each item comes into play. Item 1 (Figure 18-3) has a lead time of 50 days. The date of the study as shown by the objective chart (Figure 18-2) is August 1, 1964. To determine the accumulated number of units of item 1 which should have been on hand as of August 1, the lead time is added to the current date. At the rate of 22 working days per month, 50 days of lead time is equal to 2 and 6/22 months. On the horizontal axis of Figure 18-2, a point is marked at August 1, plus 2 and 6/22 months, which is three elevenths of the way through October. A vertical line is raised to the accumulated deliveries schedule curve, and at that point a horizontal line is carried to the units scale on the vertical axis. Thus, as of August 1, there should have been available 115 accumulated units of the materials represented by item 1. Therefore, a horizontal line is drawn on the progress chart at 115 units and across the space allotted to item 1. Each item on the plan of operations is treated in a similar manner. Note that, if the charts are arranged as shown in Figure

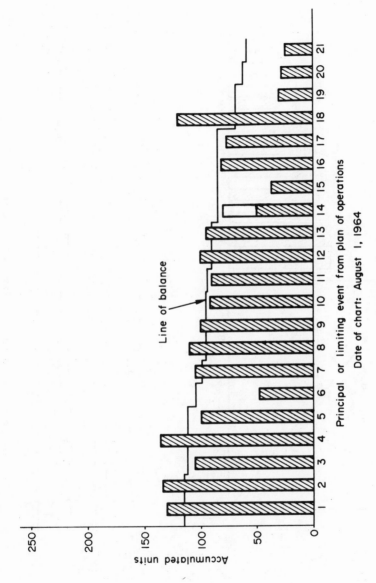

Fig. 18-5. The Progress Chart

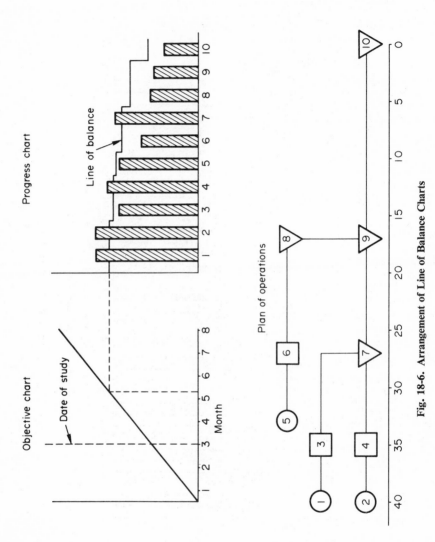

Fig. 18-6. Arrangement of Line of Balance Charts

18-6, the vertical line is raised to the schedule line and then carried horizontally to the progress chart. Since the items on the plan of operations were numbered in a left-to-right, top-to-bottom fashion, the leftmost section of the Line of Balance will be the highest portion of the line. The line will then proceed to the right in a step-down fashion.

Analyzing the Progress Chart

Inspection of the progress chart (Figure 18-5) immediately reveals that a number of items are currently out of balance with their expected positions. The analysis should begin at the right end of the chart. Item 21, the number of actual end objects shipped, is well below that scheduled to be shipped. This fact, of course, could be read directly from the objective chart, and therefore adds no new information. Item 20 shows that the number of completed aircraft assemblies is also below that scheduled, which explains the failure to ship the required number. Item 19, completed airframe assemblies, is similarly behind schedule, and a causative factor for the conditions of both items 20 and 21. A glance at item 18, receipt of engines, reveals that the failure of item 19 to be up to schedule is *not* due to the engine component not being available as required. Items 16, fuselage assemblies, and 17, landing gear assemblies, are sufficiently close to schedule; they can hardly be blamed for the badly behind schedule condition of items 19, 20, and 21. Item 15, tail assemblies, is, however, also well behind schedule, indicating that the trouble is likely to be somewhere in the tail assembly operation. The plan of operations shows that items 4, 6, and 11 are on the tail assembly sequence. The progress chart shows that items 4 and 11 appear to be reasonably close to schedule. Item 6, starting production of the horizontal stabilizers and elevators, is far behind schedule. Thus the trouble is pinpointed at item 6, and managerial attention may be concentrated on correcting this problem.

Other problem areas may be detected by further analysis of the progress chart. Items 1, 2, 4, and 18 are all well *above* the Line of Balance. Each of these processes should be investigated to see whether it should be slowed somewhat, since any out-of-balance conditions on the plus side may indicate excessive inventory investments in these items. Item 18, engine receipts, being a very high-cost component and being the farthest out of balance, should receive special attention. Items 3 and 4 appear to be sufficiently *below* the Line of Balance to cause some concern. Steps should probably be taken to bring them more closely into balance. But the item of most concern, next to item 6, is 14. If all the units were 100 per cent completed, item 14 would fall in the category of items 3 and 4. The fact that a large portion of these units are not yet completed (but are in excess of 90 per cent of completion) requires a thorough investigation as to causes and remedies.

The progress chart of Figure 18-5, because it is comparatively small, would be fairly easy to analyze as to the current condition of each class of item. This would be especially true if the vertical bars for each class of item were color coded. In the illustration, the following item classifications were included:

1. Receipt of purchased parts
2. Receipt of subcontracted parts or subassemblies
3. Start of company-made parts or subassemblies
4. Completion of company-made parts or subassemblies

For complex plans of operations, on the other hand, a supplementary progress chart for each class of item will be a valuable aid to the manager in his analysis of over-all conditions.

Supplementary charts for the progress chart of Figure 18-5 are shown in Figure 18-7. The information that these charts reveal is quite striking. A glance at chart (a) shows that all purchased parts are being received ahead of schedule. From the viewpoint of maintaining the schedule of production, this is quite an advantageous situation. From the viewpoint of the possible excess investment in inventory, however, it may be necessary to curb the enthusiasm of the purchasing department for having purchased parts on hand well in advance of requirements. The case of the engines, previously mentioned, is quite to the point here.

Chart (b) shows that the subcontracted items are being received fairly close to schedule, with some being slightly ahead and some slightly behind. If only one subcontractor is being used, he is very likely to have his scheduling under reasonable control. If several subcontractors are being used, chart (b) may reveal that some contractors are ahead of schedule and others behind. This situation could require some action on the part of the prime contractor.

Chart (c) shows that much of the actual and potential trouble lies with the activities of the prime contractor. All three basic subassemblies are being started late, with item 6 being the major trouble spot. Items 3 and 5 can easily cause future difficulties if they are not soon brought up to the Line of Balance condition. The difficulties shown by chart (d) can largely be traced to the poor scheduling revealed in chart (c).

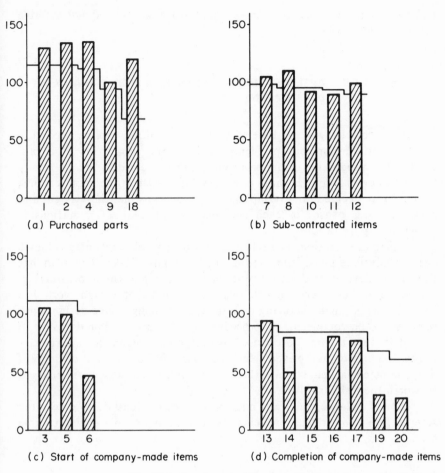

(a) Purchased parts

(b) Sub-contracted items

(c) Start of company-made items

(d) Completion of company-made items

Fig. 18-7. Supplementary Progress Charts

Future Line of Balance Studies

The Line of Balance study described here was made as of August 1, 1964. It was made in an effort to discover the cause of the major behind-schedule situation of the end object, the completed aircraft. The study has been successful in isolating out-of-balance items in the plan of operations. Naturally, as a result, the managers will initiate corrective actions. This does not terminate the usefulness of the Line of Balance method. It is highly desirable that regular studies be made—monthly is a recommended spacing. The study to be made as of September 1, 1964, would reveal whether any improvement toward bringing all items into balance

342

Line of Balance

had been achieved. Any weak spots would again be revealed and suitable action could then be taken.

SEC. 18-7. APPLYING LINE OF BALANCE TO RESEARCH AND DEVELOPMENT

With minor changes, the Line of Balance technique can be applied to research and development problems, such as the production of a prototype. The production of the prototype plane discussed in Sec. 16-1 may be used as an example. Because of a speed-up in the time requirements, it has been decided to overlap as much as possible the design and manufacturing phases of each component. The plan of operations is shown in Figure 18-8.

The plan of operations is a schedule based upon the first three columns of the analysis of phase time requirements (Figure 18-9). The plan has five phases devoted to design, five to manufacture, and three to assembly. The schedule was so arranged that as soon as sufficient design work has been completed, manufacturing may start, even though some design work remained to be completed. A procedure of this nature could result in wasted manufacturing effort caused by design changes in the later phases of the design program. Nevertheless, because of the urgency of the project, the potential reduction in the time requirements was considered to be worth the risks involved.

A Line of Balance study was made as of January 1, 1965, to determine whether the project was on schedule and to help isolate any trouble spots.

Plan of Operations

Note that the plan of operation for the research and development project differs somewhat from the plan for straight manufacturing operations. Instead of lead time, the plan is laid out in terms of months of the project. In the case of Figure 18-8, the project is planned to cover 24 months, starting in March, 1964, and to be completed as of the end of February, 1966. Each phase has a starting and ending point placed on the plan, with the estimated months required for the phase [column (3), Figure 18-9] separating the two points. The phases are then laid out on the plan so as to lead into the final product with a proper utilization of facilities and a cognizance of all related factors. As an aid in reading the plan, each phase classification is depicted with a special symbol. The starting symbol is left blank, and the ending symbol is crosshatched.

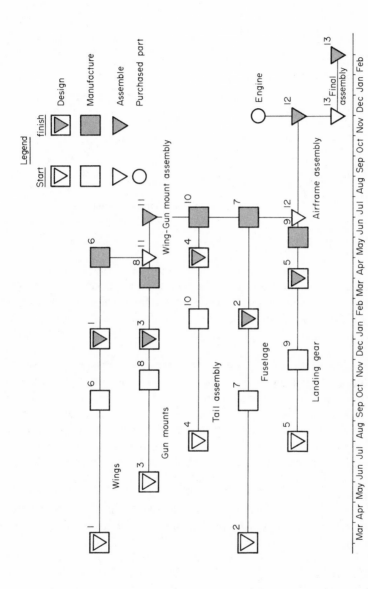

Fig. 18-8. Plan of Operations for Research and Development Project

343

Phase	Phase No.	Total Estimated Months	Estimated Months to Complete	Estimated % Complete
Wing design	1	10	0	100
Fuselage design	2	11	2	82
Gun mount design	3	7	2	71
Tail assembly design	4	9	3	66
Landing gear design	5	8	4	50
Wing manufacture	6	7	3	57
Fuselage manufacture	7	9	7	22
Gun mount manufacture	8	5	4	20
Landing gear manufacture	9	6	5.5	8
Tail assembly manufacture	10	5	5	0
Wing—gun mount assembly	11	2	2	0
Airframe assembly	12	5	4	0
Final assembly	13	3	3	0
Over-all project		87	44.5	

Fig. 18-9. Analysis of Phase Time Requirements

The Objective Chart

The objective chart also differs somewhat from that for a straight manufacturing operation. For the research and development project, the objective chart contains a schedule curve for each phase shown on the plan of operations and one for the entire project. Since in this case there are 13 phases, the objective chart contains 14 schedule curves (see Figure 18-10).

The *phase schedule curves* on Figure 18-10 are drawn as straight lines. If the planning of any of the phases shows that phase to have a curvilinear schedule, the schedule curve should be so drawn on the objective chart. Note that the vertical scale of the chart is in terms of percentage of completion. The starting point of phase 1 is March 1, 1964. The completion date is January 1, 1965. Therefore, a straight line is drawn from 0 per cent completed at March 1, 1964, to 100 per cent completed at January 1, 1965. The curve is labeled 1 at each end. Each of the other 12 phase schedules is similarly drawn.

The *total project schedule curve* is derived from the cumulative phase month schedule (Figure 18-11). Column (2) of Figure 18-11 is obtained from the plan of operations (Figure 18-8). During the month of March, 1964, two phase months were in operation, one for phase 1 and one for phase 2. During the month of December, 1964, nine phase months were in operation—one each for phases (reading top to bottom) 1, 6, 3, 8, 4, 2, 7, 5, and 9. The phase months are accumulated in column (3) of Figure 18-11 and expressed as a cumulative percentage in column (4). This cumulative percentage is then graphed on the objective chart (Figure 18-10).

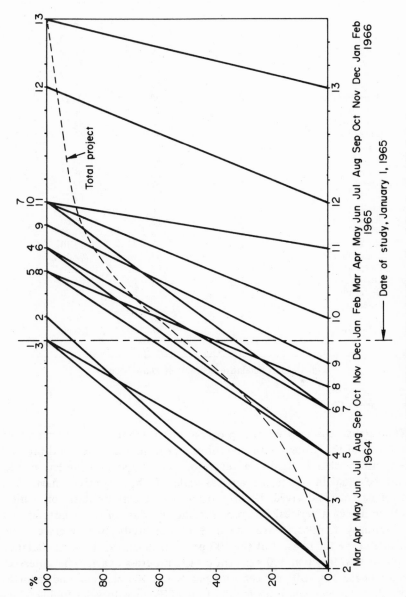

Fig. 18-10. Objective Chart for Research and Development Project

Month	Phase Months Planned per Month	Cumulative Phase Months	Cumulative % Phase Months
(1964)			
March	2	2	2.30
April	2	4	4.60
May	2	6	6.90
June	3	9	10.34
July	3	12	13.79
August	5	17	19.54
September	5	22	25.29
October	7	29	33.33
November	8	37	42.53
December	9	46	52.87
(1965)			
January	7	53	60.92
February	7	60	68.97
March	7	67	77.01
April	5	72	82.76
May	4	76	87.36
June	3	79	90.80
July	1	80	91.95
August	1	81	93.10
September	1	82	94.25
October	1	83	95.40
November	1	84	96.55
December	1	85	97.70
(1966)			
January	1	86	98.85
February	1	87	100.00
	87		

Fig. 18-11. Cumulative Schedule of Phase Months

The Progress Chart

The vertical columns on the progress chart (Figure 18-12) represent the phases of the project with one column representing the total project. The vertical scale is again in terms of percentage of completion and should be equal in size to the vertical scale of the objective chart. The Line of Balance is derived directly from the objective chart, on which has been drawn a vertical line representing the date of the study, in this case, January 1, 1965. Since the date of the study line intersects the schedule curve for phase 1 at the 100 per cent level, the Line of Balance for phase 1 is drawn at 100 per cent on the progress chart. The intersection for phase 2 is at 91 per cent, for phase 3 at 100 per cent, and so forth. (Note that the *step-down rule* for the Line of Balance does not follow when Line of Balance is applied to a research and development project.) Since the starting points, of phases 10 to 13 fall after the date of the study, the Line of Balance for these phases drops to the 0 per cent level.

The height of the vertical bars on the progress chart is derived from

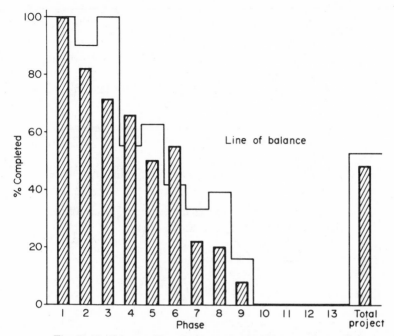

Fig. 18-12. Progress Chart for Research and Development Project

columns (4) and (5) of Figure 18-9, the analysis of phase time requirements. Column (4) represents an estimate of the months required to
complete each phase as of the date of the study. These estimates are
made independently of the original time estimates and should be realistic
in the light of unforeseen difficulties or any other considerations which
have evolved since the original estimates were made. Column (5) represents the percentage of completion in terms of time. This is derived by
subtracting the figure in column (4) from that in column (3) and dividing
the difference by the figure in column (3). The quotient is then multiplied
by 100 to convert to a percentage. This may be shown as

$$\text{phase \% completed} = 100 \left(\frac{b - a}{b}\right),$$

where a = estimated months to complete the phase

b = original estimated months required for the entire phase.

Since phase 1 is completed, the vertical bar is raised to the 100 per cent
level. The computation for phase 2 is

$$\text{\% phase 2 completed} = 100 \left(\frac{11 - 2}{11}\right) = 82 \text{ per cent.}$$

The Line of Balance for the total project is derived from the intersection of the date of the study line and the total project schedule curve. In this case the intersection is at 53 per cent. To determine the height of the vertical bar, the original total phase months for the entire project is obtained by totaling column (3) of Figure 18-9, and the total of the estimated phase months to be completed is obtained by totaling column (4). The percentage completed is then determined by

$$\text{total project } \% \text{ completed} = 100 \left(\frac{B - A}{B}\right),$$

where A = total original estimated phase months for the entire project

B = total estimated phase months required to complete the project as of the date of the study.

The computation for the illustrative case is

$$\text{total project } \% \text{ completed} = 100 \left(\frac{87 - 44.5}{87}\right) = 49 \text{ per cent.}$$

Analysis of the Progress Chart

The progress chart reveals the condition of the entire project at a glance. Three of the five design phases are behind schedule. These behind-schedule conditions have forced the related manufacturing phases also to be behind schedule. The tail assembly design is well ahead of schedule, and it appears that the related tail assembly manufacturing operation can proceed as scheduled on February 1, 1965. A possible action in this case might be to transfer some of the design engineers from the ahead-of-schedule tail assembly group to the behind-schedule fuselage design, gun mount design, and landing gear design groups. Such a transfer, of course, may not be feasible because of the different skills required by members of the various design groups. Other possible actions would be considered and evaluated.

DISCUSSION QUESTIONS

18-1. What are the three purposes of a *Line of Balance study*?

18-2. What is the *principle of management by exception*? How does it apply to the Line of Balance method?

18-3. State the four principal operations of a Line of Balance study.

18-4. Describe the *objective chart*.

18-5. How is the *delivery schedule curve* derived?

18-6. Describe the derivation and use of the *22-day month*. When, if ever, should departures from this concept be made?

18-7. Discuss the use of the *schedule of actual deliveries*. What information can be derived from a comparison of the two schedule curves?

18-8. Describe the preparation and construction of the *plan of operations*.

18-9. How are the *principal* and/or *limiting points* in the production process determined?

18-10. Discuss *lead time* in relation to (a) purchased parts, (b) subcontracted parts, (c) company-made parts, (d) subassemblies.

18-11. How are various classes of events distinguished on the plan of operations?

18-12. Explain the procedure for numbering the events on the plan of operations.

18-13. Describe the *progress chart*.

18-14. How is the *current status* of each item determined?

18-15. How is the *current status* of each item depicted on the progress chart.

18-16. What is the relationship between the vertical axis of the progress chart and that of the objective chart?

18-17. Describe the preferred layout of the three charts when placed on one sheet of paper.

18-18. Describe how to strike the *Line of Balance* on the progress chart. What is the meaning of the Line of Balance?

18-19. How are partially finished units depicted on the progress chart. Are there any limitations placed on such representations?

18-20. What effect does the recommended system of event numbering on the plan of operations have upon the appearance of the Line of Balance?

18-21. Discuss the technique of analyzing the progress chart.

18-22. In what way might *supplementary charts* be helpful in analyzing conditions as they exist at the point of time of the study? What supplementary charts would you recommend?

18-23. Discuss the purpose and timing of repeat Line of Balance studies.

18-24. Describe how the plan of operations for a research and development project differs from the plan for a production project.

18-25. Describe the objective chart for a research and development project.

18-26. How is the *total project schedule curve* derived?

18-27. What is the significance of the vertical bars on the progress chart for a research and development project?

18-28. Explain how to strike the *Line of Balance* for a research and development project.

PROBLEMS

18-1. The ABC Company manufactures complex "X" assemblies. Its contract requires the delivery of two completed assemblies each month for eight months.

However, it made no deliveries the first month and only one unit in each of the next two months. Prepare an *objective chart* as of the end of the third month.

18-2. The following is a list of principal and/or limiting events in the production of the "X" assemblies of Problem 18-1 and their lead times (in days) to the completion of the final assembly.

Principal or Limiting Factor	Source	Lead Time
Subassembly I		
Raw material for "A" received	Purchased	40
Raw material for "B" received	Purchased	40
Part "A" manufacture started	Company	35
Part "B" manufacture started	Company	35
Assembly of "A" and "B" started	Company	27
Subassembly I completed	Company	17
Subassembly II		
Purchased part received	Purchased	33
Subassembly II started	Company	27
Subassembly II completed	Company	17
Final Assembly		
Subassembly I completed	Company	17
Subassembly II completed	Company	17
Final assembly completed	Company	0

Prepare a *plan of operations.*

18-3. An investigation of inventory and other records of "X" assemblies of Problems 18-1 and 18-2 shows the cumulative units completed as of the end of the third month as follows:

Item	Number of Units
Raw material for "A" received	7
Raw material for "B" received	11
Part "A" manufacture started	10
Part "B" manufacture started	7
Assembly of "A" and "B" started	5
Subassembly I completed	4
Purchased part for subassembly II received	10
Subassembly II started	9
Subassembly II completed	8
Final assembly completed	2

Prepare a *progress chart* and strike thereon a *Line of Balance.*

18-4. The DEF Company manufactures complex "Y" assemblies. Its contract calls for the following delivery schedule:

Month	Number of Units
1	2
2	5
3	8
4	11
5	14
6	17
7	20
8	23
9	26
10	29

Actual deliveries made were as follows:

Month	Number of Units
1	0
2	2
3	4
4	6

Prepare an *objective chart* with the date of study as of the end of the fourth month.

18-5. The following is a list of principal and/or limiting events in the production of the "Y" assemblies of Problem 18-4 and their lead times (in days) to the completion of the final assembly.

Principal or Limiting Event	Source	Lead Time
Subassembly A		
Purchased part received	Purchased	37
Manufactured part started	Company	33
Subassembly A finished	Company	28
Subassembly B		
Purchased part received	Purchased	45
Manufactured part started	Company	41
Subcontracted part received	Subcontractor	37
Subassembly B finished	Company	28
Subassembly C		
Purchased part received	Purchased	37
Manufactured part started	Company	33
Subassembly C finished	Company	28
Subassembly D		
Purchased part received	Purchased	50
Manufactured part started	Company	45
Subcontracted part received	Subcontractor	41
Subassembly D finished	Company	28
Subassembly E		
Purchased part received	Purchased	24
Manufactured part started	Company	20

(Continued on page 352)

Principal or Limiting Event	Source	Lead Time
(Continued from p. 351)		
Subcontracted part E-1 received	Subcontractor	16
Subcontracted part E-2 received	Subcontractor	10
Subassembly E finished	Company	5
Subassembly F		
Purchased part received	Purchased	16
Manufactured part started	Company	12
Subcontracted part received	Subcontractor	8
Subassembly F finished	Company	5
Subassembly G		
Subassembly A finished	Company	28
Subassembly B finished	Company	28
Subassembly C finished	Company	28
Subassembly D finished	Company	28
Subcontracted part G-1 received	Subcontractor	24
Subcontracted part G-2 received	Subcontractor	16
Subcontracted part G-3 received	Subcontractor	10
Subassembly G finished	Company	5
Final Assembly		
Subassembly E finished	Company	5
Subassembly F finished	Company	5
Subassembly G finished	Company	5
Final assembly finished	Company	0

Prepare a *plan of operations.*

18-6. An investigation of inventory and other records of "Y" assemblies of Problems 18-4 and 18-5 shows the cumulative units completed as follows:

Item	Number of Units
Subassembly A	
Purchased part	48
Manufactured part started	45
Subassembly A finished	40
Subassembly B	
Purchased part	60
Manufactured part started	60
Subcontracted part received	55
Subassembly B finished	45
Subassembly C	
Purchased part received	48
Manufactured part started	45
Subassembly C finished	42
Subassembly D	
Purchased part received	65
Manufactured part started	58
Subcontracted part received	52
Subassembly D finished	40

Item	Number of Units
(Continued from p. 352)	
Subassembly E	
Purchased part received	50
Manufactured part started	45
Subcontracted part E-1 received	21
Subcontracted part E-2 received	15
Subassembly E finished	15
Subassembly F	
Purchased part received	40
Manufactured part started	35
Subcontracted part received	18
Subassembly F finished	18
Subassembly G	
Subcontracted part G-1 received	25
Subcontracted part G-2 received	20
Subcontracted part G-3 received	20
Subassembly G finished	15
Final Assembly	
Final assembly finished	12

Prepare a *progress chart* and strike thereon a *Line of Balance.*

18-7. Prepare *supplementary progress charts* using the information in Problems 18-4, 18-5, and 18-6.

18-8. Prepare a *plan of operations* for the following research and development project:

Phase	Beginning of Month	
	Start	Finish
Part A		
Design	1	8
Manufacture	5	12
Part B		
Design	2	10
Manufacture	7	12
Part C		
Design	4	10
Manufacture	7	12
Assembly D		
Assembly of Parts A, B, and C	12	15
Part E		
Design	6	11
Manufacture	9	15
Part F		
Design	2	8
Manufacture	4	15
Final Assembly		
Assembly of Assembly D and Parts E and F	15	19

18-9. From the data of Problem 18-8 prepare an *objective chart* with the date of the study as of the beginning of the eighth month.

18-10. The research and development project of Problems 18-8 and 18-9 at the beginning of the eighth month is estimated to require times (in months) for completion as follows:

Phase	Estimated Time to Completion
Part A	
Design	0
Manufacture	3
Part B	
Design	1
Manufacture	4
Part C	
Design	3
Manufacture	4.5
Assembly D	3
Part E	
Design	3
Manufacture	6
Part F	
Design	1
Manufacture	9
Final assembly	4

Prepare a *progress chart.*

BIBLIOGRAPHY

Gehringer, A. C., "Line of Balance," *Navy Management Review*, IV (April, 1959), 18-23.

"How Line of Balance Is Used to Establish Personnel Requirements," *Navy Management Review*, VI (February, 1961), 10-15.

Line of Balance Technology. Department of the Navy, Office of Naval Material, Washington, D. C.: Government Printing Office, April, 1962.

Stilian, Gabriel N., *et al., PERT: A New Management Planning and Control Technique.* New York: American Management Association, 1962, pp. 164-78.

Appendix A

Logarithms—
Basic Concepts
and Methods of Use

Where

$$A^b = C,$$

b is said to be the *logarithm* of C to the base A. Thus a logarithm is an *exponent* and the arithmetic manipulation of logarithms follows the rules of the algebraic manipulation of exponents.

RULE I. Whether the base is the same or different, *addition* may *not* be performed by the manipulation of exponents:

$$x^2 + x^3 = x^2 + x^3$$
$$x^2 + y^2 = x^2 + y^2.$$

RULE II. When the base is the same, *multiplication* may be performed by the addition of exponents:

$$x^2 \cdot x^3 = x^5,$$

but

$$x^2 \cdot y^3 = x^2 \cdot y^3.$$

RULE III. When the base is the same, *division* may be performed by the subtraction of exponents:

$$\frac{x^5}{x^2} = x^3.$$

RULE IV. *Exponentiation* may be performed by the multiplication of exponents:

$$(x^2)^3 = x^6.$$

RULE V. *Roots* may be extracted by the division of exponents:

$$\sqrt[3]{x^6} = x^{6/3} = x^2.$$

The *base* of a system of logarithms may be any real number other than 1 or 0. There are, however, two commonly used systems. The first is called *common* logarithms and uses the base 10. The second is called *natural* logarithms and uses the base *e* (see Sec. 10–1). The system under consideration here is that of common logarithms.

If 10 is raised to various positive integral powers, we have

$$10^4 = 10{,}000; \log 10{,}000 = 4.0000$$
$$10^3 = 1000; \log 1000 = 3.0000$$
$$10^2 = 100; \log 100 = 2.0000$$
$$10^1 = 10; \log 10 = 1.0000$$
$$10^0 = 1; \log 1 = 0.0000.$$

The foregoing logarithms may be divided into two parts: namely, the segment to the left of the decimal point, called the *characteristic*, and the segment to the right of the decimal point, called the *mantissa*. Note that the logarithm of any integral power of 10 has a mantissa of zero—only the characteristic changes. Note also that the logarithm of any number less than 10 but greater than, or equal to, 1 will have a characteristic equal to 0. Similarly, the logarithm of any number less than 100 and equal to, or greater than, 10 will have a characteristic equal to 1.

RULE I FOR CHARACTERISTICS. For numbers equal to, or greater than, 1, the characteristic is equal to the number of digits to the left of the decimal point, minus 1.

If 10 is raised to various negative integral powers, we have

$$10^{-1} = \frac{1}{10} = 0.1; \log 0.1 = -1.0000$$

$$10^{-2} = \frac{1}{100} = 0.01; \log 0.01 = -2.0000$$

$$10^{-3} = \frac{1}{1000} = 0.001; \log 0.001 = -3.0000$$

$$10^{-4} = \frac{1}{10{,}000} = 0.0001; \log 0.0001 = -4.0000.$$

RULE II FOR CHARACTERISTICS. For numbers less than 1, the characteristic is a negative number whose absolute value is equal to the number of 0's between the decimal point and the first nonzero digit to the right of the decimal point, plus 1.

When 10 is raised to a fractional power, the mantissa is no longer equal to zero. Take the case of $10^{0.25}$, $10^{1.25}$, $10^{2.25}$, $10^{3.25}$, and so forth, which are easy to compute:

$$10^{0.25} = \sqrt{\sqrt{10}} \doteq 1.7783; \; \log 1.7783 \doteq 0.2500$$

$$10^{1.25} = 10^{0.25} \times 10^1 \doteq 1.7783 \times 10 \doteq 17.783; \; \log 17.783 \doteq 1.2500$$

$$10^{2.25} = 10^{0.25} \times 10^2 \doteq 1.7783 \times 100 \doteq 177.83; \; \log 177.83 \doteq 2.2500$$

$$10^{3.25} = 10^{0.25} \times 10^3 \doteq 1.7783 \times 1000 \doteq 1778.3; \; \log 1778.3 \doteq 3.2500$$

Negative logarithms are somewhat different. Take the case of $10^{-0.75}$, $10^{-1.75}$, $10^{-2.75}$, and so forth.:

$$10^{-0.75} = 10^{0.25} \times 10^{-1} \doteq 1.7783 \times 0.1 \doteq 0.17783;$$
$$\log 0.17783 \doteq -0.7500$$
$$10^{-1.75} = 10^{0.25} \times 10^{-2} \doteq 1.7783 \times 0.01 \doteq 0.017783;$$
$$\log 0.017783 \doteq -1.7500$$
$$10^{-2.75} = 10^{0.25} \times 10^{-3} \doteq 1.7783 \times 0.001 \doteq 0.0017783;$$
$$\log 0.0017783 \doteq -2.7500.$$

Note two things here: (1) the characteristics do not follow *Rule II for Characteristics*; (2) the mantissa is the tens complement of the mantissa of the positive logarithms.

The first item could be taken care of by formulating a new rule for characteristics of negative logarithms, and the second by using two tables of mantissas. In practice neither of these things is done. Instead, the negative logarithm is converted to a positive logarithm by adding and subtracting a number which is absolutely larger than the negative characteristic:

$$\log 0.17783 = -0.7500$$

10.0000	-10
-0.7500	
9.2500	-10

This brings the mantissa into agreement with that of the positive logarithms and permits the use of one table of mantissas. The new characteristic is then added to the number subtracted:

$$9 - 10 = -1$$

and the adjusted logarithm becomes

$$-1.2500.$$

Since only the characteristic is now negative, this is frequently indicated by the following notation:

$$\overline{1}.2500.$$

The logarithms under consideration become

$$\log 0.17783 = -1.2500$$
$$\log 0.017783 = -2.2500$$
$$\log 0.0017783 = -3.2500.$$

Now the characteristics agree with *Rule II for Characteristics,* and the mantissas for both negative and positive logarithms are the same. The following rule for mantissas may then be used for all cases—positive logarithms and adjusted negative logarithms:

RULE FOR MANTISSAS. The value of the mantissa is independent of the position of the decimal point in the number and is determined purely by the value of the sequence of digits. Since mantissas are very difficult to compute, tables of logarithms are normally used.

The technique of computing mantissas used here is not the one used by mathematicians in producing tables of logarithms. Instead, rapidly converging mathematical series are used to compute natural logarithms, and these are then converted to common logarithms by using the proper transpositional factor.

SEC. A-2.   USING TABLES OF LOGARITHMS

Finding the Logarithm of a Number

The logarithm of a number is obtained in two steps:

1. Determine the characteristic by using the rules stated in Sec. A-1.
2. Obtain the mantissa by reference to the table of logarithms.

EXAMPLE 1. Find the logarithm of 49.9.
The characteristic is equal to the number of digits to the left of the decimal, minus 1:

$$2 - 1 = 1.$$

To find the mantissa, go down the column headed N until 49 is reached, then remaining in that row go to the column headed 9. The mantissa is 69810. Therefore,

$$\log 49.9 = 1.69810.$$

EXAMPLE 2. Find the logarithm of 0.00856.
The characteristic is equal to the number of zeros between the decimal point and the first nonzero digit to the right of the decimal point, plus 1, expressed as a negative:

$$2 + 1 = 3; \text{characteristic} = -3.$$

To find the mantissa, go down the column headed N until 85 is reached, then remaining in that row go to the column headed 6. The mantissa is 93247. Therefore,

$$\log 0.00856 = -3.93247.$$

Finding the Antilogarithm of a Logarithm

The number related to a given logarithm is referred to as the *antilogarithm* of that logarithm. The process of finding the antilogarithm is the reverse of finding the logarithm:

1. Locate the mantissa in the table of logarithms.
2. Locate the decimal point according to the characteristic.

EXAMPLE 3. Find the antilogarithm of 1.69810.
First locate the mantissa, 69810, in the table of logarithms. Follow the row to the left and write down the number in the column headed N, in this case, 49. Then to the right of the 49 write the number at the head of the column in which the mantissa is located, thus 499. The decimal point is located according to the characteristic. Since the characteristic is determined by counting the digits to the left of the decimal point and subtracting 1, the decimal position is determined by adding 1 to the *positive* characteristic. Therefore,

$$\text{antilog } 1.69810 = 49.9.$$

EXAMPLE 4. Find the antilog of -3.93247.
Locate 93247 in the table of logarithms. Column N and the heading of the

column in which the mantissa is located give 856. To locate the decimal point, place one fewer zeros than the absolute value of the *negative* characteristic between the decimal point and the number obtained from the tables:

$$\text{antilog} -3.93247 = 0.00856.$$

Interpolation

Usually neither the number for which a logarithm is sought nor the mantissa for which an antilogarithm is sought appears exactly in the table of logarithms. To obtain the desired result, a process known as *linear interpolation* is used. This merely means that a proportional amount of the difference between the figures found in the tables is added to the lower value from the tables. The following examples will clarify this concept.

EXAMPLE 5. Find the logarithm of 285.65.
From the table,

$$\log 285.00 = 2.45484$$
$$\log 286.00 = 2.45637.$$

Clearly the logarithm of 285.65 is somewhere in between.

$$2.45637 - 2.45484 = 0.00153$$
$$0.65 \times 0.00153 = 0.00025 \text{ rounded.}$$

Therefore, $\qquad \log 285.65 = 2.45484 + 0.00025 = 2.45509.$

EXAMPLE 6. Find the antilogarithm of -4.84788.
From the table,

$$\text{antilog} -4.84757 = 0.000704$$
$$\text{antilog} -4.84819 = 0.000705.$$

The antilogarithm of -4.84788 lies somewhere in between.

$$84788 - 84757 = 31$$
$$84819 - 84757 = 62$$
$$\frac{31}{62} = 0.5, \text{ or halfway between.}$$

Therefore, $\qquad \text{antilog} -4.84788 = 0.0007045.$

SEC. A-3.   COMPUTING WITH LOGARITHMS

Multiplication

$$A \cdot B = \text{antilog of } (\log A + \log B).$$

EXAMPLE 7. Find the product of 2.675 and 38.43.

$$\text{Log } 2.675 = 0.42732$$
$$\log 38.43 = \underline{1.58467}$$
$$2.01199$$

$$\text{antilog } 2.01199 = 102.7995 \doteq 102.800.$$
$$2.675 \times 38.43 \doteq 102.8.$$

Division

$$\frac{A}{B} = \text{antilog of } (\log A - \log B).$$

EXAMPLE 8. Divide 102.8 by 38.43.

$$\text{Log } 102.8 = 2.01199$$
$$\log 38.43 = \underline{1.58467}$$
$$0.42732$$

$$\text{antilog } 0.42732 \doteq 2.675.$$
$$\frac{102.8}{38.43} \doteq 2.675.$$

Exponentiation

$$A^b = \text{antilog of } b(\log A).$$

EXAMPLE 9. Find the value of $15^{3.25}$.

$$\text{Log } 15 = 1.17609$$
$$1.17609 \times 3.25 = 3.8222925.$$
$$\text{Antilog } 3.8222925 \doteq 6641.88$$
$$15^{3.25} \doteq 6641.88.$$

Extracting Roots

$$\sqrt[a]{B} = \text{antilog of} \frac{\log B}{a}.$$

EXAMPLE 10. Find the fourth root of 10.

$$\text{Log } 10 = 1.00000$$

$$\frac{1.00000}{4} = 0.25000.$$

$$\text{antilog of } 0.25000 \doteq 1.7783$$

$$\sqrt[4]{10} \doteq 1.7783.$$

True Negative Logarithms

EXAMPLE 11. Find the value of $25^{-3.6}$.

$$\text{Log } 25 = 1.39794$$

$$1.39794 \times (-3.6) = -5.032584$$

Note that -5.032584 is a true negative logarithm, and must be adjusted:

$$
\begin{array}{ll}
10.000000 & -10 \\
-5.032584 & \\
\hline
4.967416 & -10 \\
\end{array}
$$

$$\text{or} \quad -6.967416$$

$$\text{Antilog } -6.967416 \doteq 0.000009277$$

$$25^{-3.6} \doteq 0.000009277.$$

Common Logarithms

N	0	1	2	3	4	5	6	7	8	9	D
0	− ∞	00000	30103	47712	60206	69897	77815	84510	90309	95424	...
10	00000	00432	00860	01284	01703	02119	02531	02938	03342	03743	*
11	04139	04532	04922	05308	05690	06070	06446	06819	07188	07555	*
12	07918	08279	08636	08991	09342	09691	10037	10380	10721	11059	*
13	11394	11727	12057	12385	12710	13033	13354	13672	13988	14301	*
14	14613	14922	15229	15534	15836	16137	16435	16732	17026	17319	*
15	17609	17898	18184	18469	18752	19033	19312	19590	19866	20140	*
16	20412	20683	20952	21219	21484	21748	22011	22272	22531	22789	*
17	23045	23300	23553	23805	24055	24304	24551	24797	25042	25285	*
18	25527	25768	26007	26245	26482	26717	26951	27184	27416	27646	*
19	27875	28103	28330	28556	28780	29003	29226	29447	29667	29885	*
20	30103	30320	30535	30750	30963	31175	31387	31597	31806	32015	212
21	32222	32428	32634	32838	33041	33244	33445	33646	33846	34044	202
22	34242	34439	34635	34830	35025	35218	35411	35603	35793	35984	193
23	36173	36361	36549	36736	36922	37107	37291	37475	37658	37840	185
24	38021	38202	38382	38561	38739	38917	39094	39270	39445	39620	177
25	39794	39967	40140	40312	40483	40654	40824	40993	41162	41330	170
26	41497	41664	41830	41996	42160	42325	42488	42651	42813	42975	164
27	43136	43297	43457	43616	43775	43933	44091	44248	44404	44560	158
28	44716	44871	45025	45179	45332	45484	45637	45788	45939	46090	152
29	46240	46389	46538	46687	46835	46982	47129	47276	47422	47567	147
30	47712	47857	48001	48144	48287	48430	48572	48714	48855	48996	142
31	49136	49276	49415	49554	49693	49831	49969	50106	50243	50379	138
32	50515	50651	50786	50920	51055	51188	51322	51455	51587	51720	134
33	51851	51983	52114	52244	52375	52504	52634	52763	52892	53020	130
34	53148	53275	53403	53529	53656	53782	53908	54033	54158	54283	126
35	54407	54531	54654	54777	54900	55023	55145	55267	55388	55509	122
36	55630	55751	55871	55991	56110	56229	56348	56467	56585	56703	119
37	56820	56937	57054	57171	57287	57403	57519	57634	57749	57864	116
38	57978	58092	58206	58320	58433	58546	58659	58771	58883	58995	113
39	59106	59218	59329	59439	59550	59660	59770	59879	59988	60097	110
40	60206	60314	60423	60531	60638	60746	60853	60959	61066	61172	107
41	61278	61384	61490	61595	61700	61805	61909	62014	62118	62221	105
42	62325	62428	62531	62634	62737	62839	62941	63043	63144	63246	102
43	63347	63448	63548	63649	63749	63849	63949	64048	64147	64246	100
44	64345	64444	64542	64640	64738	64836	64933	65031	65128	65225	98
45	65321	65418	65514	65610	65706	65801	65896	65992	66087	66181	96
46	66276	66370	66464	66558	66652	66745	66839	66932	67025	67117	93
47	67210	67302	67394	67486	67578	67669	67761	67852	67943	68034	91
48	68124	68215	68305	68395	68485	68574	68664	68753	68842	68931	90
49	69020	69108	69197	69285	69373	69461	69548	69636	69723	69810	88

Common Logarithms

N	0	1	2	3	4	5	6	7	8	9	D
50	69897	69984	70070	70157	70243	70329	70415	70501	70586	70672	86
51	70757	70842	70927	71012	71096	71181	71265	71349	71433	71517	84
52	71600	71684	71767	71850	71933	72016	72099	72181	72263	72346	83
53	72428	72509	72591	72673	72754	72835	72916	72997	73078	73159	81
54	73239	73320	73400	73480	73560	73640	73719	73799	73878	73957	80
55	74036	74115	74194	74273	74351	74429	74507	74586	74663	74741	78
56	74819	74896	74974	75051	75128	75205	75282	75358	75435	75511	77
57	75587	75664	75740	75815	75891	75967	76042	76118	76193	76268	76
58	76343	76418	76492	76567	76641	76716	76790	76864	76938	77012	74
59	77085	77159	77232	77305	77379	77452	77525	77597	77670	77743	73
60	77815	77887	77960	78032	78104	78176	78247	78319	78390	78462	72
61	78533	78604	78675	78746	78817	78888	78958	79029	79099	79169	71
62	79239	79309	79379	79449	79518	79588	79657	79727	79796	79865	70
63	79934	80003	80072	80140	80209	80277	80346	80414	80482	80550	68
64	80618	80686	80754	80821	80889	80956	81023	81090	81158	81224	67
65	81291	81358	81425	81491	81558	81624	81690	81757	81823	81889	66
66	81954	82020	82086	82151	82217	82282	82347	82413	82478	82543	65
67	82607	82672	82737	82802	82866	82930	82995	83059	83123	83187	64
68	83251	83315	83378	83442	83506	83569	83632	83696	83759	83822	63
69	83885	83948	84011	84073	84136	84198	84261	84323	84386	84448	62
70	84510	84572	84634	84696	84757	84819	84880	84942	85003	85065	62
71	85126	85187	85248	85309	85370	85431	85491	85552	85612	85673	61
72	85733	85794	85854	85914	85974	86034	86094	86153	86213	86273	60
73	86332	86392	86451	86510	86570	86629	86688	86747	86806	86864	59
74	86923	86982	87040	87099	87157	87216	87274	87332	87390	87448	58
75	87506	87564	87622	87679	87737	87795	87852	87910	87967	88024	58
76	88081	88138	88195	88252	88309	88366	88423	88480	88536	88593	57
77	88649	88705	88762	88818	88874	88930	88986	89042	89098	89154	56
78	89209	89265	89321	89376	89432	89487	89542	89597	89653	89708	55
79	89763	89818	89873	89927	89982	90037	90091	90146	90200	90255	55
80	90309	90363	90417	90472	90526	90580	90634	90687	90741	90795	54
81	90849	90902	90956	91009	91062	91116	91169	91222	91275	91328	53
82	91381	91434	91487	91540	91593	91645	91698	91751	91803	91855	53
83	91908	91960	92012	92065	92117	92169	92221	92273	92324	92376	52
84	92428	92480	92531	92583	92634	92686	92737	92788	92840	92891	51
85	92942	92993	93044	93095	93146	93197	93247	93298	93349	93399	51
86	93450	93500	93551	93601	93651	93702	93752	93802	93852	93902	50
87	93952	94002	94052	94101	94151	94201	94250	94300	94349	94399	50
88	94448	94498	94547	94596	94645	94694	94743	94792	94841	94890	49
89	94939	94988	95036	95085	95134	95182	95231	95279	95328	95376	49
90	95424	95472	95521	95569	95617	95665	95713	95761	95809	95856	48
91	95904	95952	95999	96047	96095	96142	96190	96237	96284	96332	48
92	96379	96426	96473	96520	96567	96614	96661	96708	96755	96802	47
93	96848	96895	96942	96988	97035	97081	97128	97174	97220	97267	47
94	97313	97359	97405	97451	97497	97543	97589	97635	97681	97727	46
95	97772	97818	97864	97909	97955	98000	98046	98091	98137	98182	46
96	98227	98272	98318	98363	98408	98453	98498	98543	98588	98632	45
97	98677	98722	98767	98811	98856	98900	98945	98989	99034	99078	45
98	99123	99167	99211	99255	99300	99344	99388	99432	99476	99520	44
99	99564	99607	99651	99695	99739	99782	99826	99870	99913	99957	44

SOURCE: Dudley J. Cowden, *Statistical Methods in Quality Control* (Englewood Cliffs, N.J.: Prentice-Hall, Inc., 1957), pp. 648–49. (*Reprinted by permission of the author and publishers.*)

Appendix B

Values of χ^2 for Specified Probabilities and Given Degrees of Freedom

This table shows $Q(\chi^2|\nu)$, the probability of obtaining a value of χ^2 as large as the sample value or larger. See the diagram below.

This table shows
the black area:

for $\nu = 1$ and $\nu = 2$

ν	Probability										
	.999	.995	.99	.98	.975	.95	.90	.80	.75	.70	.50
1	$.0^4157$	$.0^4393$	$.0^3157$	$.0^3628$	$.0^3982$	.00393	.0158	.0642	.102	.148	.455
2	.00200	.0100	.0201	.0404	.0506	.103	.211	.446	.575	.713	1.386
3	.0243	.0717	.115	.185	.216	.352	.584	1.005	1.213	1.424	2.366
4	.0908	.207	.297	.429	.484	.711	1.064	1.649	1.923	2.195	3.357
5	.210	.412	.554	.752	.831	1.145	1.610	2.343	2.675	3.000	4.351
6	.381	.676	.872	1.134	1.237	1.635	2.204	3.070	3.455	3.828	5.348
7	.598	.989	1.239	1.564	1.690	2.167	2.833	3.822	4.255	4.671	6.346
8	.857	1.344	1.646	2.032	2.180	2.733	3.490	4.594	5.071	5.527	7.344
9	1.152	1.735	2.088	2.532	2.700	3.325	4.168	5.380	5.899	6.393	8.343
10	1.479	2.156	2.558	3.059	3.247	3.940	4.865	6.179	6.737	7.267	9.342
11	1.834	2.603	3.053	3.609	3.816	4.575	5.578	6.989	7.584	8.148	10.341
12	2.214	3.074	3.571	4.178	4.404	5.226	6.304	7.807	8.438	9.034	11.340
13	2.617	3.565	4.107	4.765	5.009	5.892	7.042	8.634	9.299	9.926	12.340
14	3.041	4.075	4.660	5.368	5.629	6.571	7.790	9.467	10.165	10.821	13.339
15	3.483	4.601	5.229	5.985	6.262	7.261	8.547	10.307	11.036	11.721	14.339
16	3.942	5.142	5.812	6.614	6.908	7.962	9.312	11.152	11.912	12.624	15.338
17	4.416	5.697	6.408	7.255	7.564	8.672	10.085	12.002	12.792	13.531	16.338
18	4.905	6.265	7.015	7.906	8.231	9.390	10.865	12.857	13.675	14.440	17.338
19	5.407	6.844	7.633	8.567	8.907	10.117	11.651	13.716	14.562	15.352	18.338
20	5.921	7.434	8.260	9.237	9.591	10.851	12.443	14.578	15.452	16.266	19.337
21	6.447	8.034	8.897	9.915	10.283	11.591	13.240	15.445	16.344	17.182	20.337
22	6.983	8.643	9.542	10.600	10.982	12.338	14.041	16.314	17.240	18.101	21.337
23	7.529	9.260	10.196	11.293	11.688	13.091	14.848	17.187	18.137	19.021	22.337
24	8.085	9.886	10.856	11.992	12.401	13.848	15.659	18.062	19.037	19.943	23.337
25	8.649	10.520	11.524	12.697	13.120	14.611	16.473	18.940	19.939	20.867	24.337
26	9.222	11.160	12.198	13.409	13.844	15.379	17.292	19.820	20.843	21.792	25.336
27	9.803	11.808	12.879	14.125	14.573	16.151	18.114	20.703	21.749	22.719	26.336
28	10.391	12.461	13.565	14.847	15.308	16.928	18.939	21.588	22.657	23.647	27.336
29	10.986	13.121	14.256	15.574	16.047	17.708	19.768	22.475	23.567	24.577	28.336
30	11.588	13.787	14.953	16.306	16.791	18.493	20.599	23.364	24.478	25.508	29.336

SOURCE: Dudley J. Cowden, *Statistical Methods in Quality Control* (Englewood Cliffs, N.J.: Prentice-Hall, Inc., 1957), pp. 672–73. (*Reprinted by permission of the author and publishers.*)

Values of χ^2 for Specified Probabilities and Given Degrees of Freedom

This table shows the black area:

for $\nu \geq 3$

Probability										ν
.30	.25	.20	.10	.05	.025	.02	.01	.005	.001	
1.074	1.323	1.642	2.706	3.841	5.024	5.412	6.635	7.879	10.827	1
2.408	2.773	3.219	4.605	5.991	7.378	7.824	9.210	10.597	13.815	2
3.665	4.108	4.642	6.251	7.815	9.348	9.837	11.345	12.838	16.268	3
4.878	5.385	5.989	7.779	9.488	11.143	11.668	13.277	14.860	18.465	4
6.064	6.626	7.289	9.236	11.070	12.832	13.388	15.086	16.750	20.517	5
7.231	7.841	8.558	10.645	12.592	14.449	15.033	16.812	18.548	22.457	6
8.383	9.037	9.803	12.017	14.067	16.013	16.622	18.475	20.278	24.322	7
9.524	10.219	11.030	13.362	15.507	17.535	18.168	20.090	21.955	26.125	8
10.656	11.389	12.242	14.684	16.919	19.023	19.679	21.666	23.589	27.877	9
11.781	12.549	13.442	15.987	18.307	20.483	21.161	23.209	25.188	29.588	10
12.899	13.701	14.631	17.275	19.675	21.920	22.618	24.725	26.757	31.264	11
14.011	14.845	15.812	18.549	21.026	23.337	24.054	26.217	28.300	32.909	12
15.119	15.984	16.985	19.812	22.362	24.736	25.472	27.688	29.819	34.528	13
16.222	17.117	18.151	21.064	23.685	26.119	26.873	29.141	31.319	36.123	14
17.322	18.245	19.311	22.307	24.996	27.488	28.259	30.578	32.801	37.697	15
18.418	19.369	20.465	23.542	26.296	28.845	29.633	32.000	34.267	39.252	16
19.511	20.489	21.615	24.769	27.587	30.191	30.995	33.409	35.718	40.790	17
20.601	21.605	22.760	25.989	28.869	31.526	32.346	34.805	37.156	42.312	18
21.689	22.718	23.900	27.204	30.144	32.852	33.687	36.191	38.582	43.820	19
22.775	23.828	25.038	28.412	31.410	34.170	35.020	37.566	39.997	45.315	20
23.858	24.935	26.171	29.615	32.671	35.479	36.343	38.932	41.401	46.797	21
24.939	26.039	27.301	30.813	33.924	36.781	37.659	40.289	42.796	48.268	22
26.018	27.141	28.429	32.007	35.172	38.076	38.968	41.638	44.181	49.728	23
27.096	28.241	29.553	33.196	36.415	39.364	40.270	42.980	45.558	51.179	24
28.172	29.339	30.675	34.382	37.652	40.646	41.566	44.314	46.928	52.620	25
29.246	30.434	31.795	35.563	38.885	41.923	42.856	45.642	48.290	54.052	26
30.319	31.528	32.912	36.741	40.113	43.194	44.140	46.963	49.645	55.476	27
31.391	32.620	34.027	37.916	41.337	44.461	45.419	48.278	50.993	56.893	28
32.461	33.711	35.139	39.087	42.557	45.722	46.693	49.588	52.336	58.302	29
33.530	34.800	36.250	40.256	43.773	46.979	47.962	50.892	53.672	59.703	30

For large values of ν,

$$\chi^2 \doteq \nu \left(1 - \frac{2}{9\nu} \pm z_Q \sqrt{\frac{2}{9\nu}} \right)^3.$$

where z_Q is the normal deviate cutting off the corresponding tails of a normal distribution. Thus if $z_Q = 1.96$, we obtain values of χ^2 for $Q = .975$ and .025, or $P = .025$ and .975.

For very large values of ν,

$$\chi^2 \doteq \tfrac{1}{2}(z_Q \pm \sqrt{2\nu - 1})^2.$$

Appendix C

Table of Areas Under the Normal Curve

z	0.00	0.01	0.02	0.03	0.04	0.05	0.06	0.07	0.08	0.09
0.0	0.5000	0.5040	0.5080	0.5120	0.5160	0.5199	0.5239	0.5279	0.5319	0.5359
0.1	0.5398	0.5438	0.5478	0.5517	0.5557	0.5596	0.5636	0.5675	0.5714	0.5753
0.2	0.5793	0.5832	0.5871	0.5910	0.5948	0.5987	0.6026	0.6064	0.6103	0.6141
0.3	0.6179	0.6217	0.6255	0.6293	0.6331	0.6368	0.6406	0.6443	0.6480	0.6517
0.4	0.6554	0.6591	0.6628	0.6664	0.6700	0.6736	0.6772	0.6808	0.6844	0.6879
0.5	0.6915	0.6950	0.6985	0.7019	0.7054	0.7088	0.7123	0.7157	0.7190	0.7224
0.6	0.7257	0.7291	0.7324	0.7357	0.7389	0.7422	0.7454	0.7486	0.7517	0.7549
0.7	0.7580	0.7611	0.7642	0.7673	0.7703	0.7734	0.7764	0.7794	0.7823	0.7852
0.8	0.7881	0.7910	0.7939	0.7967	0.7995	0.8023	0.8051	0.8078	0.8106	0.8133
0.9	0.8159	0.8186	0.8212	0.8238	0.8264	0.8289	0.8315	0.8340	0.8365	0.8389
1.0	0.8413	0.8438	0.8461	0.8485	0.8508	0.8531	0.8554	0.8577	0.8599	0.8621
1.1	0.8643	0.8665	0.8686	0.8708	0.8729	0.8749	0.8770	0.8790	0.8810	0.8830
1.2	0.8849	0.8869	0.8888	0.8907	0.8925	0.8944	0.8962	0.8980	0.8997	0.90147
1.3	0.90320	0.90490	0.90658	0.90824	0.90988	0.91149	0.91309	0.91466	0.91621	0.91774
1.4	0.91924	0.92073	0.92220	0.92364	0.92507	0.92647	0.92785	0.92922	0.93056	0.93189
1.5	0.93319	0.93448	0.93574	0.93699	0.93822	0.93943	0.94062	0.94179	0.94295	0.94408
1.6	0.94520	0.94630	0.94738	0.94845	0.94950	0.95053	0.95154	0.95254	0.95352	0.95449
1.7	0.95543	0.95637	0.95728	0.95818	0.95907	0.95994	0.96080	0.96164	0.96246	0.96327
1.8	0.96407	0.96485	0.96562	0.96638	0.96712	0.96784	0.96856	0.96926	0.96995	0.97062
1.9	0.97128	0.97193	0.97257	0.97320	0.97381	0.97441	0.97500	0.97558	0.97615	0.97670
2.0	0.97725	0.97778	0.97831	0.97882	0.97932	0.97982	0.98030	0.98077	0.98124	0.98169
2.1	0.98214	0.98257	0.98300	0.98341	0.98382	0.98422	0.98461	0.98500	0.98537	0.98574
2.2	0.98610	0.98645	0.98679	0.98713	0.98745	0.98778	0.98809	0.98840	0.98870	0.98899
2.3	0.98928	0.98956	0.98983	$0.9^2 0097$	$0.9^2 0358$	$0.9^2 0613$	$0.9^2 0863$	$0.9^2 1106$	$0.9^2 1344$	$0.9^2 1576$
2.4	$0.9^2 1802$	$0.9^2 2024$	$0.9^2 2240$	$0.9^2 2451$	$0.9^2 2656$	$0.9^2 2857$	$0.9^2 3053$	$0.9^2 3244$	$0.9^2 3431$	$0.9^2 3613$
2.5	$0.9^2 3790$	$0.9^2 3963$	$0.9^2 4132$	$0.9^2 4297$	$0.9^2 4457$	$0.9^2 4614$	$0.9^2 4766$	$0.9^2 4915$	$0.9^2 5060$	$0.8^2 5201$
3.0	$0.9^2 8650$	$0.9^2 8694$	$0.9^2 8736$	$0.9^2 8777$	$0.9^2 8817$	$0.9^3 8856$	$0.9^2 8893$	$0.9^2 8930$	$0.9^2 8965$	$0.9^2 8999$
3.5	$0.9^3 7674$	$0.9^3 7759$	$0.9^3 7842$	$0.9^3 7922$	$0.9^3 7999$	$0.9^3 8074$	$0.9^3 8146$	$0.9^3 8215$	$0.9^3 8282$	$0.9^3 8347$
4.0	$0.9^4 6833$	$0.9^4 6964$	$0.9^4 7090$	$0.9^4 7211$	$0.9^4 7327$	$0.9^4 7439$	$0.9^4 7546$	$0.9^4 7649$	$0.9^4 7748$	$0.9^4 7843$

For example: $F(2.41) = .9^2 2024 = .992024$.

SOURCE: A. Hald, *Statistical Tables and Formulas* (New York: John Wiley & Sons, Inc., 1952). (*Reprinted by permission of the author and publishers.*)

Appendix D

Table of Random Digits

55137	82186	02022	19819	97725	06155	86444	97001	06484	86919
84654	88775	90804	09556	14353	73773	24234	39083	39694	71643
67174	75190	01901	77980	25654	79451	23582	13207	94733	32791
05255	34134	98400	79075	54472	36928	50124	13555	29845	13909
00235	96293	03124	71690	98752	96812	72626	52417	33567	26196
29605	80606	87879	85698	26797	28253	65415	13365	58586	84943
25757	50161	43566	46440	12929	12661	15012	26241	56591	74542
83842	92537	91557	59709	78215	57385	30125	82729	68228	59704
72233	36841	80054	37564	40911	77163	84171	29433	83985	60279
95320	32603	60944	49534	13621	84971	94910	91249	12893	79344
59595	73510	80382	32807	80201	84359	49516	56644	53010	08086
90430	56275	68710	67302	66767	92925	18303	91717	15745	98740
52911	09472	03056	42875	33143	79326	65090	11792	92261	91803
38783	69167	63440	73968	65974	20385	11375	94262	41711	56529
03145	93482	89916	69453	45940	58913	32775	43326	80560	14231
54422	91366	92427	31083	87967	77612	71073	65010	79361	24811
87060	28611	17713	70763	98353	65918	51331	55469	77225	28474
02809	41314	16998	21967	85589	13587	64293	86317	14521	67861
21349	49152	42548	36963	73718	44663	81281	28875	42996	94717
92446	01888	53982	51988	93686	52605	91355	09242	33405	51083
30504	11458	37339	94300	68369	17963	85143	24707	59462	25988
70595	76848	42744	78139	26984	92856	62880	64114	74407	92107
46678	99099	35575	00763	37726	15711	12358	29164	80035	64689
03067	97539	87839	95244	73497	87490	01601	61952	46210	17200
15921	14242	79148	93153	94559	48437	70725	99452	89172	85171
81739	98257	01280	41284	52612	40670	94773	19755	75615	91170
06744	41201	27110	82283	15785	29847	86046	84178	57473	98427
87980	80264	01343	63440	79508	58686	41060	56015	71244	29348
98602	64443	20876	88293	41088	83932	09166	31963	30663	08704
24932	78198	58031	09083	35726	38829	70159	54699	30218	36183
53075	43820	30710	97962	62838	19684	54898	15985	91293	06403
14879	88835	62132	69432	34534	30165	34805	83160	05531	80632
46881	78222	73879	43190	95697	08022	42562	10445	57443	40048
49929	74655	59425	71942	41676	98199	55045	90902	49355	16018
47178	21198	76332	90237	53578	28064	25590	71463	97830	28416
23033	15727	81220	38825	14725	91399	37766	28946	56497	14104
08047	00308	73551	56388	81532	14447	07860	52598	53097	37582
77206	54505	02462	72637	39645	78126	88146	06060	04468	32581
65994	76525	33399	11192	72791	93164	51482	37056	22637	87518
57983	35441	73080	74695	68731	55915	32078	45173	32545	93955
31635	56389	57574	88321	11326	51048	28582	18754	18199	19533
47217	44309	04374	39648	71512	94319	20395	76376	62677	74228
40839	68433	10622	76108	71935	64715	43918	71801	48196	66125
80925	18153	25209	85134	34436	85216	12702	88065	20087	93436
40256	16645	39491	17197	90474	32775	03903	02393	04429	35607
66598	65500	86227	28500	99962	80223	78654	34426	23353	13768
68015	63272	31686	65114	93022	28248	51488	07980	21541	23580
23512	15319	10064	54461	42509	69267	17612	67379	19464	99584
00756	49791	36477	11445	44108	46651	77421	97365	78898	20879
81764	86200	45091	18929	25351	20762	19637	53329	78850	71672

SOURCE: Generated by computer at California State College at Los Angeles.

Appendix E

Table of Random Exponential Numbers

1	0.20	51	1.27	101	1.51	151	0.00	201	0.46	251	0.15
2	2.04	52	2.66	102	1.11	152	0.99	202	0.13	252	3.22
3	1.61	53	0.13	103	0.13	153	0.07	203	0.97	253	1.02
4	0.33	54	0.94	104	0.17	154	0.36	204	2.53	254	1.20
5	3.91	55	0.00	105	4.83	155	0.29	205	0.25	255	0.63
6	0.15	56	0.06	106	0.12	156	0.46	206	1.51	256	0.01
7	0.71	57	0.65	107	0.36	157	0.27	207	0.03	257	0.63
8	2.04	58	0.92	108	0.45	158	0.13	208	1.24	158	1.20
9	3.91	59	3.91	109	0.06	159	0.40	209	0.42	259	3.91
10	0.39	60	0.10	110	0.60	160	0.14	210	0.12	260	0.24
11	0.10	61	0.26	111	1.35	161	0.94	211	1.51	261	0.16
12	1.83	62	2.12	112	0.12	162	0.69	212	0.12	262	0.36
13	2.04	63	1.11	113	0.53	163	0.07	213	0.84	263	0.20
14	0.62	64	0.60	114	0.19	164	0.31	214	0.99	264	3.51
15	0.84	65	0.13	115	0.17	165	0.02	215	1.24	265	1.27
16	0.19	66	0.48	116	0.10	166	0.63	216	1.77	266	0.03
17	1.11	67	0.42	117	0.19	167	0.92	217	0.13	267	1.20
18	0.97	68	2.30	118	1.71	168	0.08	218	0.71	268	0.65
19	1.71	69	1.24	119	0.07	169	0.13	219	0.69	269	3.91
20	1.05	70	0.03	120	1.35	170	0.84	220	0.26	270	0.53
21	0.19	71	0.05	121	0.36	171	1.97	221	0.58	271	0.07
22	0.27	72	5.32	122	0.07	172	0.92	222	0.10	272	0.08
23	1.66	73	1.97	123	0.94	173	0.07	223	0.87	273	0.60
24	0.15	74	0.58	124	0.01	174	1.20	224	0.27	274	0.07
25	2.04	75	0.05	125	0.46	175	0.40	225	1.39	275	0.53
26	0.03	76	0.22	126	0.20	176	0.29	226	1.11	276	0.16
27	0.10	77	2.12	127	0.99	177	1.71	227	0.17	277	0.62
28	0.46	78	1.43	128	0.56	178	0.05	228	2.12	278	0.17
29	0.77	79	1.08	129	0.15	179	0.58	229	1.47	279	0.25
30	0.29	80	0.03	130	0.15	180	0.54	230	0.13	280	0.12
31	0.05	81	0.60	131	2.53	181	0.36	231	0.39	281	0.02
32	0.62	82	0.43	132	0.16	182	0.73	232	0.13	282	0.99
33	0.12	83	1.24	133	2.41	183	0.17	233	0.87	283	0.17
34	1.20	84	2.30	134	0.04	184	0.58	234	1.43	284	0.94
35	0.69	85	0.08	135	0.60	185	0.39	235	2.30	285	0.05
36	0.00	86	0.53	136	0.07	186	0.67	236	1.77	286	0.14
37	1.35	87	0.65	137	0.63	187	1.24	237	0.00	287	0.24
38	0.00	88	0.24	138	0.97	188	0.08	238	1.20	288	0.92
39	0.05	89	2.41	139	0.03	189	1.08	239	0.00	289	0.84
40	1.08	90	0.00	140	1.35	190	0.29	240	2.04	290	0.30
41	0.06	91	0.10	141	0.15	191	0.94	241	1.71	291	0.03
42	0.27	92	1.24	142	0.43	192	1.24	242	0.03	292	0.56
43	0.65	93	2.30	143	0.05	193	0.04	243	0.13	293	1.71
44	0.73	94	2.04	144	0.12	194	0.25	244	1.27	294	0.99
45	1.51	95	0.19	145	2.30	195	0.33	245	0.36	295	0.99
46	0.01	96	0.58	146	0.20	196	1.02	246	0.71	296	0.20
47	0.29	97	1.83	147	2.04	197	0.97	247	0.17	297	1.14
48	0.99	98	0.30	148	0.45	198	0.06	248	0.99	298	0.33
49	1.27	99	0.46	149	0.01	199	0.99	249	2.04	299	1.71
50	2.53	100	0.12	150	1.66	200	0.99	250	1.05	300	1.71

SOURCE: Generated by computer at California State College at Los Angeles.

Appendix F

Table of Correction
Factors for Control Charts

n	c'	d'	A_1	A_2	B'	D_3	D_4
2	1.772	0.8865	3.7599	1.881	1.7843	$\cdots$	3.267
3	1.382	0.5907	2.3937	1.023	1.4568	$\cdots$	2.575
4	1.253	0.4857	1.8800	0.7285	1.2617	$\cdots$	2.282
5	1.189	0.4299	1.5958	0.5768	1.1285	$\cdots$	2.115
6	1.151	0.3946	1.4100	0.4833	1.0310	$\cdots$	2.004
7	1.126	0.3698	1.2766	0.4193	0.9537	0.076	1.924
8	1.108	0.3512	1.1750	0.3726	0.8921	0.136	1.864
9	1.094	0.3367	1.0942	0.3367	0.8411	0.184	1.816
10	1.084	0.3249	1.0281	0.3082	0.7979	0.223	1.777
11	1.075	0.3152	0.9727	0.2851	0.7608	0.256	1.744
12	1.068	0.3069	0.9253	0.2658	0.7284	0.284	1.716
13	1.063		0.8842		0.6998		
14	1.058		0.8482		0.6744		
15	1.054		0.8162		0.6515		
16	1.050		0.7876		0.6308		
17	1.047		0.7618		0.6120		
18	1.044		0.7384		0.5948		
19	1.042		0.7170		0.5789		
20	1.040		0.6974		0.5642		
21	1.038		0.6793		0·5506		
22	1.036		0.6625		0.5380		
23	1.034		0.6469		0.5261		
24	1.033		0.6324		0.5151		
25	1.031		0.6188		0.5047		

SOURCES: Dudley J. Cowden, *Statistical Methods in Quality Control* (Englewood Cliffs, N.J.: Prentice-Hall, Inc., 1957). (*Reprinted by permission of the author and publishers.*)
B' values were computed by the author from the formula

$$B' = \frac{3c'}{\sqrt{2n}}$$

The D_3 and D_4 values were taken, by permission, from American Society for Testing Materials, *A. S. T. M. Manual on Quality Control of Materials* (1951) Table B 2, p. 115.

Index

Index